# DAVID WAUGH

The
# UK&Europe

# Questions compiled by Tony Bushell

## Nelson

# Contents

# CONTENTS

## Temperatures in Europe

### Winter

The isotherms for January show that the warmest parts of Europe are in the south and west, and that temperatures decrease rapidly towards the north and east (Figure 1.1). Many parts of southern Spain, Italy and Greece are warm enough to allow farming to continue, and to attract tourists and retired people. In contrast, places in the Alps, Scandinavia and eastern Europe are cold enough for snow to lie for several months. While this discourages farming, it can encourage winter sports.

### Summer

The isotherms for July show that while southern Europe is very warm, temperatures decrease fairly evenly towards the north (Figure 1.2). Although temperatures are too low in northern Scandinavia for cereals and fruit to ripen, they are high enough for olives, vines and subtropical fruit to grow around the Mediterranean Sea. The high temperatures of these southern areas attract large numbers of tourists but, by increasing evaporation rates, can cause seasonal water shortages.

## Factors affecting temperature

### Distance from the sea

As the sea is a liquid and is less dense than the land, it can be heated to a greater depth. This means that the sea takes much longer to heat up in summer than the land. Once the sea is warmed, however, it retains its heat longer, and so cools down more slowly in winter than the land. This is why places in the west of Europe, near to the Atlantic Ocean, are colder in summer and warmer in winter than places further inland (Figures 1.1 and 1.2). Britain, which is surrounded by the sea, tends to have cool summers, mild winters and a small annual range of temperature.

### Ocean currents

Coastal areas of western Europe are affected by the North Atlantic Drift. This warm current of water, which originates in the Gulf of Mexico, keeps the western coasts of Britain and Norway much warmer than other places in similar latitudes (Figure 1.3).

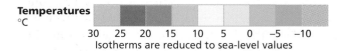

Temperatures °C

30  25  20  15  10  5  0  −5  −10

Isotherms are reduced to sea-level values

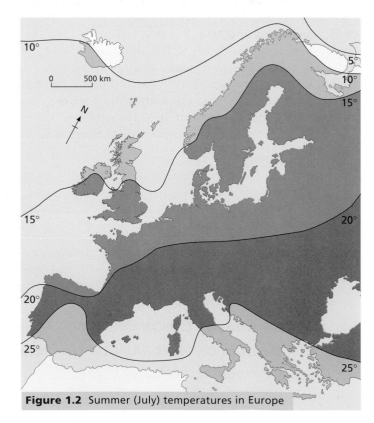

**Figure 1.1** Winter (January) temperatures in Europe

**Figure 1.2** Summer (July) temperatures in Europe

## Prevailing winds

The prevailing winds over Europe in winter come from the south-west. As they cross the warm Atlantic Ocean and North Atlantic Drift, they raise temperatures, especially in western areas (Figure 1.3). Similarly in summer to the north of 40°N, the south-westerlies remain the prevailing winds. However, at this time of year, when the sea is colder than the land, they bring much cooler conditions to western areas. South of 40°N, Mediterranean countries experience warm, gentle prevailing winds from the warmer land areas to the east and south.

## Latitude

Places in southern Europe, being nearer the Equator, are much warmer than places in northern Europe. This is due to the curvature of the earth and the angle of the sun in the sky (Figure 1.4). In southern Europe the sun is always high in the sky, especially in summer, although it is never directly overhead. The higher the sun is in the sky, the more its heat will be concentrated onto a small area and the warmer will be the land. In contrast, in northern Scandinavia the sun is always low in the sky (in mid-winter it may never rise above the horizon). As its heat is now spread out over a wider area, temperatures remain much lower.

   Notice also that the lower the angle of the sun, the greater the amount of atmosphere through which the rays have to pass. This allows more heat to be lost to dust and cloud in the atmosphere.

## Altitude

Temperatures decrease, on average, by 1°C for every 100 metres in height. As parts of the Alps are over 4,000 metres, they are at least 40°C colder than Mediterranean coastal areas to the south. With the wind-chill factor making them even colder, many parts remain snow-covered throughout the year.

## Aspect

Hillsides facing south are usually warmer than those facing north. This is because they receive more sun, while those facing north are more likely to remain in shadow.

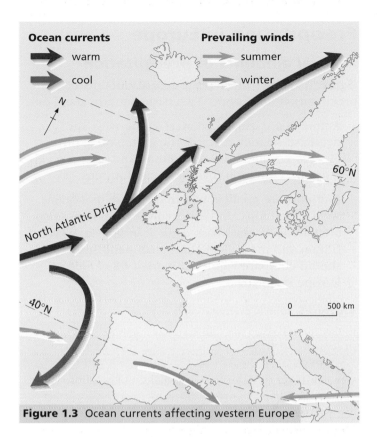

**Figure 1.3** Ocean currents affecting western Europe

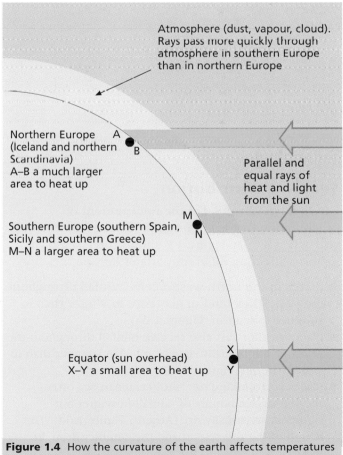

**Figure 1.4** How the curvature of the earth affects temperatures

# Precipitation in Europe

## Annual amounts of precipitation

Figure 1.5 shows the average annual amounts of precipitation for Europe. Two basic patterns stand out.

1 Amounts are usually greatest in the west and decrease steadily towards the east. Notice on Figures 1.5 and 1.6 that Shannon and Lisbon receive more precipitation than Berlin and Athens.

2 Amounts are greatest where there are mountains, such as the Alps, and especially where mountains are parallel to the coast, as in Scandinavia, western Britain and the Balkan and Italian peninsulas (you should compare Figure 1.5 with a relief map of Europe in an atlas).

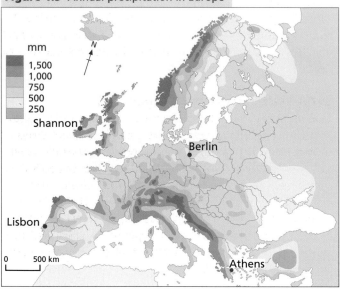

**Figure 1.5** Annual precipitation in Europe

## Seasonal distribution

Often, however, it is not the total amount of precipitation that is important but rather the time of year when it falls. Figure 1.6 shows three seasonal patterns affecting different parts of Europe.

- Places in the north-west receive rainfall throughout the year. They tend to get more in winter than in summer (Shannon, Figure 1.6a).
- Places further east also receive rainfall throughout the year but they usually receive more in summer than in winter (Berlin, Figure 1.6b).
- Places surrounding the Mediterranean Sea often receive large amounts of rainfall in winter but summers are usually dry (Athens, Figure 1.6d). The length of the dry season and the summer drought increase towards the south.

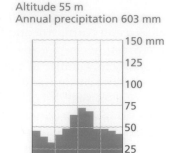

**a** Shannon

Altitude 2 m
Annual precipitation 929 mm

**b** Berlin

Altitude 55 m
Annual precipitation 603 mm

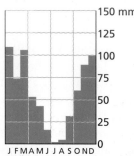

**c** Lisbon

Altitude 77 m
Annual precipitation 708 mm

**d** Athens

Altitude 107 m
Annual precipitation 402 mm

**Figure 1.6** Seasonal distribution of precipitation

## Reliability and type of precipitation

Other important concerns about precipitation include its reliability, intensity and type. In Britain, where it can usually be relied upon to rain every few days, there is rarely a water shortage. Even after a dry summer, as in 1976, supplies are usually replenished the following winter – the dry winter following the 1995 drought in England and Wales proved to be an exception. When it does rain in Britain, it is likely to fall steadily for several hours, allowing it to infiltrate into the ground.

Other places in Europe are less fortunate. Mediterranean areas expect a drought each summer. Although they receive winter rainfall, they cannot always rely on enough to last them over the summer period. When it does fall in summer it is often in the form of thunderstorms with heavy rain and, possibly, hail. The intensive rainfall, which is often unable to soak into the hard ground, can cause flooding and soil erosion, while hail can damage crops. In northern and mountainous parts of Europe, heavy snowfalls are liable to disrupt human activity.

**Figure 1.7** Relief rainfall

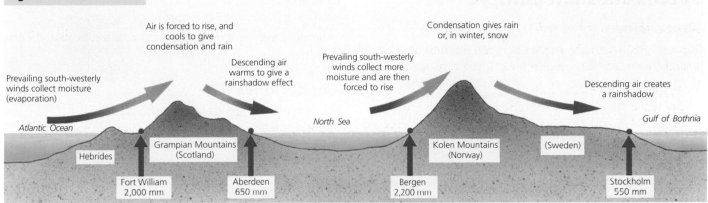

## Causes of rainfall

There are three main types of rainfall: relief, frontal and convectional. In each case precipitation is caused by warm air, which contains water vapour, being forced to rise until it cools sufficiently for condensation to occur.

### 1 Relief rainfall (Figure 1.7)

Relief rainfall occurs when the prevailing south-westerly winds pick up moisture as they cross the Atlantic Ocean. Where these winds meet coastal mountains, as in western Britain and Norway, the warm, moist air is forced to rise and cool. If cooling is sufficient to cause condensation, then heavy rainfall is likely. Once over the mountains, the air descends and warms, giving the drier 'rainshadow' conditions of eastern Britain and Sweden (Figure 1.5).

### 2 Frontal rainfall (Figure 1.8)

Frontal rain is associated with depressions (page 8) which form over the Atlantic Ocean and move eastwards across northern Europe at most times of the year, and over southern Europe in winter. They result from warm, moist tropical air meeting cooler, drier polar air. As warm and cold air have different densities and do not mix easily, the warmer, lighter air is forced to rise over the cooler, denser air. Depressions are most frequent in winter, giving north-west Europe their winter rainfall maximum (Figure 1.6a and c) and Mediterranean areas their seasonal rainfall (Figure 1.6c and d).

### 3 Convectional rainfall (Figure 1.9)

Convectional rainfall occurs when the ground is heated by the sun. The air next to the ground is heated and moisture on the ground evaporates. The warm, moist air rises in convection currents. As it rises it cools and condenses to give large cumulonimbus clouds and, often, heavy thunderstorms. Convectional rainfall, associated with high temperatures, is more likely to occur in southern parts of Europe and is responsible for the summer rainfall maximum of places in eastern Europe (Figure 1.6b).

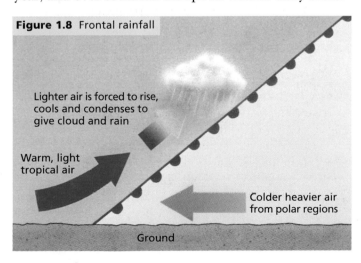

**Figure 1.8** Frontal rainfall

Lighter air is forced to rise, cools and condenses to give cloud and rain

Warm, light tropical air

Colder heavier air from polar regions

Ground

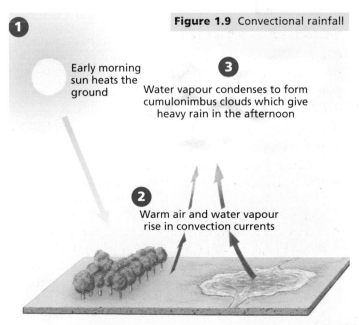

**Figure 1.9** Convectional rainfall

1 Early morning sun heats the ground

3 Water vapour condenses to form cumulonimbus clouds which give heavy rain in the afternoon

2 Warm air and water vapour rise in convection currents

# Depressions and anticyclones

## Depressions

Depressions dominate the weather of north-western Europe for most of the year, and Mediterranean areas in winter. Depressions are areas of low pressure which bring cloud, rain and wind. They form over the Atlantic Ocean when a mass of warm, moist tropical air from the south meets a mass of cooler, drier polar air from the north. The two air masses do not mix easily due to differences in temperature and density. The boundary between the two air masses is called a *front*. When warmer, lighter air moves towards colder, denser air, it is forced to rise over the cold air at a *warm front* (Figure 1.10). When cooler, denser air moves towards warm air, it undercuts the warm air, forcing it to rise at a *cold front*. In both cases the rising air is cooled and some of the vapour condenses, producing cloud and frontal rain. As the cold front moves faster than the warm front, it catches it up to form an *occluded front*. Although each depression is unique, the weather they bring as they move eastwards tends to have an easily recognisable pattern (Figure 1.10).

## Anticyclones

While anticyclones dominate the weather of Mediterranean areas in summer, they are experienced far less frequently than depressions in northern Europe. Their main characteristics are the opposite to those of depressions. Anticyclones are areas of high pressure which bring dry, settled weather which can last for several weeks. Winds are light, at times non-existent. As air in an anticyclone descends, it warms and so picks up moisture. This results in clear skies which give very warm conditions, especially in southern Europe in summer. However, in winter anticyclones often bring very cold weather.

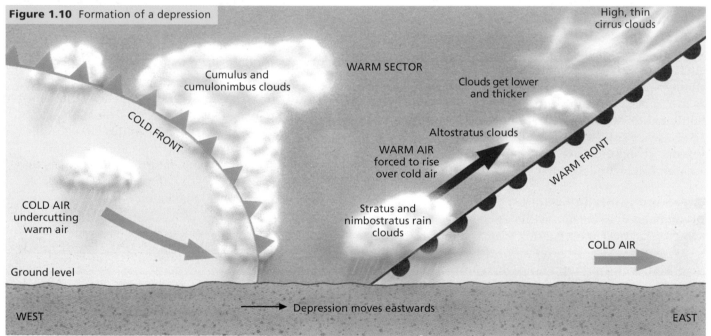

**Figure 1.10** Formation of a depression

High, thin cirrus clouds

WARM SECTOR

Cumulus and cumulonimbus clouds

Clouds get lower and thicker

COLD FRONT

Altostratus clouds

WARM AIR forced to rise over cold air

WARM FRONT

COLD AIR undercutting warm air

Stratus and nimbostratus rain clouds

COLD AIR

Ground level

Depression moves eastwards

WEST

EAST

| STAGE 5 After the cold front | STAGE 4 As the cold front passes | STAGE 3 In the warm sector | STAGE 2 As the warm front passes | STAGE 1 Before the arrival of the warm front |
|---|---|---|---|---|
| • Lower temperatures | • Sudden drop in temperature | • Warmer temperatures | • Sudden rise in temperature | • At first it is sunny with clear skies or high cloud |
| • Winds still strong and from the north-west | • Winds usually strong to gale force | • Winds decrease and come from the south-west | • A lengthy period of steady rain, low cloud | • Winds are gentle and from the south-east |
| • Heavy showers, perhaps with hail, and sunny intervals | • Relatively short period of heavy rainfall | • Low or broken cloud, either fair or light rain and drizzle | • Winds are often strong | • In time clouds get lower and thicken, winds slowly increase in strength |
| • Pressure rises | | • Low pressure | | • Pressure falls |

**Figure 1.11** Satellite image of a depression

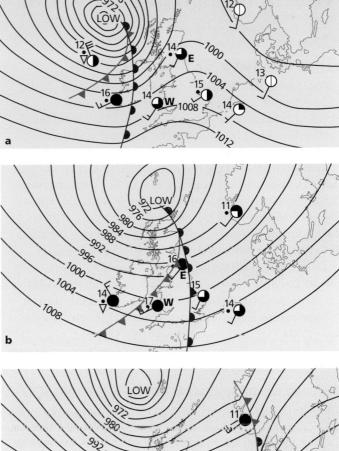

a

b

c

**Figure 1.12** Synoptic charts to show the progress of a depression

## Satellite images and synoptic charts

Depressions can be seen on *satellite images* as masses of swirling cloud (Figure 1.11), and anticyclones as areas of cloudless sky (Figure 1.13). Satellite images are photos taken from space and relayed back to earth. They are invaluable when trying to predict short-term changes in the weather. The state of the weather at any one time is shown on a *synoptic chart* (a weather map). The three synoptic charts in Figure 1.12 show the passing of a typical depression, with Figure 1.12a matching the satellite image in Figure 1.11. The synoptic chart and corresponding satellite image in Figure 1.13 illustrate a typical anticyclone.

Synoptic maps produced by the Meteorological Office use official symbols to show conditions at specific weather stations (Figure 1.14). The weather stations on Figures 1.12 and 1.13 show five elements: temperature, wind speed, wind direction, amount of cloud cover, and type of precipitation. A sixth element – atmospheric pressure – can be obtained by interpreting the isobars.

Figure 1.12 also shows how the weather at Edinburgh (E) and in west Wales (W) changes as the depression passes. Notice that the weather in both places in Figure 1.12a, b and c is similar to stages 1, 3 and 5 in Figure 1.10.

**ure 1.13** Satellite image and synoptic chart of an anticyclone

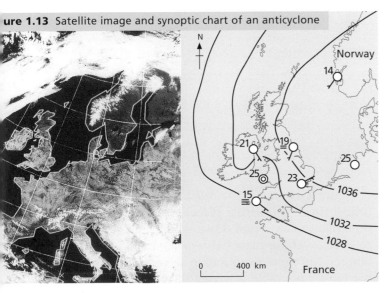

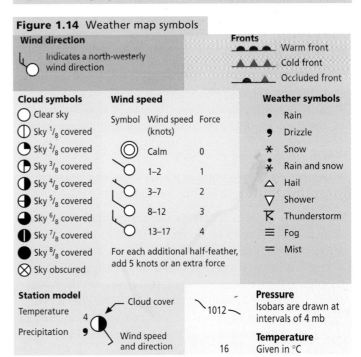

**Figure 1.14** Weather map symbols

**Wind direction**

Indicates a north-westerly wind direction

**Fronts**
Warm front
Cold front
Occluded front

**Cloud symbols**
Clear sky
Sky ¹/₈ covered
Sky ²/₈ covered
Sky ³/₈ covered
Sky ⁴/₈ covered
Sky ⁵/₈ covered
Sky ⁶/₈ covered
Sky ⁷/₈ covered
Sky ⁸/₈ covered
Sky obscured

**Wind speed**

| Symbol | Wind speed (knots) | Force |
|---|---|---|
| | Calm | 0 |
| | 1–2 | 1 |
| | 3–7 | 2 |
| | 8–12 | 3 |
| | 13–17 | 4 |

For each additional half-feather, add 5 knots or an extra force

**Weather symbols**
• Rain
, Drizzle
✱ Snow
⁎ Rain and snow
△ Hail
▽ Shower
Ҡ Thunderstorm
≡ Fog
= Mist

**Station model**

Temperature
Precipitation

Cloud cover

Wind speed and direction

**Pressure**
Isobars are drawn at intervals of 4 mb

**Temperature**
Given in °C

**9**

# The climate of the UK

*Weather* is the hour-to-hour, day-by-day state of the atmosphere. It includes temperature, sunshine, precipitation, cloud and wind. It is short-term and is often localised. *Climate* is the average weather conditions for a place taken over a period of time, usually 30 years. It is the expected, rather than the actual, conditions for that place. It is long-term and often applies to large areas of the world (e.g. the Mediterranean climate). Britain has:

- a variable climate, which means that the weather changes from day to day – this makes weather forecasting difficult
- an equable climate, which means that extremes of heat or cold, or of drought or prolonged rainfall, are rarely experienced.

If we wish to generalise about Britain's climate, we can say that it has cool summers, mild winters and a steady, reliable rainfall which is spread fairly evenly throughout the year. However, there are variations within this general pattern.

- There are important differences between places in the extreme north and south of the UK, as well as between places on the east and west coasts.
- The actual weather is often very different from the predicted average climate. For example, very heavy rain in early 1995 caused many rivers to flood, whereas by the end of that year's dry summer, some were at record low levels; and while November 1995 was the warmest ever recorded, May 1996 was the coldest for 73 years.

## *Precipitation*

Western areas receive more rainfall than places in the east (Figure 1.15). This is due to:

- the prevailing south-westerly winds which bring moist air from the Atlantic Ocean and cause relief rainfall as they cross the mountains of western Britain
- depressions moving eastwards from the Atlantic Ocean which give frontal rainfall.

Western areas also receive a winter rainfall maximum, as depressions tend to be more frequent at that time of year (see Figure 1.19).

Eastern areas receive less rainfall as they are in the rainshadow of the mountains. However, as they are usually warmer in summer than places to the west, they can expect to receive more convectional rainfall and a rainfall maximum in that season (see Figure 1.19).

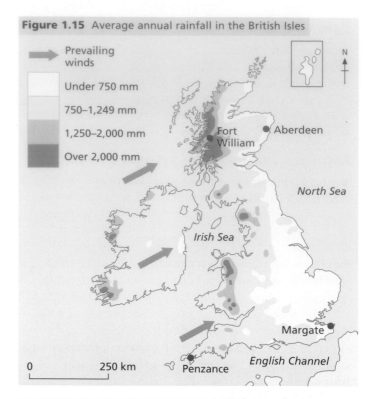

**Figure 1.15** Average annual rainfall in the British Isles

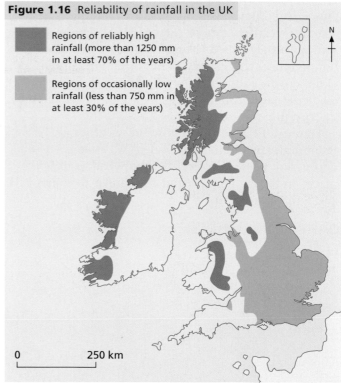

**Figure 1.16** Reliability of rainfall in the UK

Figure 1.16 shows the reliability of rainfall in the British Isles. Notice that places which receive least precipitation are often those where rainfall is the least reliable. As these places also experience high summer temperatures and evaporation rates then they become the most vulnerable to water shortages.

## Temperature

In winter, western areas are warmer than places to the east (Figure 1.17). This is due to:

- the moderating influence of the sea, which is warmer than the land at that time of year
- the influence of the warm North Atlantic Drift
- the prevailing south-westerly winds which cross the relatively warm Atlantic Ocean and North Atlantic Drift
- eastern areas being more likely to receive cold winds from the continent.

In summer, southern areas are warmer than places to the north (Figure 1.18). This is due to:

- the sun being at a higher angle in the sky (the effect of latitude)
- warm winds from the continent, which is warmer than the sea at that time of year
- longer hours of sunshine and less cloud per day.

Figure 1.19 shows, in a simplified form, the seasonal and regional differences in climate in the British Isles. The four quadrants result from using the 5°C isotherm for January, which divides the warmer west from the colder east, and the 15°C isotherm for July, which divides the warmer south from the colder north.

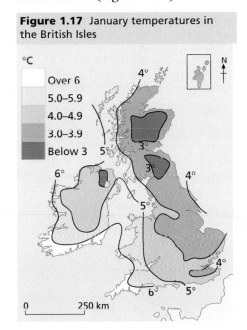

**Figure 1.17** January temperatures in the British Isles

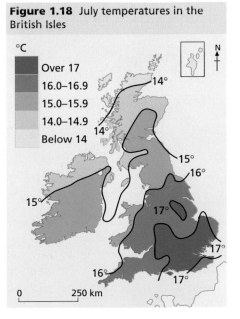

**Figure 1.18** July temperatures in the British Isles

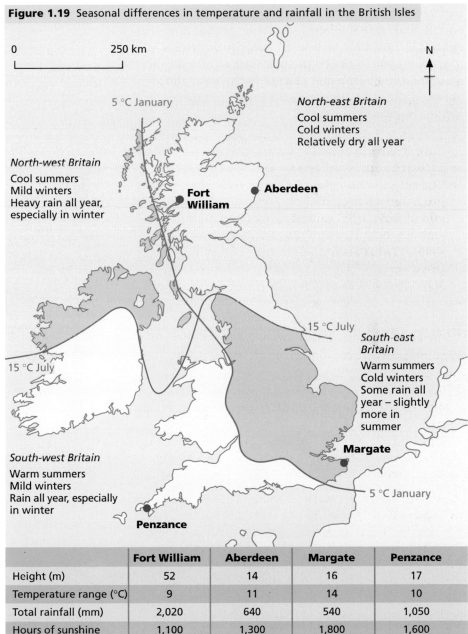

**Figure 1.19** Seasonal differences in temperature and rainfall in the British Isles

| | Fort William | Aberdeen | Margate | Penzance |
|---|---|---|---|---|
| Height (m) | 52 | 14 | 16 | 17 |
| Temperature range (°C) | 9 | 11 | 14 | 10 |
| Total rainfall (mm) | 2,020 | 640 | 540 | 1,050 |
| Hours of sunshine | 1,100 | 1,300 | 1,800 | 1,600 |

# Europe's climate and natural vegetation

## Climate

Figure 1.20 shows the main types of climate in Europe. You should be aware that:

- the map is simplified and does not show local variations
- the divisions between each climate type are shown as very generalised lines – in reality the change between two climates is often very gradual, and it would be more accurate to show the boundaries as broad transition zones.

Of the major world climates, five occur in Europe: arctic, cold, temperate maritime, temperate continental, and Mediterranean. The central European climate is, however, unique to Europe. It forms a transition zone between the maritime climate in the west and the continental climate to the east, and between the cold climate in the north and the Mediterranean to the south.

## Natural vegetation

Figure 1.21 shows the main natural vegetation types in Europe. Like the previous map showing climate, this map has also been simplified. It:

- disregards variations in vegetation caused by local differences in climate, soils and relief
- shows divisions as thin lines rather than broad zones
- assumes that large areas of Europe are still covered by their natural vegetation – in fact, while some areas of tundra and coniferous forest may still be natural, elsewhere most of the natural vegetation has been cleared or altered by human activity.

By simplifying the maps it is possible to see a close similarity between the climate of an area and its natural vegetation.

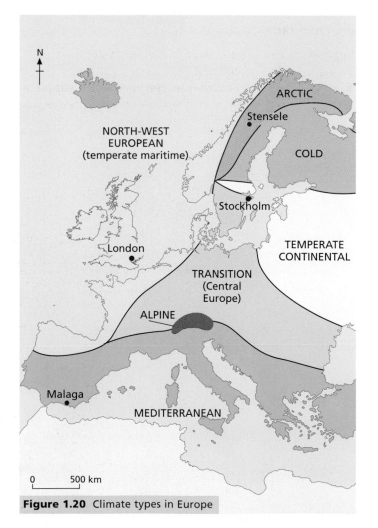

**Figure 1.20** Climate types in Europe

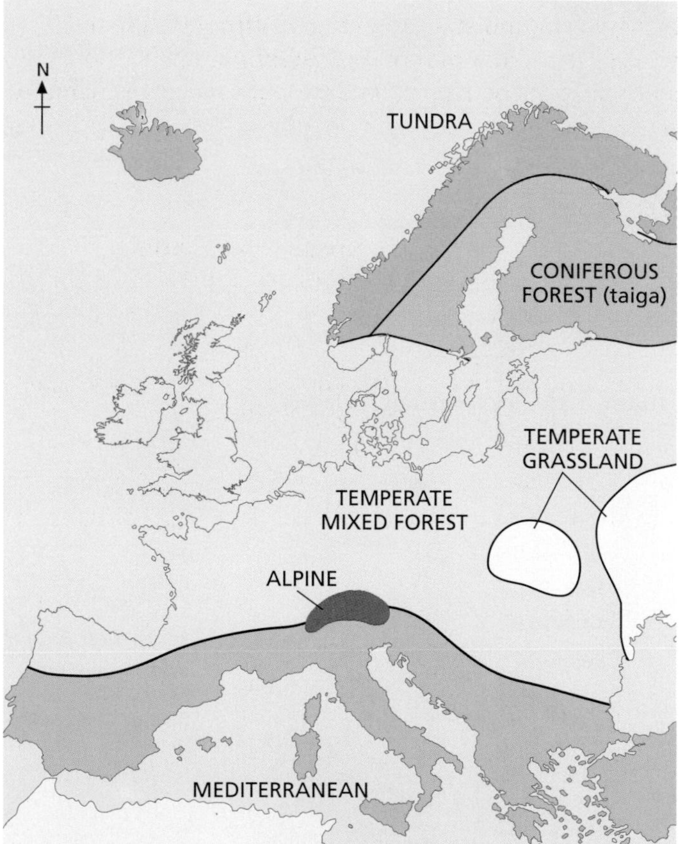

**Figure 1.21** Natural vegetation types in Europe

# Mediterranean climate and vegetation

The Mediterranean climate, as shown by the graph for Malaga in south-east Spain (Figure 1.22), is characterised by hot, dry summers and warm, wet winters.

*Summers* are hot and dry. Although the sun never shines directly from overhead, it does reach a high angle in the sky. The weather is dominated by anticyclones which give cloudless skies and settled conditions. The easterly prevailing winds are warm as they come from the land which is hot at this time of year. They are also dry as they cross land surfaces which lack moisture. The length of the dry season and the effects of the summer drought increase southwards. Rain, when it does fall, often comes in heavy convectional thunderstorms.

*Winters* are warm, partly because the sun is still at a relatively high angle in the sky and partly because the westerly prevailing winds come from the Atlantic Ocean which is warmer than the land at this time of year. The prevailing winds and associated depressions bring warm, moist air which gives frontal rain and, where they cross mountains, relief rainfall. Although amounts may be heavy, wet days are usually separated by several warm and sunny days.

## Vegetation

At one time most Mediterranean hillsides were extensively wooded. Where this is still the case, the trees include evergreen oaks (e.g. cork oak) and conifers (e.g. Corsican pine). Most slopes have, however, been deforested, allowing a secondary scrub type of vegetation to develop. There are two main types of scrub:

- *maquis*, which is a dense, tangled undergrowth more typical of granite and other impermeable rocks (Figure 1.23)

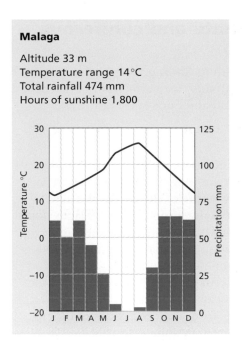

**Malaga**

Altitude 33 m
Temperature range 14°C
Total rainfall 474 mm
Hours of sunshine 1,800

**Figure 1.22**
Climate graph for Malaga, Spain

- *garrigue*, which is a sparser, lower-lying scrub with many aromatic plants such as rosemary and lavender associated with limestone and other permeable rocks (Figure 1.24).

Vegetation has had to adapt to the summer heat and drought. Plants often have:
- long tap roots to reach underground water supplies
- either small, waxy, glossy leaves or sharp thorns, to reduce moisture loss
- a protective bark as defence against the heat
- a short life cycle to avoid growth during the summer drought.

As a result of human activity, grazing animals and fire, little of the natural woodland survives today.

**Figure 1.23** Maquis vegetation

**Figure 1.24** Garrigue vegetation

# The cold climate and coniferous forest (taiga)

The cold climate, with its short growing season and coniferous forest, extends eastwards from northern Sweden across Finland and Eurasia (Figure 1.20).

## Temperature

Summers are short and cool (Figure 1.25). Although the hours of daylight are long, temperatures remain low owing to the low angle of the sun in the sky. Winters are both very long and very cold. Places north of the Arctic Circle have a period when the sun never rises above the horizon. Most places are inland and away from any warming influence of the Atlantic Ocean and the North Atlantic Drift. It is usual for the Gulf of Bothnia to freeze each winter (Figure 1.26). Strong easterly winds from the cold continent mean there is a high wind-chill factor.

## Precipitation

Precipitation is light throughout the year (Figure 1.25). This is partly because the air is cold and cannot hold much moisture, and partly because amounts of relief and frontal rain are reduced by the rainshadow effect caused by the Norwegian mountains (Figure 1.7). Precipitation falls mainly as short convectional showers in summer, when there is a rainfall maximum, and as snow in winter. However, precipitation amounts are less critical to vegetation growth than are temperatures.

## Vegetation

Vegetation consists of vast uninterrupted stands of coniferous forest or *taiga* (Figure 1.27). The most common trees are Norwegian spruce, Scots pine, and fir. Often, in contrast to deciduous forests, there can be extensive 'stands' of a single species. The trees, which are softwoods, have developed characteristics which allow them to adapt to the severe climate. These characteristics include:

- being evergreen, so that they do not need to renew leaves during the short growing season
- needles as leaves to reduce moisture loss (transpiration)
- thick, resinous bark to protect against cold winds
- cones to protect the seeds during the winter
- a compact conical shape to help stability in strong winds
- springy, sloping branches to allow snow to slide off.

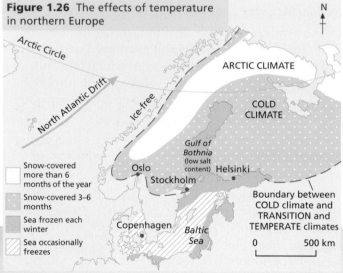

**Figure 1.26** The effects of temperature in northern Europe

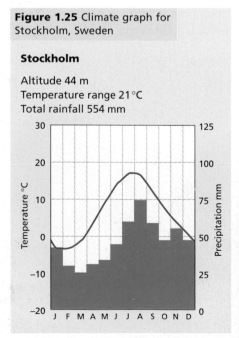

**Figure 1.25** Climate graph for Stockholm, Sweden

**Stockholm**

Altitude 44 m
Temperature range 21°C
Total rainfall 554 mm

**Figure 1.27** Coniferous forest in Sweden

# The arctic climate and tundra vegetation

The arctic climate occurs in parts of Iceland and northern Scandinavia (Figure 1.20) as well as in alpine areas to the south.

## Temperature

While mid-summers may have a period of continuous daylight, monthly temperatures only rise a few degrees above freezing-point due to the sun's low angle in the sky (Figure 1.28). The growing season is, therefore, very short. Winters are long, dark and extremely cold. Strong prevailing easterly winds from Siberia, with a high wind-chill factor, increase the feeling of cold. The ground may be permanently frozen – the so-called *permafrost*. Where the surface layer thaws in summer, it forms a shallow *active* layer. The surface may become waterlogged as the subsoil remains frozen and evaporation rates are low.

Alpine areas of central Europe experience a similar climate due to their extremes of altitude.

## Precipitation

Precipitation is light and, for much of the year, falls as snow (Figure 1.28). The snow, which is dry and powdery, is often blown about by strong winds giving blizzard conditions. Short convectional rainshowers give the summer precipitation maximum.

## Vegetation

The natural vegetation of arctic climates is the tundra. Tundra in Finnish means 'a barren or treeless land', which it is in winter (Figure 1.29), and in Russian 'a marshy plain', which it is in summer (Figure 1.30). The vegetation has had to adapt to the very cold conditions and short growing season. These adaptations include:
- a life cycle of less than two months
- being low-growing and compact to gain protection against the biting wind
- short roots as the soil is thin and the subsoil frozen
- being able to withstand marshy conditions
- small leaves to limit transpiration.

Mosses predominate in poorly drained areas and lichens on exposed rock. On drier south-facing slopes, there are carpets of brightly coloured flowers, known as *bloom-mats* (Figure 1.30), and berry-bearing plants, such as bilberry. Nearer rivers, stunted willow, alder and birch struggle for survival.

**Figure 1.30** Bloom-mats: patches of brightly coloured flowers blooming in the tundra in summer

**Figure 1.28** Climate graph for Stensele, Sweden

**Stensele**

Altitude 370 m
Temperature range 27°C
Total rainfall 494 mm

**Figure 1.29** Tundra vegetation in summer

**1** *(Pages 4, 5, 10, 11)*

Study the map.

**a** i) What is the North Atlantic Drift?

ii) From which direction are the prevailing winds?

**b** i) Which is the warmest area of Britain in January?

ii) Which is the coldest area of Britain in January?

iii) Suggest reasons for the pattern of temperatures across Britain in January.

**c** Explain why snow is most common in the area shown on the map.

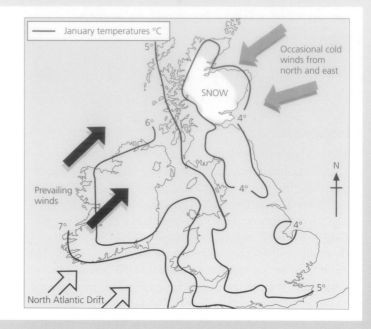

**2** *(Page 4)*

Look at the information in the map and table.

**a** Describe the pattern of temperature across Europe:

i) in January

ii) in July.

**b** Explain how distance from the sea is the main cause of these different temperature patterns.

| Temp °C | London | Berlin | Warsaw | Moscow |
|---------|--------|--------|--------|--------|
| January | 4 | −1 | −3 | −15 |
| July | 1 7 | 18 | 19 | 20 |

**3** *(Pages 7, 8, 9)*

Look at the satellite image.

**a** Answer A, B, C, D, E, F or G to the following:

i) Which place has the lowest pressure?

ii) Which place has the highest pressure?

iii) Which place has the strongest winds?

iv) Which is the warm front?

**b** The weather system over south and central Europe is an anticyclone. Describe the weather that it will bring to the area.

**c** The storms at B on the chart are caused by convection. Explain how they happen.

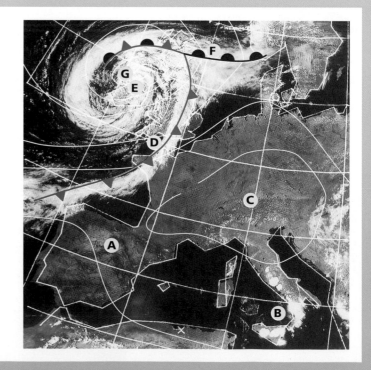

**4** *(Pages 8 and 9)*

Depressions are low-pressure systems which are common over the UK. Look at the weather map, and look back at the symbols on page 8.

**a** Copy and complete the table below to show the weather at Stations A and B.

| | Station A | Station B |
|---|---|---|
| Temperature | | 12°C |
| Weather | Rain | |
| Cloud cover | | |
| Wind speed | | 23–27 knots |
| Wind direction | South-west | |

**b** Suggest reasons for the different weather at Stations A and B.

**c** The weather system is moving eastwards and the warm front will be over Station C in 24 hours. Give a weather forecast for the next 24 hours for Station C.

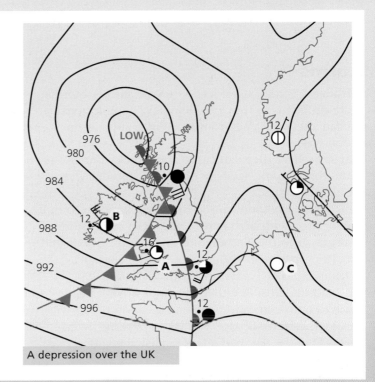

A depression over the UK

**5** *(Pages 7, 10, 11)*

Look at Figure 1.15 on page 10, which shows rainfall distribution.

**a** i) Which are the two wettest towns?
   ii) Which are the two driest towns?
   iii) Describe the pattern of rainfall across Britain.

**b** With help from the cross-section, explain how the rainfall amounts change from west to east.

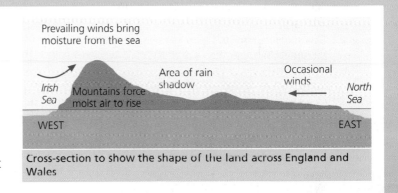

Cross-section to show the shape of the land across England and Wales

**6** *(Pages 12, 13, 14, 15)*

**a** Name the three climate types labelled Ⓐ, Ⓑ and Ⓒ on the map.

**b** Choose one of the three climates and describe its main features using the headings below.

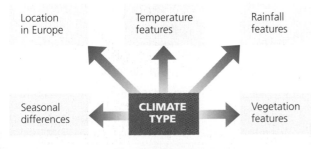

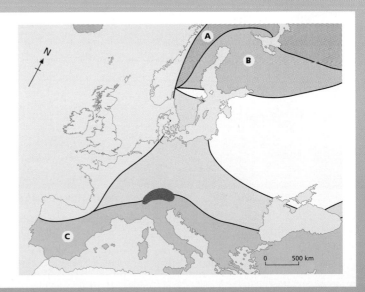

## Storms

North-west Europe is subject to severe storms. Storms create problems as they can disrupt economic activity and can affect our daily routine. Winds affect us in several ways.

- At sea where they can cause shipwrecks and loss of life, threaten the security of oil-rigs, and delay cross-Channel ferries.
- By coastal flooding caused by strong winds which, if associated with high spring tides, can cause storm surges, as in the Netherlands and south-east England in 1953 (pages 58–59), or can breach coastal defences, as at Towyn in North Wales in 1990.
- By causing erosion either by winds driving huge waves onto cliffs and promenades as on the Holderness coast (page 74), or by blowing away topsoil in the flat, hedgeless English fenlands (page 137).
- By causing snow to drift during blizzards.

- By disrupting power supplies and communications either by pulling down electricity and telephone wires or causing trees to block roads as in 'the Great Storm' of south-east England in October 1987.
- By creating a source of renewable energy (page187).

### The *Braer* disaster, January 1993

The worst week of storms ever to affect parts of the British Isles occurred in early January 1993. A series of deep Atlantic depressions crossed the extreme northern parts of Scotland. One depression caused the running aground of the *Braer* oiltanker on Shetland (Figure 2.1). Another, which had the lowest pressure ever recorded in a depression and which caused the eventual break-up of the tanker, has become known as the '*Braer* storm' (Figure 2.2). Figure 2.3 describes the weather events leading to the grounding and eventual breaking up of the *Braer*.

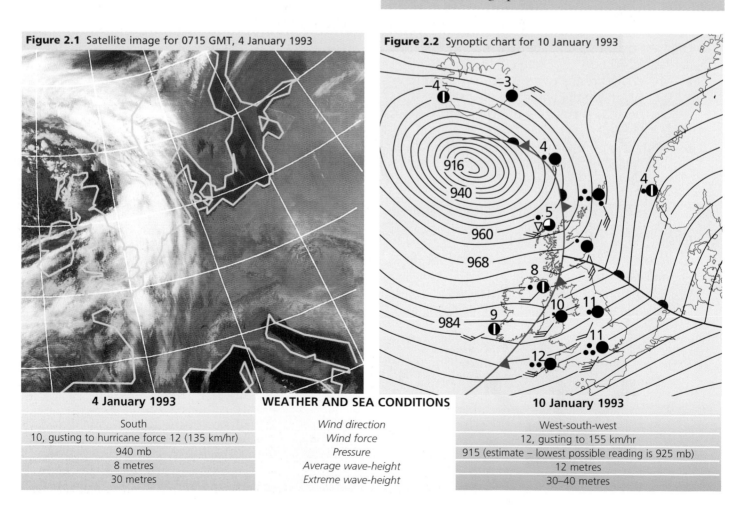

**Figure 2.1** Satellite image for 0715 GMT, 4 January 1993

**Figure 2.2** Synoptic chart for 10 January 1993

| 4 January 1993 | WEATHER AND SEA CONDITIONS | 10 January 1993 |
|---|---|---|
| South | *Wind direction* | West-south-west |
| 10, gusting to hurricane force 12 (135 km/hr) | *Wind force* | 12, gusting to 155 km/hr |
| 940 mb | *Pressure* | 915 (estimate – lowest possible reading is 925 mb) |
| 8 metres | *Average wave-height* | 12 metres |
| 30 metres | *Extreme wave-height* | 30–40 metres |

| | | |
|---|---|---|
| **5 January** | 0000 | Deep Atlantic depression moving rapidly eastwards. |
| | 0520 | *Braer* reports engine failure. |
| | 0535 | Two tugs at Sullom Voe (112 km by sea) alerted, and soon sail. |
| | 0700 | Rescue helicopter begins winching men off. Dangerous job in the southerly force 10 winds. *Braer* continues to drift northwards. |
| | 1015 | Tugs return to Sullom Voe, unable to make progress in gale and mountainous waves (they are too small to help anyway). |
| | 1115 | *Braer* runs aground. Some leakage, but ship remains intact. Winds too strong for spray-dispersant planes to fly. |
| **6 January** | | Severe weather conditions prevent salvage operations but spray-dispersant planes operate for several hours. |
| **7–9 January** | | Continuous gales and high waves cause *Braer* to slowly break up and to discharge more and more oil. Strong winds blow oil inland. |
| **10 January** | 1800 | Arrival of deepest depression ever recorded in North Atlantic. Pressure 915 mb (estimated, as off bottom of scale), hurricane-force winds gusting to 150 km/hour. Complete break-up of *Braer*. Turbulent sea, hurricane-force winds, huge waves. |
| **11–16 January** | | Centre of the '*Braer* storm' begins to move away very slowly to north-east. Hurricane-force winds continue to generate huge waves which dash against the rocky coastline. Oil is broken into tiny droplets, which are carried out to sea by waves rebounding from the cliffs. Wet weather also prevents oil particles from settling on the beach. |

**Figure 2.3**
Events leading to the grounding and break-up of the *Braer*, January 1993

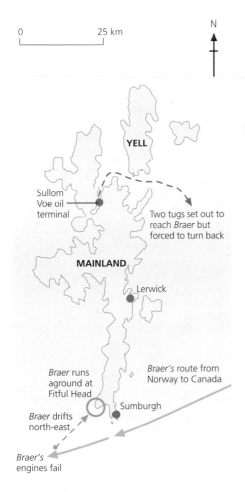

0    25 km

N

YELL

Sullom Voe oil terminal

Two tugs set out to reach *Braer* but forced to turn back

MAINLAND

Lerwick

*Braer* runs aground at Fitful Head

*Braer*'s route from Norway to Canada

Sumburgh

*Braer* drifts north-east

*Braer*'s engines fail

**Figure 2.4** Events of 5 January 1993

**Figure 2.5** Storm waves breaking over the *Braer*, January 1993

## Water supply and drought

We have already seen that it is not always the amount of precipitation that falls in a year that is important, but rather its seasonal distribution, intensity and reliability (page 6).

- If there is a very wet season then surplus moisture is likely to return rapidly to rivers and the sea.
- During a long dry season the water supply may be insufficient for crops, animals and domestic use.
- Farmers need rain, but not too much, during the growing season.
- Summer rainfall is less effective than winter rainfall as the higher temperatures increase *evapotranspiration* (the loss of moisture from the ground and plants).
- Run-off of water is fastest after summer convectional storms when the rain is heavy and the ground surface is hard.

### The water balance

Figure 2.6 shows the balance between precipitation and evapotranspiration over Europe. Those areas where precipitation exceeds evapotranspiration have a *water surplus*, while those where evapotranspiration exceeds precipitation have a *water deficit*. Notice the following:

- North-west Europe, with rainfall throughout the year and cooler temperatures, has a water surplus.
- Southern Europe, with its summer drought and higher temperatures, has a water deficit (Figure 2.8).
- Often, places that are sparsely populated (see Figure 8.1) have a water deficit, while places that are more densely populated have a water surplus.

This has meant that even since times of early settlement, people have had to transfer water from one place to another (Figure 2.7).

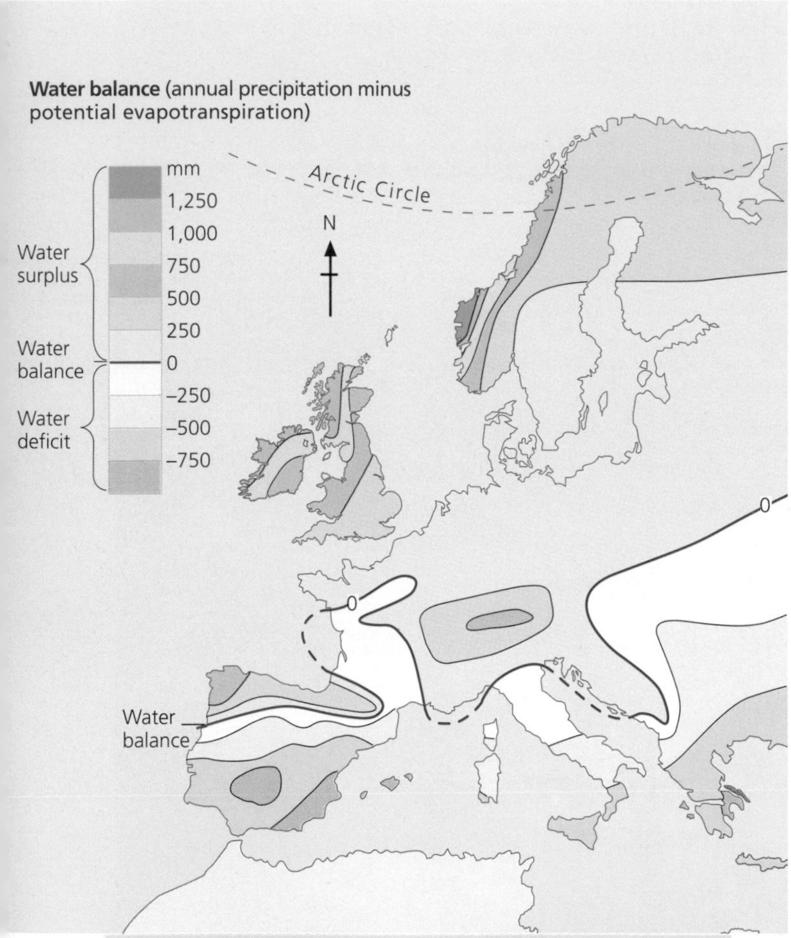

**Figure 2.7** The Pont du Gard in France, an aqueduct built in the 1st century AD to carry water over the River Gard to the city of Nîmes

**Figure 2.6** Europe's water balance: areas with a surplus or deficit of water

**Water balance** (annual precipitation minus potential evapotranspiration)

**Figure 2.8** A dried-up river bed showing the annual water shortage experienced in Mediterranean countries

## Water shortage in England 1995

Perhaps it is because drought is less frequent in the UK than in Mediterranean lands that Britain seems unable to cope with a water shortage. Although people still talked about the 1975–1976 drought, water authorities seemed unprepared for the hot, dry summer of 1995. The National Rivers Authority (NRA) claimed in late August that river levels across the country were falling rapidly. Many rivers were flowing at less than half their average for the time of year, with some flowing at under 10 per cent (Figure 2.9). The NRA claimed this was the result of many areas having experienced more than six consecutive months with below-average rainfall at a time when they had had exceptionally high temperatures. Low river levels mean less water can be extracted by water companies, less water to dilute pollutants and less oxygen for fish.

The dry spell continued throughout the autumn and by November water supplies in West Yorkshire had become dangerously low. Reservoirs feeding Calderdale were only 9.7 per cent full, and those feeding Kirklees 11.9 per cent (Figure 2.10). Yorkshire Water was forced to buy water from Northumbrian Water's Kielder reservoir (pages 22–23). This water had to be pumped from the River Tees to a reservoir in Cleveland before being transported by road to West Yorkshire by a fleet of 200 tankers working 24 hours a day, seven days a week (Figure 2.11).

The 1995 drought showed the need, even in Britain, for good, sustainable water management by water authorities.

**Figure 2.10** A dried-up reservoir in Yorkshire in the summer of 1995

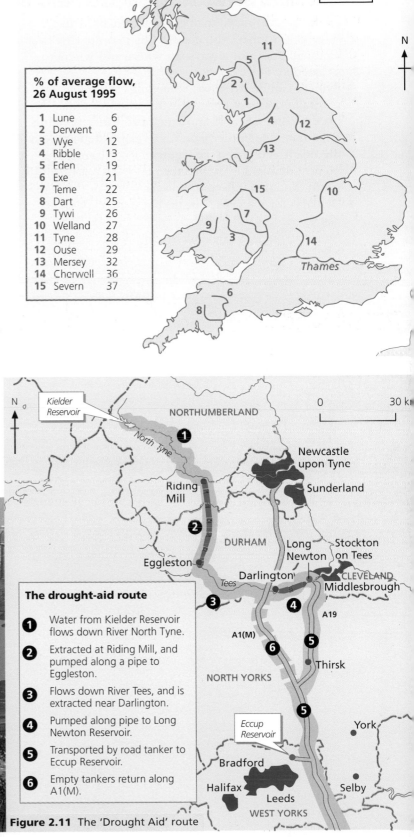

**Figure 2.9** Low-flow rivers in England and Wales

0     100 km

| % of average flow, 26 August 1995 | |
|---|---|
| 1 Lune | 6 |
| 2 Derwent | 9 |
| 3 Wye | 12 |
| 4 Ribble | 13 |
| 5 Eden | 19 |
| 6 Exe | 21 |
| 7 Teme | 22 |
| 8 Dart | 25 |
| 9 Tywi | 26 |
| 10 Welland | 27 |
| 11 Tyne | 28 |
| 12 Ouse | 29 |
| 13 Mersey | 32 |
| 14 Cherwell | 36 |
| 15 Severn | 37 |

### The drought-aid route

**1** Water from Kielder Reservoir flows down River North Tyne.

**2** Extracted at Riding Mill, and pumped along a pipe to Eggleston.

**3** Flows down River Tees, and is extracted near Darlington.

**4** Pumped along pipe to Long Newton Reservoir.

**5** Transported by road tanker to Eccup Reservoir.

**6** Empty tankers return along A1(M).

**Figure 2.11** The 'Drought Aid' route

# Water transfers in the UK

## A mismatch between supply and demand

The UK receives more than enough rainfall in an average year to meet the needs of its people. However, this rainfall does not always fall where and when it is most needed. For example:

- Rainfall can be irregular. Sometimes there may be several months of drought while at other times excess rain and rapid snowmelt can cause flooding.
- Most rain falls in the higher, less populated areas in the north and west (see Figure 1.15) whereas the highest demand is in the more populated areas in the south, the Midlands and the east.
- Demand for water is least during winter when many places receive most of their rainfall, and highest in summer when rainfall is less and temperatures and evapotranspiration are highest.
- The areas of highest demand change over time as people and industries move.

As a result, water has to be stored in reservoirs in areas where there is a surplus and transferred to places which have a water deficit (Figure 2.12).

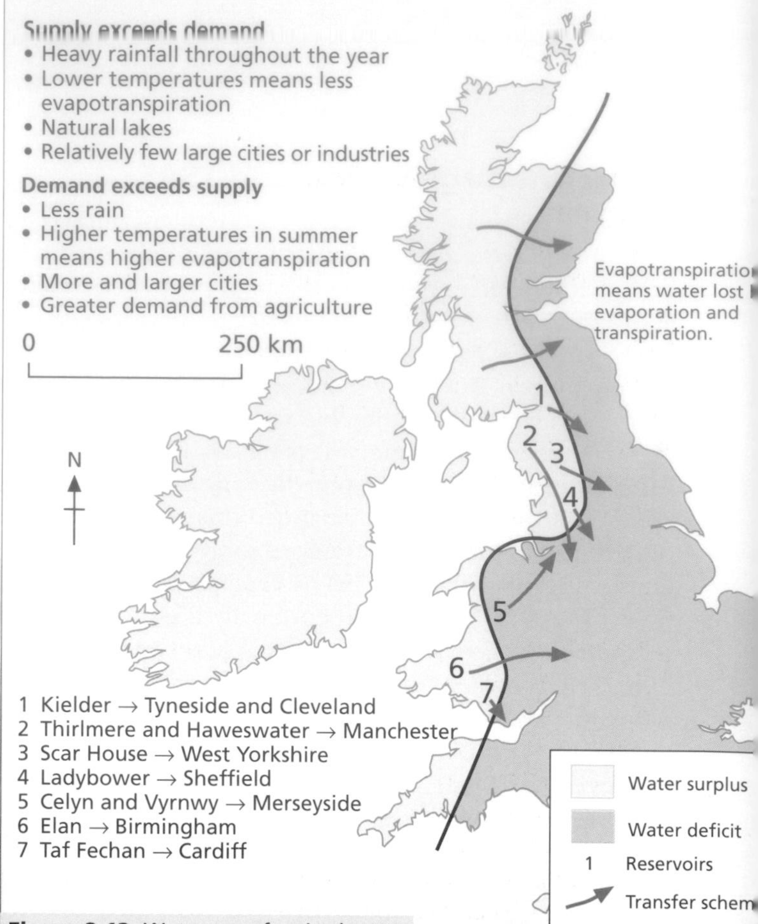

## The Kielder Project

### The 1970s – Europe's largest reservoir

In the early 1970s the demand for water by industries and domestic users in the north-east of England was expected by the early 1980s to exceed supply. Not everyone was in favour of the project, and it was not until after two public enquiries that work began in 1975. The scheme involved two stages.

**Supply exceeds demand**
- Heavy rainfall throughout the year
- Lower temperatures means less evapotranspiration
- Natural lakes
- Relatively few large cities or industries

**Demand exceeds supply**
- Less rain
- Higher temperatures in summer means higher evapotranspiration
- More and larger cities
- Greater demand from agriculture

0 _____ 250 km

N

Evapotranspiration means water lost evaporation and transpiration.

1 Kielder → Tyneside and Cleveland
2 Thirlmere and Haweswater → Manchester
3 Scar House → West Yorkshire
4 Ladybower → Sheffield
5 Celyn and Vyrnwy → Merseyside
6 Elan → Birmingham
7 Taf Fechan → Cardiff

Water surplus

Water deficit

1 Reservoirs

Transfer scheme

**Figure 2.12** Water transfers in the UK

1 Building a dam 1.2 km long and 50 metres high and creating a reservoir – Kielder Water – which was the largest artificial lake in western Europe (Figure 2.13).
2 Pumping water through huge pipes uphill from the River Tyne to a holding reservoir. From here water is transferred by an aqueduct, much of which is underground, to the Rivers Wear and Tees (Figure 2.14a). The Kielder reservoir was allowed to begin to fill in autumn 1980. By spring 1982 it was completely filled.

**Figure 2.13** Kielder Water

## The 1980s – a multipurpose reservoir

Due to economic recession in the early 1980s, the demand for water was less than had originally been anticipated. However, other uses were found for Kielder Water. These included the following:

● Regulating the flow of the Tyne, preventing it from getting too low during times of drought and reducing the flood risk after heavy rain.

● Constructing a small hydro-electric power station. The power produced – enough to satisfy the needs of a small town of 10,000 people – is connected to the National Grid.

● Using the 43 km shoreline, the water surface, and the surrounding Kielder Forest as resources to encourage tourism and recreation. Tourism has now become such an important activity that to many of its 300,000 annual visitors, Kielder Water appears to have been created for recreation. Leaplish for example has become one of several 'honeypot' sites (page 177), with water ski-ing, yachting, forest walks, picnic sites, camping and caravanning.

## 1995–1996

Even during the extreme drought conditions of 1995, Northumbrian Water was able to provide an assured and uninterrupted supply of water to its customers. In November it made an agreement with Yorkshire Water to 'export' some of its surplus (see Figure 2.11). In April 1996, Yorkshire Water announced that it was to ask the Environment Agency for permission to begin a £40 million rivers transfer operation allowing water from Kielder to be transferred to the rivers Wiske, Swale, Ure and Ouse (Figure

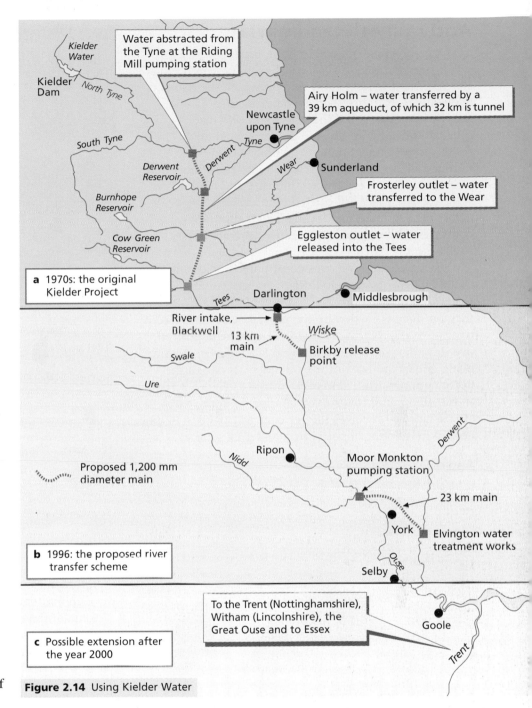

**Figure 2.14** Using Kielder Water

12.14b). This scheme, if accepted, could be available within six months but would only be used should Yorkshire's own water supplies be insufficient to meet demand. However, many people fear that the scheme would be environmentally damaging.

## Into the next century . . .

Conservation groups, who claim that the river transfer scheme is environmentally unacceptable, suggest that Yorkshire Water could, at little extra cost, secure its supply by piping water from Kielder. More ambitious proposals suggest that water from Kielder could be transferred, by river, to meet the large demand in the drier south-east of England (Figure 2.14c).

## Acid rain in Scandinavia

Acid rain was first noticed in Scandinavia in the 1950s when large numbers of fish there died. Research showed that the rivers and lakes in which the fish had lived contained more than average amounts of acid. Later it was discovered that this extra acid had originated from rain – hence the term 'acid rain'. The main sources of acid rain are sulphur dioxide and nitrogen oxide, two gases released into the atmosphere from thermal power stations, industry and motor vehicles. The gases are carried by prevailing winds across seas and national frontiers and, after being converted into sulphuric and nitric acid, are deposited back onto the earth's surface.

Most European countries contribute to acid rain, but the main culprits include Britain, France, Germany and eastern Europe (Figure 2.15). Much of the acid which they produce is carried by the prevailing south-westerly winds over the North and Baltic Seas to be deposited over Scandinavia. This means that Scandinavia, despite being one of the least of the offenders, is one of the major sufferers from acid rain. Indeed as Figure 2.16 shows, according to a survey conducted in the early 1980s, Norway receives 92 per cent and Sweden 82 per cent of its sulphur deposits from external sources,

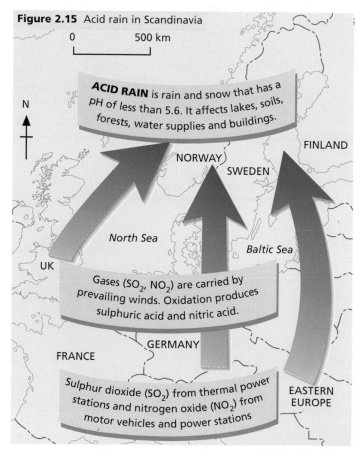

**Figure 2.15** Acid rain in Scandinavia

ACID RAIN is rain and snow that has a pH of less than 5.6. It affects lakes, soils, forests, water supplies and buildings.

Gases ($SO_2$, $NO_2$) are carried by prevailing winds. Oxidation produces sulphuric acid and nitric acid.

Sulphur dioxide ($SO_2$) from thermal power stations and nitrogen oxide ($NO_2$) from motor vehicles and power stations

**Figure 2.16** Europe: sulphur originating in external countries

| Country | % |
|---|---|
| Norway | 92 |
| Sweden | 82 |
| Finland | 75 |
| Denmark | 64 |
| UK | 20 |
| Netherlands | 58 |
| Germany | 44 |
| Poland | 58 |
| Belgium | 77 |
| Czech Rep. | 85 |
| Austria | 65 |
| France | 48 |
| Switzerland | 90 |
| Former Yugoslavia | 49 |
| Spain | 20 |
| Italy | 30 |

compared with only 20 per cent in the UK. Acid rain is, therefore, a global problem which can only be solved through international co-operation and management.

Some of the more serious effects of acid rain in Scandinavia are summarised in Figure 2.17.

| | |
|---|---|
| **Lakes** | Increased acidity kills fish and plant life. Latest estimates suggest that over 75 per cent of lakes and rivers in southern Norway and Sweden have no fish in them. |
| **Soils** | Increased acidity of soils can reduce farm output. Worst affected are acid soils overlying granite and sandy-glacial soils covered in coniferous trees – both of which are common in Scandinavia. |
| **Forests** | Trees die as important nutrients (calcium and potassium) are washed out by acid rain and are replaced by manganese and aluminium which poison the roots. |
| **Others** | Acids in water supplies may become a health hazard; buildings and monuments decay; sulphur dioxide is believed to be a cause of lung cancer and is a cause of smog. |

**Figure 2.17** Effects of acid rain

# Ozone

## High-level ozone

Ozone is a gas. It is concentrated in a layer 25–30 km above the earth's surface. Ozone acts as a shield, protecting the earth from the damaging effects of ultraviolet radiation from the sun. Ultraviolet radiation is responsible for sunburn and skin cancer, snow-blindness, cataracts and eye damage, ageing and wrinkling of skin, and reduced immunity to disease.

There is serious concern as parts of the ozone shield appear to be breaking down. A depletion of ozone above the Antarctic was observed by the British Antarctic Survey in 1977 and the first 'hole' discovered there in 1985 (a 'hole' is where ozone depletion is over 50 per cent). This hole, which appears each spring, develops when very low temperatures allow the ozone to be destroyed in a chemical reaction involving chlorine. The main sources of chlorine are:

- the release of chlorofluorocarbons (CFCs), especially from aerosols, by humans into the atmosphere (a long-term effect)
- from major volcanic eruptions (a short-term effect).

The first observed 'hole' over the Arctic followed the coldest-ever January of 1989. Since then depletions have increased annually over northern Europe. This has resulted, in the UK, in a 40 per cent increase in skin cancer a year. In the spring of 1995 Britain recorded its lowest-ever ozone levels with a 40 per cent depletion (Figure 2.18). The Meteorological Office now publishes a daily radiation map (Figure 2.19) and people are advised to use sunblocks (Figure 2.20) and to limit exposure to direct sunlight.

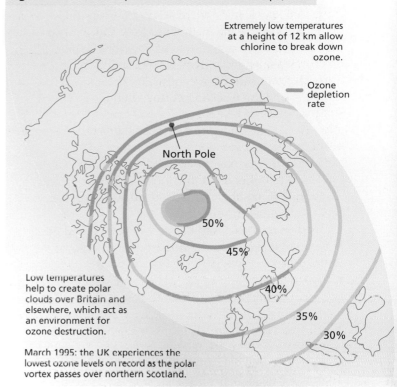

**Figure 2.18** Ozone depletion over north-west Europe, 1995

Extremely low temperatures at a height of 12 km allow chlorine to break down ozone.

Ozone depletion rate

North Pole

50%

45%

40%

35%

30%

Low temperatures help to create polar clouds over Britain and elsewhere, which act as an environment for ozone destruction.

March 1995: the UK experiences the lowest ozone levels on record as the polar vortex passes over northern Scotland.

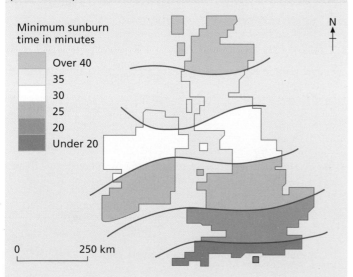

**Figure 2.19** Ultraviolet forecast for a sunny summer day in the UK (as on Ceefax)

Minimum sunburn time in minutes

Over 40
35
30
25
20
Under 20

N

0    250 km

**Figure 2.20** Wearing sun block against the sun

## Low-level ozone

In contrast, motor vehicle exhaust fumes create increasing amounts of ozone close to the earth's surface, especially under anticyclonic weather conditions. High levels of ozone damage plants and affect the health of people and animals. High asthma levels in children, particularly in London during the hot summers of 1994 and 1995, have been linked to traffic pollution. In Paris during 1994, 16 alerts were issued when ozone levels were above the danger limit. The problem has become so acute that daily health warnings are now broadcast in both the UK and France.

## 1 (Pages 18 and 19)

**a** Describe the main features of the weather system that affected the Shetland Islands in January 1993.

**b** With help from pages 18 and 19 and the labelled information on this map:
  i) describe the effects of the first storm
  ii) describe the effects of the second storm.

**c** Explain how the second storm actually helped reduce the damage caused by the wreck of the *Braer*.

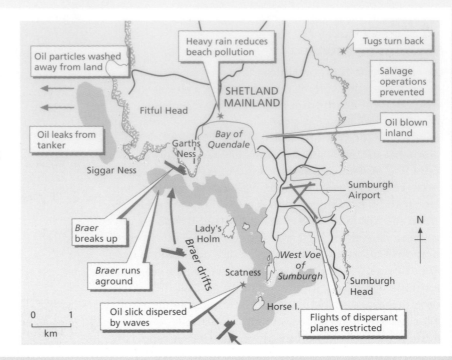

## 2 (Pages 22 and 23)

Look at the diagram.

**a** Why is the supply graph stepped, while the demand graph shows a fairly smooth increase?

**b** i) What was the supply of water in 1961?
  ii) What was the supply of water after the Derwent and Cow Green reservoirs were opened?
  iii) Why was a new reservoir needed by 1991?

**c** i) How much spare (surplus) water was held by Northumbrian Water in 1991?
  ii) Explain why Northumbrian Water has been able to export water from Kielder since the early 1980s.

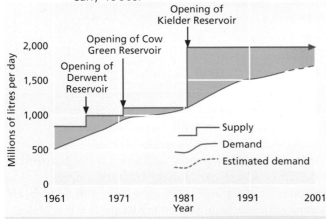

Supply and demand for water in the Northumbrian Water area of north-east England

## 3 (Pages 22 and 23)

Look at Figure 2.14 on page 23, and the map here.

**a** i) Name four reservoirs in north-east England.
  ii) Describe the route along which water from Kielder can reach Middlesbrough.
  iii) Suggest why a pumping station is needed at point A in order to move water towards point B.

**b** i) Kielder is a *multipurpose* scheme. What is meant by this term?
  ii) Give four uses for Kielder Water.

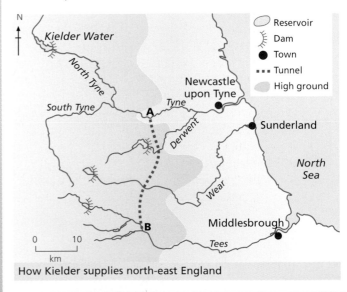

How Kielder supplies north-east England

**4** (Pages 21, 22, 23)

**a** Look at Figure 2.12 on page 22, and read the newspaper article here.
  i) Explain why East Anglia has problems providing water.
  ii) Which areas of Britain are most likely to be able to provide a regular supply of water? Give reasons for your answer.
**b** A water authority may try to reduce or overcome its water shortage problem by transferring water. With the help of simple maps, briefly describe how Yorkshire Water:
  i) transferred water after the 1995 drought
  ii) plans to transfer water in the future.

## Drought worries hit East Anglia

'The biggest problem we have is water shortages. Here we get less than 600 mm of rainfall a year, and that doesn't provide enough water for domestic use or farms and industry. It is also a difficult area for providing reservoirs as there is no high land for building a dam.'

**Water Board official**

**5** (Page 24)

**a** What is acid rain?
**b** Explain how cars, factories and power stations can cause acid rain.
**c** Britain has been blamed for damaging lakes and rivers in Norway and Sweden. Explain how pollution from Britain could be causing acid rain to fall in such countries.
**d** Describe the damaging effects of acid rain

Trees damaged by acid rain

**6** (Page 24)

**a** Look at the information here and at Figure 2.16 on page 24.
  i) Which four countries produce most sulphur?
  ii) Which four countries receive the largest deposits of sulphur?
  iii) Which four countries receive the largest percentage of sulphur from other countries?
**b** 'Acid rain is an international problem and can only be controlled by international co operation.'
  i) Explain this statement.
  ii) Which of your answers to question **a** best supports the statement? Give reasons for your answer.

Sulphur deposited in Europe (thousand tonnes per year)

Sulphur produced in Europe (thousand tonnes per year)

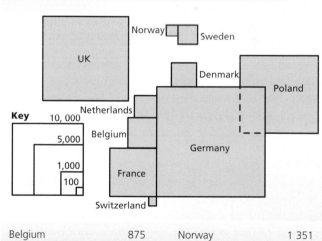

| Belgium | 875 | Norway | 1 351 |
|---|---|---|---|
| Denmark | 612 | Poland | 10 712 |
| France | 5 024 | Sweden | 1 995 |
| Germany | 13 502 | Switzerland | 754 |
| Netherlands | 851 | UK | 6 160 |

## Rock types and structure

### Rock types

The earth's crust consists of many different types of rock. It is usual to group these rocks into three main types.

1 *Igneous* rocks result from volcanic activity. They consist of crystals which formed as the volcanic rock cooled down, e.g. granite (Figure 3.1) and basalt.

2 *Sedimentary* rocks are laid down in layers, e.g. sandstone (Figure 3.2), limestone, chalk and coal.

3 *Metamorphic* rocks are those that have been altered by extremes of heat and pressure, e.g. shale which is compressed to form slate (Figure 3.3), and limestone which is changed by heat to give marble.

### Rock structure

The structure of a rock can, among other things, affect its *resistance* to erosion and its *permeability* to water.

### Resistance

Rocks have different strengths and so produce different landforms. The following are some examples.

- A hard rock is resistant to erosion and is more likely to form hills and mountains. A softer, less compact rock is more likely to be either broken up or worn away and so forms valleys.
- In a drainage basin, resistant rock across a valley will create waterfalls and rapids (see page 45).
- On coasts, resistant rocks stand out as headlands whereas softer rocks form bays (see page 55).

The resistance of a rock, therefore, affects the shape of the landscape. Rocks that are hard and resistant to erosion tend to produce steep cliffs at the coast or steep valley sides in drainage basins. In contrast, softer, less resistant rocks produce gentler cliffs and valley sides.

### Permeability

An *impermeable* rock is one that will not let water pass through it while a *permeable* rock is one that does let water pass through it. Permeable rocks may:

- consist of tiny pores through which water can pass, e.g. chalk
- contain areas of weakness, such as bedding planes and joints, along which water can flow, e.g. Carboniferous limestone. Figure 3.2 shows horizontal bedding planes, which separate individual layers, and vertical joints.

**Figure 3.1** Crystals in Shap granite, an igneous rock

**Figure 3.2** Layers of Old Red Sandstone in the Orkneys – a sedimentary rock

**Figure 3.3** A slate quarry in North Wales – slate is a metamorphic rock

## *Carboniferous limestone*

Carboniferous limestone consists mainly of calcium carbonate and often contains fossils including corals. It develops its own landforms and scenery due mainly to three characteristics.

### 1 Structure

Carboniferous limestone is a hard, grey sedimentary rock which was laid down in layers on the sea bed. The junctions between layers are called *bedding planes*. Joints occur at right-angles to the bedding planes. Bedding planes and joints are areas of weakness in the rock.

### 2 Permeability

Limestone is permeable, but not porous, which means water can flow along bedding planes and down joints but not through the rock itself.

### 3 Chemical weathering (see page 30)

Carbonic acid in rainwater slowly dissolves limestone and removes it in solution. Chemical weathering widens weaknesses in the rock such as bedding planes and joints.

Limestone scenery can be seen in the Yorkshire Dales and Peak District National Parks, in the Grands Causses in southern France and the Karst region of the former Yugoslavia (Figure 3.4).

### Landforms in the Grands Causses

*Causses* is the French term for limestone plateau. This wide plateau includes numerous areas where bare rock is exposed as limestone pavements. A limestone pavement, whose surface corresponds to exposed bedding planes, gives the appearance of being flat. In reality it is very uneven as rainwater has dissolved the joints to form *grykes* (*lapiés* in French), leaving detached blocks of limestone called *clints* (see Figure 3.9).

Because limestone is permeable there is very little surface drainage apart from where rivers like the Tarn have cut deep gorges (Figure 3.5). Elsewhere surface water soon drains underground down *swallow holes* and widened joints. Where solution is strong, *underground caves* such as the Grotto de la Gourniers develop (Figure 3.6). If water dripping from the ceiling of these caves evaporates then limestone is redeposited to form *stalactites*, which hang from the roof, and *stalagmites*, which grow upwards from the floor. Where an underground river reaches underlying impermeable rock, it flows over this rock until it reappears at the surface as a spring or *resurgence* (Figure 13.32).

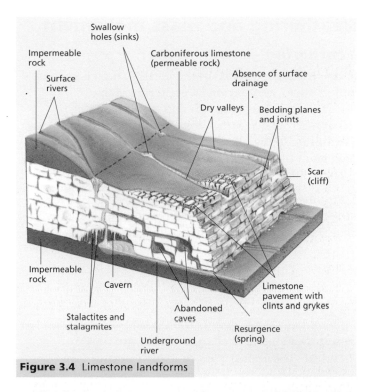

Figure 3.4 Limestone landforms

Figure 3.5 Les Gorges du Tarn, south-west France

Figure 3.6 Grotto de la Gourniers, Vercors in southern France

# Weathering and mass movement

## Weathering

Rocks that are exposed on the earth's surface become vulnerable to weathering. Weathering is the disintegration (breaking up) and decomposition (decay) of rocks *in situ* – that is, in their original place. Weathering, unlike erosion, need not involve the movement of any material.

There are two main types of weathering.

1 *Physical weathering* is the disintegration of rock into smaller pieces by physical processes without any change in the chemical composition of the rock. Physical weathering is most likely to occur in areas of bare rock where there is no vegetation to protect the rock from extremes of weather. Two examples of physical weathering are *freeze-thaw* and *exfoliation*.

2 *Chemical weathering* is the decomposition of rocks caused by a chemical change within the rock. Chemical weathering is more likely to occur in warm, moist climates as these encourage chemical reactions. An example of chemical weathering is *limestone solution*.

## Freeze–thaw

Freeze-thaw, or *frost shattering* as it is sometimes called, occurs in cold climates when temperatures are often around freezing point and where exposed rocks contain many cracks. Water enters the cracks during the warmer day and freezes during the colder night. As the water turns into ice it expands and exerts pressure on the surrounding rock. When temperatures rise the ice melts and pressure is released. Repeated freezing and thawing widens the cracks and causes pieces of rock to break off. When the broken-off rocks collect at the foot of a steep slope it is called *scree* (Figure 3.7).

**Figure 3.7** Screes formed by freeze–thaw weathering

## Exfoliation

Exfoliation, or *onion weathering*, occurs in very warm climates when a rock is repeatedly heated and cooled. Surface layers of exposed rock heat up and expand more rapidly during the day and cool and contract more rapidly at night than do the inner layers. This sets up stresses which cause the surface layers to peel off, like the layers of an onion, to leave rounded rocks and hills (Figure 3.8).

**Figure 3.8** A rock dome produced by exfoliation

## Limestone solution

Rainwater contains carbonic acid which is carbon dioxide in solution. Although it is only a weak acid it reacts chemically with rocks such as limestone which contain calcium carbonate (see page 29). As the limestone slowly dissolves, it is removed in solution by running water. Solution widens bedding planes and joints in the limestone to create a distinctive set of landforms (Figure 3.9).

**Figure 3.9** A limestone pavement with clints and grykes – a result of limestone solution

## Mass movement

Mass movement describes the downhill movement of weathered material under the force of gravity. The movement can include soil, stones and rock. Mass movement occurs on all slopes and is an almost continuous process. However, the speed of movement can vary considerably between *soil creep*, where movement is barely noticeable, and *landslides*, where movement is very rapid.

### Soil creep

Soil creep is the slowest downhill movement, occurring on very gentle and well-vegetated slopes. Although material may move by less than 1 cm a year, its results can be seen as step-like terracettes on banks and hillsides (Figure 3.10). Other effects of soil creep are shown in Figure 3.11.

### Landslides

Landslides are very rapid movements which are more likely on steep slopes and after periods of heavy rain. Some of Britain's most spectacular landslides occur along the south coast, especially in areas where softer rock overlies harder rock. As the softer rock becomes saturated and heavier, it can flow over the underlying rock.

The worst landslide disaster in Britain was at Aberfan in 1966. Like many other settlements in South Wales, Aberfan grew up around its colliery. Because the valley floors here are so narrow, it became common practice to tip the coal waste high up on the steep valley sides. Following a wet October and after a night of heavy rain, tip number 7 became saturated and suddenly and rapidly flowed downhill (Figure 3.12). It was just after 9 o'clock in the morning, and local children had already assembled in the infant and junior school. They were unaware of the millions of tonnes of coal waste, rocks and sludge, followed by a second wave consisting of liquid mud, which rushed down the steep valley side towards them. The flow, 15 metres deep, engulfed the school, a row of terraced houses and a farm (see the photograph on page 38). Of the 147 people who died (most were suffocated), 116 were children. Almost a whole generation of the community was wiped out within seconds.

Although landslides in Britain may damage property and cause inconvenience to people, fortunately events such as the one at Aberfan are rare.

**Figure 3.10** Terracettes on a hillside in the Alps

**Figure 3.12** The Aberfan landslide and mudflow

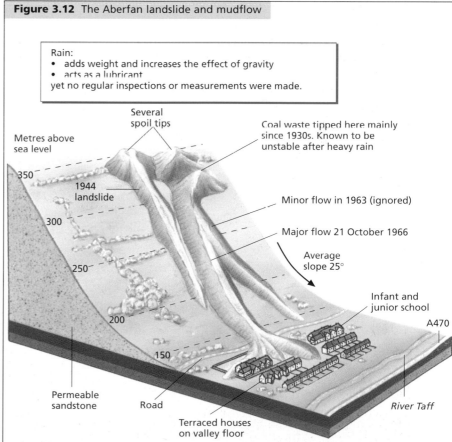

Rain:
• adds weight and increases the effect of gravity
• acts as a lubricant
yet no regular inspections or measurements were made.

Several spoil tips

Metres above sea level

Coal waste tipped here mainly since 1930s. Known to be unstable after heavy rain

350

1944 landslide

Minor flow in 1963 (ignored)

300

Major flow 21 October 1966

250

Average slope 25°

Infant and junior school

A470

200

150

Permeable sandstone

Road

Terraced houses on valley floor

*River Taff*

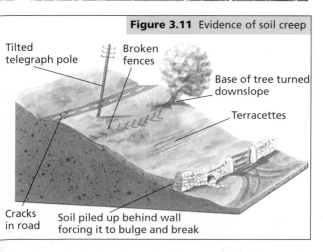

**Figure 3.11** Evidence of soil creep

Tilted telegraph pole

Broken fences

Base of tree turned downslope

Terracettes

Cracks in road

Soil piled up behind wall forcing it to bulge and break

# Plate tectonics and crustal instability

If the earth were the size of an apple, its crust would be no thicker than the apple's skin. The crust is divided into seven large segments and several smaller ones called *plates* (Figure 3.13). These plates float, like rafts, on the molten (semi-solid) mantle which lies beneath the crust.

Heat from within the earth creates convection currents in the mantle which cause the plates to move, even if only by a few centimetres a year. Plates can move either towards, away from, or sideways relative to neighbouring plates. Plates meet at *plate boundaries* and it is at these boundaries that most of the world's earthquakes and volcanic eruptions occur and where the high fold mountains are located.

## About crusts and plates

- There are two types of crust (Figure 3.14). *Continental crust* is permanent, whereas *oceanic crust* is continually being formed and destroyed. Continental crust cannot sink whereas oceanic crust, which is heavier, can.
- Most changes take place at, or near, plate boundaries. In contrast the centres of plates are rigid and usually very stable.
- There are no gaps in the earth's surface, so if two plates move apart, new oceanic crust, originating from under the crust, must form.
- Plates cannot overlap. If two plates move towards each other then they must either be pushed upwards on impact to form fold mountains, or one plate must be forced downwards and destroyed.

**Figure 3.13** Plate boundaries and zones of activity

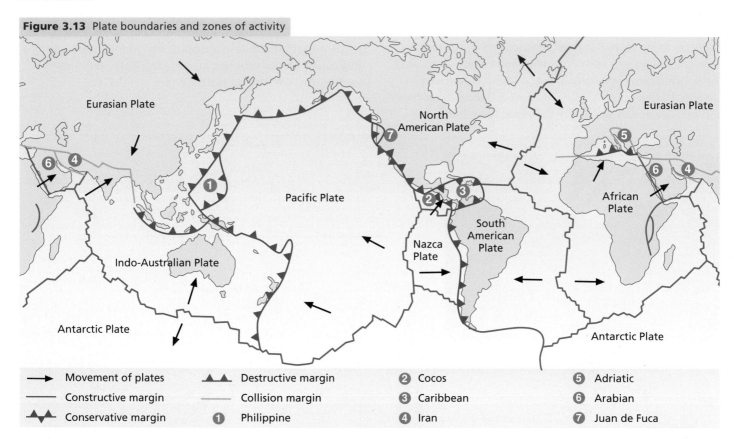

| Legend | | |
|---|---|---|
| → Movement of plates | ▲▲ Destructive margin | ② Cocos |
| — Constructive margin | — Collision margin | ③ Caribbean |
| ▼▼ Conservative margin | ① Philippine | ④ Iran |
| | | ⑤ Adriatic |
| | | ⑥ Arabian |
| | | ⑦ Juan de Fuca |

| | Continental crust (sial) | Oceanic crust (sima) |
|---|---|---|
| Thickness | 35–70 km (average) | 6–10 km (average) |
| Age of rocks | Very old, most over 1,500 million years | Very young, most less than 200 million years |
| Weight of rocks | Lighter, with an average density of 2.6 | Heavier, with an average density of 3.0 |
| Nature of rocks | Light in colour; numerous types – granite is the most common | Dark in colour; few types, mainly basalt |

**Figure 3.14** Differences between continental crust and oceanic crust

| Type of plate boundary | Description of changes | Earthquake/volcanic activity | Examples |
|---|---|---|---|
| A   Constructive margins | Two plates move away from each other. New oceanic crust appears, forming mid-ocean ridges with volcanoes. | Relatively gentle volcanic and earthquake activity | Mid-Atlantic Ridge, e.g. Iceland (pages 36–37) |
| B   (i) Destructive margins | Oceanic crust moves towards continental crust but being heavier it sinks and is destroyed, forming deep-sea trenches and island arcs with volcanoes. | Violent volcanic and earthquake activity | Etna and Vesuvius (pages 34–35) |
| (ii) Collision zones | Two continental crusts collide and as neither can sink, they are forced up into fold mountains. | Earthquake activity (no volcanic activity) | Alps (page 35), Sierra Nevada |
| C   Conservative margins | Two plates move sideways past each other – land is neither formed nor destroyed. | Can be violent earthquake activity (no volcanic activity) | None in present-day Europe |
| Note: Centres of plates are rigid | Rigid plate centres form shield-lands of ancient, worn-down rocks. | No activity | Baltic Shield |

**Figure 3.15** Different types of plate movement, with European examples of resultant landforms

**Figure 3.16** The effects of plate movement on places and people in Europe

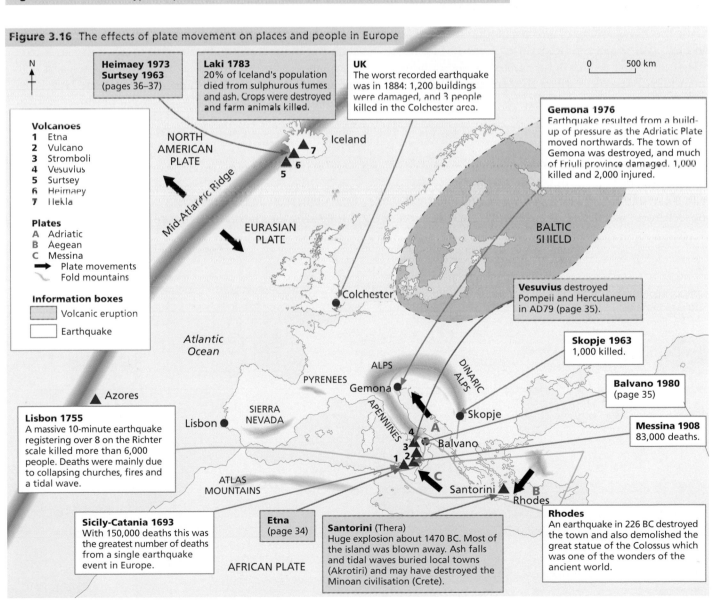

**Heimaey 1973**
**Surtsey 1963**
(pages 36–37)

**Laki 1783**
20% of Iceland's population died from sulphurous fumes and ash. Crops were destroyed and farm animals killed.

**UK**
The worst recorded earthquake was in 1884: 1,200 buildings were damaged, and 3 people killed in the Colchester area.

0      500 km

**Gemona 1976**
Earthquake resulted from a build-up of pressure as the Adriatic Plate moved northwards. The town of Gemona was destroyed, and much of Friuli province damaged. 1,000 killed and 2,000 injured.

NORTH AMERICAN PLATE

Iceland

**Volcanoes**
1   Etna
2   Vulcano
3   Stromboli
4   Vesuvius
5   Surtsey
6   Heimaey
7   Hekla

**Plates**
A   Adriatic
B   Aegean
C   Messina
→   Plate movements
     Fold mountains

**Information boxes**
☐   Volcanic eruption
☐   Earthquake

Mid-Atlantic Ridge

EURASIAN PLATE

BALTIC SHIELD

**Vesuvius** destroyed Pompeii and Herculaneum in AD79 (page 35).

Colchester

Atlantic Ocean

**Skopje 1963**
1,000 killed.

ALPS

DINARIC ALPS

PYRENEES

Gemona

**Balvano 1980**
(page 35)

Azores

SIERRA NEVADA

APENNINES

Skopje

**Messina 1908**
83,000 deaths.

**Lisbon 1755**
A massive 10-minute earthquake registering over 8 on the Richter scale killed more than 6,000 people. Deaths were mainly due to collapsing churches, fires and a tidal wave.

Lisbon

4   A
3   Balvano
1 2
C

ATLAS MOUNTAINS

Santorini

Rhodes

B

**Sicily-Catania 1693**
With 150,000 deaths this was the greatest number of deaths from a single earthquake event in Europe.

**Etna**
(page 34)

**Santorini** (Thera)
Huge explosion about 1470 BC. Most of the island was blown away. Ash falls and tidal waves buried local towns (Akrotiri) and may have destroyed the Minoan civilisation (Crete).

AFRICAN PLATE

**Rhodes**
An earthquake in 226 BC destroyed the town and also demolished the great statue of the Colossus which was one of the wonders of the ancient world.

# Crustal instability in Italy

## Destructive plate margins

To the south of Italy lies the African Plate which consists of continental crust. Between this plate and the Eurasian Plate is a small area of oceanic crust known as the Messina Plate. As the African Plate moves northwards it pushes the oceanic crust of the Messina Plate into the continental crust of the Eurasian Plate (Figure 3.17). Where these two plates meet, the oceanic crust is forced downwards to form a subduction zone with its associated deep-sea trench (the Tyrrhenian Sea). The increase in pressure, caused by the plate being forced downwards, can trigger severe earthquakes, especially in Sicily (see page 33) and southern Italy (Balvano 1980).

As the crust continues to descend it melts, partly due to heat resulting from friction caused by contact with the Eurasian Plate, and partly due to the increase in heat as it re-enters the mantle. Some of the newly formed magma, being lighter than the surrounding mantle, rises to the surface to form volcanoes. Volcanoes occur in an island arc which includes Sicily (where Mount Etna erupts frequently), Vulcano and Stromboli, and on the mainland (where Mount Vesuvius erupts less frequently).

Mount Etna has erupted 14 times this century. During the 1971 eruption most of the ski slopes and cable-car stations, together with the vulcanological observatory, were destroyed by lava. The eruption of

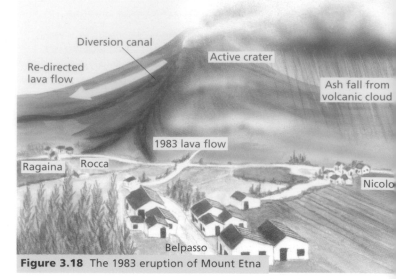

**Figure 3.18** The 1983 eruption of Mount Etna

1983 began in March and lasted for several months. Millions of tonnes of lava gushed out of a small crater on the mountainside. By the end of April the lava had engulfed a hotel, three restaurants, 25 houses and numerous orange groves and vineyards. The lava, flowing at an average speed of 15 km per hour along a channel bounded by ridges of solidified rock, began to threaten several villages in its track (Figure 3.18). On 15 May a series of controlled explosions were made to try to divert the lava into a diversion channel. Although only 30 per cent of the lava was diverted, it proved to be sufficient. The Italian Army repeated this operation following another large eruption in April 1992.

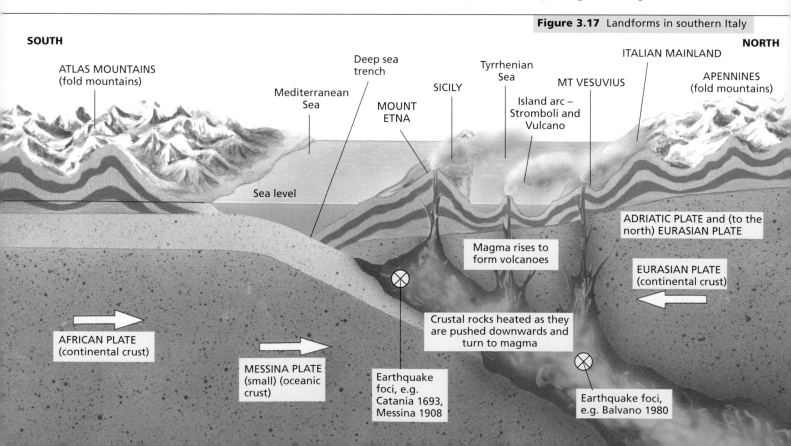

**Figure 3.17** Landforms in southern Italy

The eruption of Vesuvius in AD 79 destroyed the towns of Pompeii and Herculaneum. Thousands of people died when Pompeii was covered to a depth of 5 metres by ash (Figure 3.19), and Herculaneum to a depth of 20 metres by mudflows. Between 1631 and 1944 Vesuvius erupted, on average, every seven years. Since 1944, the date of the last eruption, the city of Naples has slowly expanded up the lower slopes of the volcano (Figure 3.20) and most of its inhabitants are too young to have witnessed any life-threatening activity. Scientists, who expect renewed activity, exploded dynamite within the volcano in mid-1996 to try to help them predict when the next eruption might occur.

An earthquake which measured 6.8 on the Richter scale devastated a large area around the town of Balvano in southern Italy on 23 November 1980 (see Figure 3.16). The main tremor lasted 1 minute 20 seconds and was followed by several secondary shocks. It led to 3,000 deaths, and 180,000 people became homeless. The earthquake caused damage as far away as Naples.

**Figure 3.20** The modern city and port of Naples showing urban growth on the lower slopes of Vesuvius

**Figure 3.19** The ruins of Pompeii with Vesuvius in the background

## Collision zones

Present-day Italy is believed to have been formed when the small Adriatic Plate, originally part of the African Plate, moved northwards and collided with the Eurasian Plate (Figure 3.21). As both plates consisted of continental crust, neither could sink and so parts of what had been an earlier much larger Mediterranean Sea (the Tethys Sea) were forced upwards to form young fold mountains – the Alps and the Apennines. The force of the collision was great enough for deposited sediments, including sea shells, to be lifted high up to the summit of the Matterhorn (now 4,478 metres above sea level). The continuing movement of these plates produces severe earthquakes, including the one at Gemona in 1976 (Figure 3.16) which caused over 1,000 deaths.

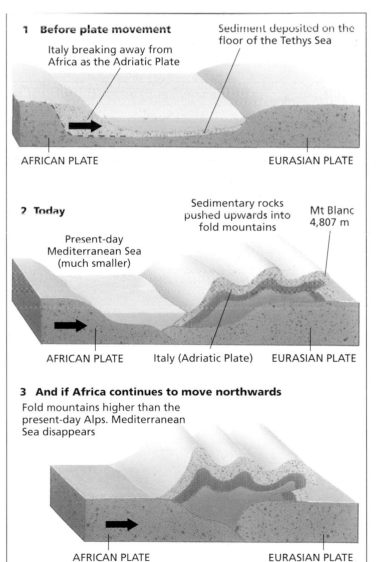

**1 Before plate movement**

Italy breaking away from Africa as the Adriatic Plate

Sediment deposited on the floor of the Tethys Sea

AFRICAN PLATE                    EURASIAN PLATE

**2 Today**

Sedimentary rocks pushed upwards into fold mountains

Mt Blanc 4,807 m

Present-day Mediterranean Sea (much smaller)

AFRICAN PLATE    Italy (Adriatic Plate)    EURASIAN PLATE

**3 And if Africa continues to move northwards**

Fold mountains higher than the present-day Alps. Mediterranean Sea disappears

AFRICAN PLATE                    EURASIAN PLATE

**Figure 3.21** The formation of the Alps

# Crustal instability in Iceland

## Constructive plate margins

At constructive margins, convection currents cause two plates to move away from each other (Figure 3.22). This movement allows magma to rise to the surface to fill any possible 'gap' and, in doing so, creates new oceanic crust.

In the North Atlantic Ocean, the North American Plate is moving away from the Eurasian Plate by some 5 cm a year. Magma, rising through weaknesses in the sea floor, creates volcanoes which have formed a range of underwater mountains called the Mid-Atlantic Ridge. In places, as in Iceland and the Azores, some of the volcanoes have built up above sea level to create new islands (e.g. Surtsey). Iceland itself is composed almost entirely of lava and other volcanic rocks. One-third of the lava poured out onto the earth's surface in the last 500 years has been in Iceland, and over 200 volcanoes have erupted there in recent geological times (Figure 3.23).

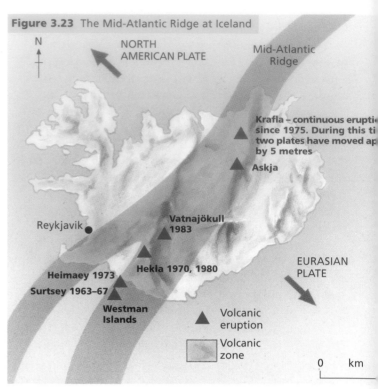

**Figure 3.23** The Mid-Atlantic Ridge at Iceland

Krafla – continuous erupti since 1975. During this ti two plates have moved ap by 5 metres

Askja

Vatnajökull 1983

Reykjavik

Hekla 1970, 1980

EURASIAN PLATE

Heimaey 1973

Surtsey 1963–67

Westman Islands

Volcanic eruption

Volcanic zone

0 km

## Surtsey

On 14 November 1963 an Icelandic fishing boat reported an explosion under the sea to the south-west of the Westman Islands (Figure 3.23). Further explosions were accompanied by the ejection of smoke, steam, ash and pumice-stone. After the submarine eruptions had built up an ash cone 130 metres above the sea bed, the new island of Surtsey appeared above the ocean surface (Figure 3.24). On 4 April 1964 the permanence of the island was guaranteed when lava began to flow from the central vent. When eruptions ceased in 1967, the island measured 2.8 km² in area and rose to a height of 178 metres. Within months, plants and insects had begun to colonise the new island.

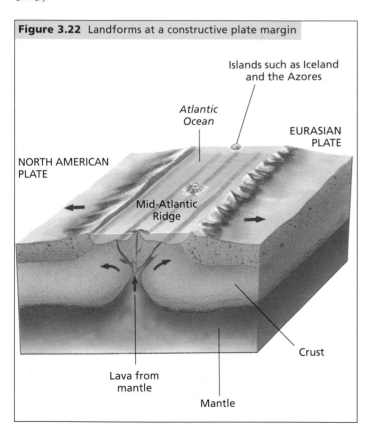

**Figure 3.22** Landforms at a constructive plate margin

Islands such as Iceland and the Azores

Atlantic Ocean

EURASIAN PLATE

NORTH AMERICAN PLATE

Mid-Atlantic Ridge

Crust

Lava from mantle

Mantle

**Figure 3.24** The creation of Surtsey

## Heimaey

Just before 0200 hours on 23 January 1973, an earth tremor stopped the clock in the main street of Heimaey, Iceland's major fishing port, in the Westman Islands (Figure 3.23). Soon afterwards, fishermen witnessed the earth's crust, east of the island's main volcanic cone of Helgafell, breaking open (Figure 3.25). Lava and ash poured out of a fissure 2 km in length, igniting some houses nearby and covering others in ash. The town's 5,300 inhabitants were evacuated as the new cone of Kirkefell began to form (Figure 3.26).

A month later and with the town still threatened, workers started to spray the still advancing lava with 12,000 tonnes of water per hour. The idea was to try to cool the lava so as to let it solidify into a natural defence and to try to prevent it blocking the harbour entrance. However, two rapid lava surges in March, destroying first 70 houses and then a further 40, meant that over one-quarter of Heimaey had been engulfed by lava. Many other buildings had also collapsed under the weight of 5 metres of ash. The eruption began to subside in April, and ended by early July. Villagers, returning soon after, found the harbour entrance narrower but better protected against bad weather.

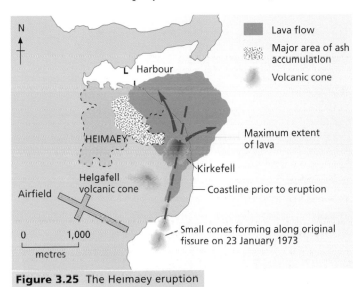

**Figure 3.25** The Heimaey eruption

**Figure 3.26** Kirkefell, the new volcanic cone which threatened Heimaey

## Why do people live in areas of crustal instability?

Many people, especially farmers, have always been prepared to take the risk of living near to volcanoes. Recently other forms of economic activity have also attracted settlement.

- **Farming** Magma contains many important minerals and nutrients necessary for plant growth. Volcanic ash and most lavas break down rapidly through weathering to give easily cultivated, fertile soils. Ash, which is destructive when it first falls, soon acts as a fertiliser. The result is that the lower slopes of volcanoes like Etna and Vesuvius can be used as vineyards, olive groves and orchards, so farmers readily return after each eruption.
- **Fishing** People are attracted to places like the Westman Islands because the seas around Iceland are rich in fish.
- **Tourism** Volcanic areas offer a range of attractions to visitors. Most landscapes are scenic, Iceland has hot springs and geysers, Etna has ski-slopes, and Pompeii and Herculaneum are visited for their ruins.
- **Geothermal power** Water heated naturally underground in Iceland is used to heat homes, swimming pools and greenhouses.
- **Urban growth** As Naples continues to expand, new buildings are spreading up the lower slopes of Vesuvius (Figure 3.20). However, this is a far less serious problem in Europe than in several economically less developed continents where urban growth is very rapid.
- **Bad luck!** People living in Pompeii and Herculaneum did not realise that Vesuvius was a volcano. In other places too volcanoes may erupt after being quiet for many centuries.

**1** *(Pages 28, 29, 30)*

**a** i)  How is limestone formed?

ii)  Give three features of limestone rock.

**b** Look carefully at the cross-section.

i)  Which of the letters A, B, C, D or E shows where you would find:
  • a limestone pavement
  • a swallow hole
  • a limestone cave or cavern?

ii)  Describe and explain the course of the river from X to Y.

iii)  Explain how the solution of limestone helped to form Gaping Gill.

**c** With the help of diagrams, describe and explain the formation of:

i)  stalactites and stalagmites

ii)  limestone pavement.

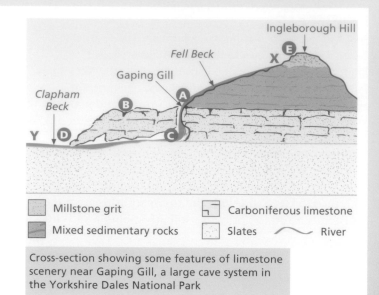

Millstone grit

Mixed sedimentary rocks

Carboniferous limestone

Slates

River

Cross-section showing some features of limestone scenery near Gaping Gill, a large cave system in the Yorkshire Dales National Park

**2** *(Pages 30 and 31)*

**a** Look at the photo and map. Match the letters A, B, C, D, E, F and G to each of the following:
  • Aberfan village
  • school
  • railway
  • tipping of coal waste
  • unexplained 1944 landslide
  • unreported 1963 mudflow
  • disaster landslide of 1966.

**b** i)  How many waste tips were there in the Aberfan area?

ii)  How was waste transported to the tips?

iii)  Why was waste tipped on the mountainside?

**c** What evidence is there to suggest that the area was unstable?

**d** Explain how water was a main cause of the Aberfan landslide.

**e** What measures could be taken to reduce the chances of a disaster like this happening again?

The Aberfan disaster, October 1966

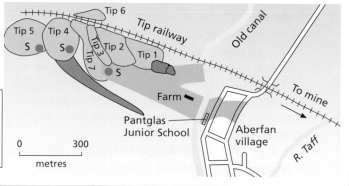

Landslides

■ 1944
■ 1963
□ 1966
S ● Spring

0    300
metres

**3** *(Pages 32 to 35)*

Look at the map.
**a** What are plates?
**b** i) Which two plates meet near Mount Etna?
   ii) Is the boundary between these plates constructive or destructive? Give reasons for your answer.
**c** The plate boundary at X is a collision zone. Describe and explain what happens here.

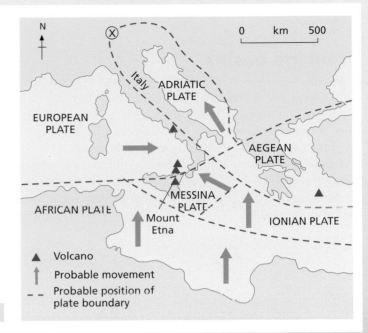

Plate boundaries and probable movements around Italy

**4** *(Pages 32, 33, 34, 35, 37)*

Look at the cross-section.
**a** Explain how Mount Etna erupts by describing what happens at locations 1, 2, 3, 4 and 5.
**b** Describe the problems caused by volcanic eruptions.
**c** What can be done to reduce the problems caused by volcanic eruptions? Answer under these headings:
   • Before the eruption
   • During the eruption
   • After the eruption.
**d** Suggest why people continue to live in areas near active volcanoes.

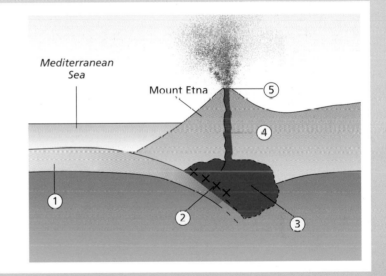

**5** *(Pages 36 and 37)*

**a** Look at the diagram.
   i) Name the plates at A and B.
   ii) Are the plates coming together or moving apart?
   iii) What is happening at C?
   iv) Why are the rocks at D older than those at E?
**b** Iceland lies on a constructive plate boundary. Explain why volcanoes are common here.
**c** What was done on Heimaey in 1973 to help reduce the danger and damage caused by the eruption?

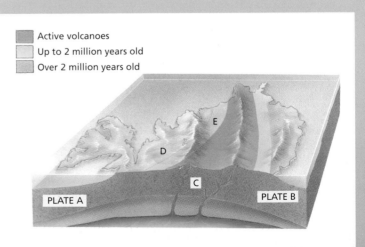

## Drainage basins

A *drainage* or *river basin* is an area of land drained by a main river and its tributaries (Figure 4.1). The boundary of a drainage basin, marked by a ridge of high land, is called a *watershed*. A watershed, therefore, separates one drainage basin from neighbouring drainage basins. Some drainage basins, like the Danube and Rhine (Figure 4.2), are very large and can cover several countries. Others, possibly that of your local river, can be small.

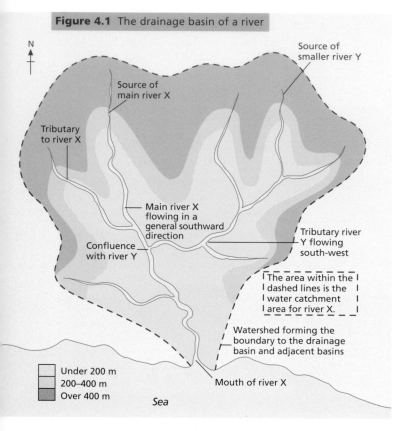

**Figure 4.1** The drainage basin of a river

## Hydrological cycle

Plants, people and animals need water in order to survive. Unfortunately 97 per cent of the earth's water is found in a salty state in seas and oceans and 2 per cent is stored as ice and snow. This means there is only 1 per cent which is either fresh water on land or water vapour in the atmosphere. As the amount of fresh water and vapour is limited, it has to be recycled over and over again. The continual recycling of water between the land, air and sea is known as the hydrological, or water, cycle (Figure 4.3). As no water is said to be added to or lost from the hydrological cycle, it is said to be a *closed system*.

**Figure 4.2** The Rhine drainage basin

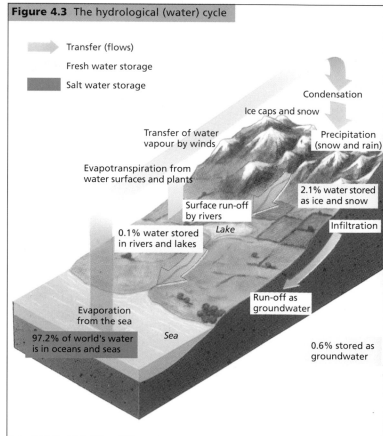

**Figure 4.3** The hydrological (water) cycle

## The drainage basin system

The drainage basin forms that part of the hydrological cycle which operates on land. However, unlike the hydrological cycle, it is an *open system*, because it has:

- *inputs* where water enters the system through precipitation (rain and snow)
- *outputs* where water is lost to the system either by rivers carrying it to the sea or through *evapotranspiration*. Evapotranspiration is the loss of moisture either directly from rivers and lakes (evaporation) or from vegetation (transpiration).

Within the system there are:

- *stores* where water is held, e.g. in pools or lakes on the surface or in soil and rocks underground
- *transfers* which are processes by which water is able to flow, or pass, through the system, e.g. infiltration, surface run-off and throughflow.

A typical drainage basin system is shown in Figure 4.4.

When it begins to rain, most water droplets are *intercepted* by trees and plants. Interception is greatest in summer and in wooded areas. If the rain falls as a short, light shower then little water reaches the ground. Instead it is stored on vegetation and eventually lost to

the system through evaporation. If the rain is heavy and lasts longer, water drips onto the ground or flows down tree trunks as *stemflow*. Water may at first form pools on the surface (*surface storage*), but as the ground becomes increasingly wet and soft, the water begins to infiltrate. *Infiltration* is the downward movement of water. It is fastest in permeable rock or soil (e.g. chalk and sands) and slowest in impermeable rock or soil (e.g. granite and clay).

Water is then either stored in the soil (*soil moisture storage*) or transferred slowly either sideways as *throughflow* or downwards as *percolation*. While throughflow is likely to create springs on valley sides, percolation forms *groundwater* which is water stored at a depth in rocks. *Groundwater* flow is the slowest form of transfer.

In contrast, *surface run-off* provides the fastest movement. Surface run-off occurs when either the storm is too heavy for infiltration, when the ground is impermeable, or when the soil has become saturated. The level of saturation, which varies seasonally, is known as the *water table*. Rivers carry water back to the sea and it is then lost from the drainage basin system.

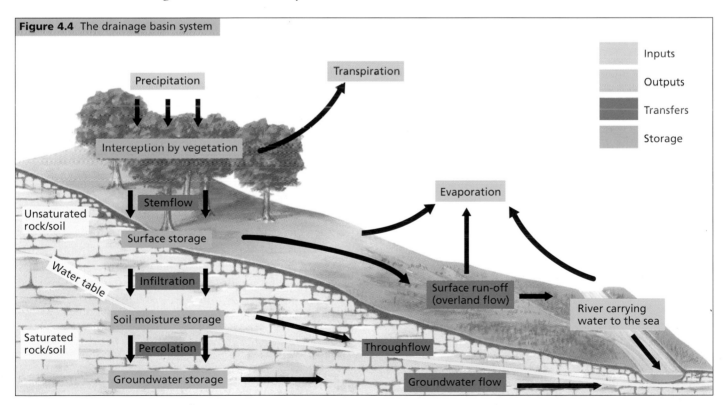

**Figure 4.4** The drainage basin system

# The water balance and flood hydrographs

## The water balance

The water balance is the balance between the inputs and outputs in the drainage basin system. It can be expressed as a formula:

$$\text{Precipitation} = \text{Run-off} + \text{Evapotranspiration}$$
$$(\textit{input}) \qquad\qquad (\textit{outputs})$$

Over much of Britain most precipitation usually falls in winter when temperatures, and therefore evapotranspiration, are lowest. This causes a water *surplus*, with large amounts of moisture stored in the soil, and high river levels. As rainfall tends to decrease in summer and as temperatures rise, river levels fall. Vegetation, now growing rapidly, has to *utilise* some of the moisture stored within the soil (Figure 4.5). Usually most parts of Britain, except the extreme south-east, receive sufficient rain in winter to last throughout the summer. However, if there is a drought, as happened in 1976 and 1995, the reserve of soil moisture may be used up. This will create a soil moisture *deficiency* and, because of the shortage of water, plants will begin to die (Figure 4.6). In the autumn, as temperatures decrease, rainfall increases and vegetation stops growing, the soil is *recharged* with moisture until, eventually, there is a water surplus again.

Different climates have different water balances. Mediterranean areas, for example, have a seasonal water deficiency due to their summer drought (Figure 4.6).

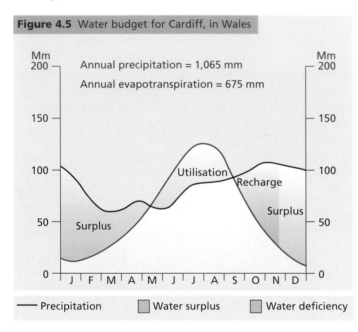

**Figure 4.5** Water budget for Cardiff, in Wales

Annual precipitation = 1,065 mm
Annual evapotranspiration = 675 mm

— Precipitation　　☐ Water surplus　　☐ Water deficiency

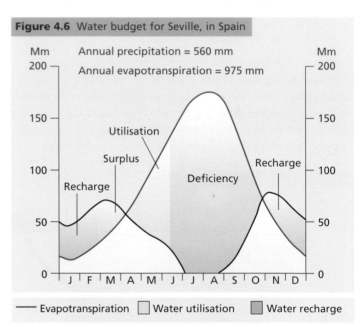

**Figure 4.6** Water budget for Seville, in Spain

Annual precipitation = 560 mm
Annual evapotranspiration = 975 mm

— Evapotranspiration　　☐ Water utilisation　　☐ Water recharge

## Discharge

The discharge of a river depends upon its velocity and volume.

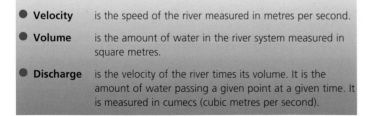

- **Velocity** is the speed of the river measured in metres per second.
- **Volume** is the amount of water in the river system measured in square metres.
- **Discharge** is the velocity of the river times its volume. It is the amount of water passing a given point at a given time. It is measured in cumecs (cubic metres per second).

In some drainage basins, discharge and river levels rise rapidly after a storm. This can cause frequent, and occasionally serious, flooding. Later, both discharge and river levels can fall almost as rapidly and, especially after dry spells, become very low. In other drainage basins, rivers seem to maintain a more even flow.

## The flood (storm) hydrograph

A hydrograph shows the discharge of a river at a given point (a gauging station) over a period of time. A flood, or storm, hydrograph shows how a river responds to a particular storm (Figure 4.7).

When a storm begins, discharge and river levels do not increase immediately as only a little of the rain falls directly into the channel. The first water to reach the river comes from surface run-off. This is later supplemented by throughflow and, finally, groundwater flow. The increase in discharge is shown by the rising limb. The gap between the time of peak (maximum) rainfall and peak discharge (the highest river level) is called the *lag time*. A river with a short lag time and a high discharge is more likely to flood than a river with a lengthy lag time and a low discharge (Figure 4.8).

**Figure 4.7** A flood, or storm, hydrograph

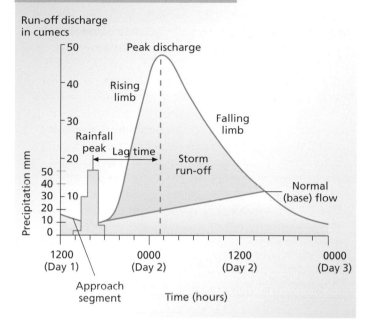

## Differences in the shape of the hydrograph

It is possible that two neighbouring drainage basins, despite having similar amounts of rainfall, can produce very different hydrograph shapes. In Figure 4.9, the river in drainage basin A is likely to flood regularly, while the river in basin B may never flood. The reasons for this difference may be due to a single factor, or to a combination of factors (Figure 4.8).

**Figure 4.9** Drainage densities of two neighbouring drainage basins

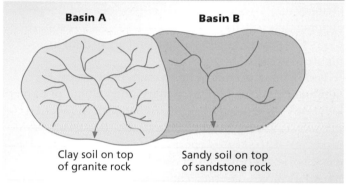

**Figure 4.8** Reasons for differences in the flood hydrographs of two neighbouring river basins

| | Drainage basin A | Drainage basin B |
|---|---|---|
| *Storm hydrograph* | 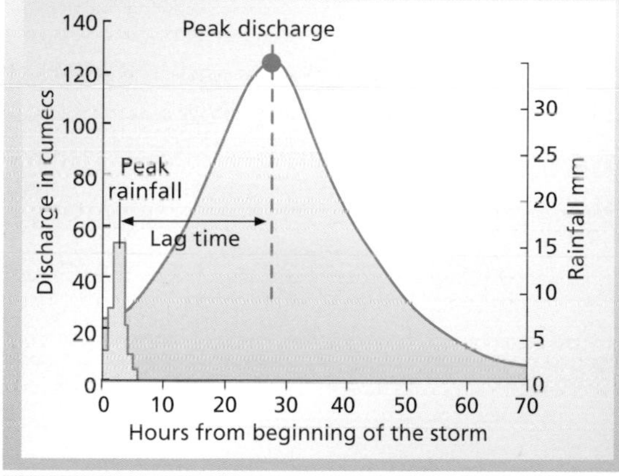 (graph: Peak discharge, Peak rainfall, Lag time) | 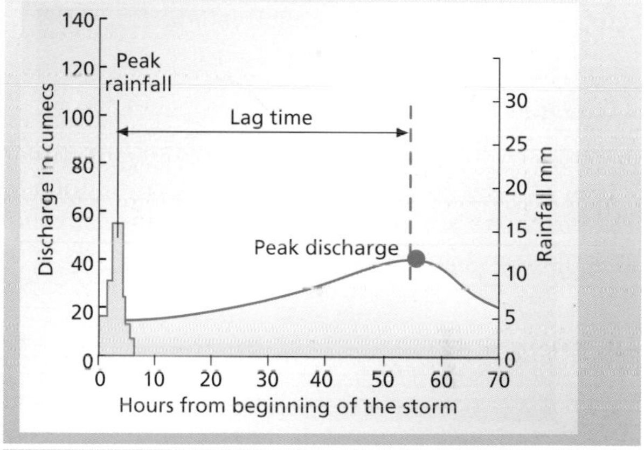 (graph: Peak rainfall, Lag time, Peak discharge) |
| **Factor** | | |
| *Weather* | Thunderstorm, torrential rain or rapid snowmelt. Ground freezes in winter or bakes hard in summer. | Gentle rain or drizzle. Ground soft and damp, allowing infiltration. |
| *Relief* | Faster run-off on steep slopes | Slower run-off on more gentle slopes |
| *Rock type* (Figure 4.9) | Surface run-off on impermeable rock | Throughflow and groundwater flow as rainfall infiltrates into permeable (porous) rock. |
| *Soil* (Figure 4.9) | Very thin soil, less infiltration. | Deeper soil, more infiltration. |
| *Natural vegetation* | Thin grass and moorland, less interception. | Forest: most interception. Roots delay throughflow and absorb moisture. Evapotranspiration reduces chances of water reaching river. |
| *Land use* | Urbanisation, increased tarmac (impermeable layer) and drains (increased run-off). Arable land – more exposed soil. | Rural area with little tarmac, concrete or drains. Tree crops and arable farming increase interception. |
| *Use of river* | Limited use. | Water extracted for industry, domestic use and irrigation. Dam built to store water. |
| *Drainage density* (Figure 4.9) | Higher density means more streams to collect water quickly. | Lower density, fewer streams to collect water. |

# River processes and landforms

## Processes

Energy is needed in any system. In the drainage basin system the source of energy is moving water. It is estimated that under normal conditions 95 per cent of the river's total energy is needed to overcome friction. Most friction occurs at the *wetted perimeter* – that is, where the river comes into contact with its banks and bed. The channel of a mountain stream, often filled with boulders, creates much friction whereas the channel of a lowland river, with its wider and deeper channel, has less friction (Figure 4.10). As a result, rivers flow more quickly in lowland areas than in highland areas.

Following a period of heavy rain, or after the confluence with a major tributary, the volume of a river increases. As less water is in contact with the wetted perimeter, friction is reduced and the river's velocity increases. The surplus energy, resulting from the decrease in friction, can be used to pick up and transport more material. The greater the velocity of the river, the greater the amount of material, both in quantity and size, that can be carried. The material transported by a river is called its *load*.

## Transportation

A river can transport its load by one of four processes. These processes – *traction* and *saltation* along its bed and *suspension* and *solution* within the river itself – are described in Figure 4.11.

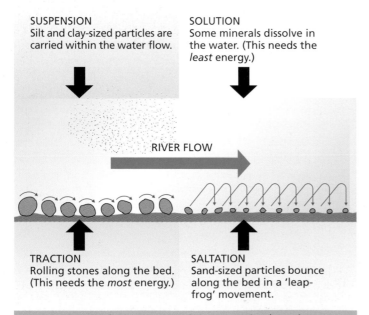

SUSPENSION
Silt and clay-sized particles are carried within the water flow.

SOLUTION
Some minerals dissolve in the water. (This needs the *least* energy.)

RIVER FLOW

TRACTION
Rolling stones along the bed. (This needs the *most* energy.)

SALTATION
Sand-sized particles bounce along the bed in a 'leap-frog' movement.

**Figure 4.11** The four processes of transportation by a river

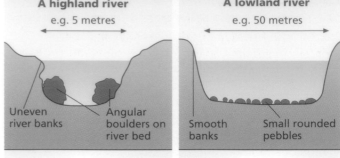

**Figure 4.10** Differences in velocity and discharge between a river in a highland area and a river in a lowland area

**A highland river**
e.g. 5 metres

Uneven river banks     Angular boulders on river bed

**A lowland river**
e.g. 50 metres

Smooth banks     Small rounded pebbles

Here the river banks and bed are rough and there are many boulders in the channel. This gives a large wetted perimeter which increases friction and reduces velocity.

Here the river banks and bed are much smoother and material in the channel is small in size. This gives a smaller wetted perimeter which reduces friction and increases velocity.

## Erosion

A river uses its load to erode (wear away) its banks and bed. As the velocity and, therefore, the amount of material which the river can transport increase, so too does the rate at which it can erode. The four processes by which a river can erode are explained in Figure 4.12.

**Figure 4.12** The four processes of river erosion

| | |
|---|---|
| **Attrition** | When bed-load (which includes boulders) collides and breaks into smaller particles – this is more likely to occur in highland areas. |
| **Abrasion** (corrasion) | When material in suspension rubs against the banks of a river. This is more likely in lowland areas where the load is small-sized and acts like sandpaper. |
| **Solution** (corrosion) | When acids in the river dissolve rocks such as limestone, which form the banks and bed. This can occur anywhere along the river's course. |
| **Hydraulic action** | When the sheer force of water dislodges particles from the river banks and bed. |

## Deposition

Deposition occurs when a river loses the energy needed to transport its load. Deposition, beginning with the heaviest material first, can take place:

- when the velocity and discharge decrease after a dry spell of weather
- where the current slows down (e.g. on the inside of a meander or where the river enters the sea).

# Landforms in highland areas

## V-shaped valleys and truncated spurs

The channel of a river in a highland area is usually choked with boulders. Under normal conditions the river has insufficient spare energy to transport these boulders and so erosion is limited. Following periods of heavy rain, which may be frequent in mountainous areas, the discharge of the river is likely to increase rapidly. This gives the river spare energy with which it can move the large boulders and enables it to cut downwards rapidly, a process called *vertical erosion*. Vertical erosion leads to the development of narrow, steep-sided valleys shaped like the letter V (Figure 4.13, and see grid square 2926 on page 207). The valley sides are steep due to rain washing down loose rock and soil. This material is then added to the river's load. The river itself is forced to wind around protruding hillsides. These protrusions, called *interlocking spurs*, restrict views up or down the valley (Figure 4.13).

**Figure 4.13** A V-shaped valley, interlocking spurs and rapids

## Waterfalls, rapids and gorges

Waterfalls usually form when a river, after flowing over a band of hard, resistant rock, meets a band of softer, less resistant rock (see page 28). The underlying less resistant rock is worn away more quickly, and the harder rock is undercut. In time the overhanging harder rock becomes unsupported and collapses. Some of the collapsed material is likely to be swirled around by the river, especially during times of high discharge, carving out a deep plunge pool. As the whole process is repeated, the waterfall retreats upstream leaving, in its place, a steep-sided gorge.

## The River Tees

Figure 4.14 shows High Force on the River Tees. At this point the river, after crossing a band of hard volcanic rock known as the Whin Sill, has eroded the underlying resistant limestone and shales (Figure 4.15). The Tees, after falling vertically for 22 metres, continues its course through a steep-sided gorge.

Several kilometres upriver from High Force is Cauldron Snout. Here the Tees tumbles 50 metres down a natural stairway of rapids, also formed by outcrops of volcanic rock. The layers of hard and softer rock are relatively thin at this point.

**Figure 4.15** Formation of High Force, Upper Teesdale

**Figure 4.14** High Force, Upper Teesdale

Relatively gentle valley sides

River Tees

A  Hard, resistant volcanic rock (the Whin Sill)

B  Layers of softer shales and less resistant limestone

4  Waterfall retreats upstream

3  Collapse

2  Overhang

22 metres

1  Undercutting

5  Steep-sided gorge

Plunge pool

Fallen rocks

River Tees

# Landforms in lowland areas

As rivers near the sea, they flow in increasingly wider and more gentle-sided valleys. As their channels increase in size, to hold the extra water received from tributaries, friction decreases (Figure 4.10) allowing the river to transport more material. Due to its reduced size, much of this material is carried in suspension. These changing circumstances mean that landforms produced by a river in a lowland area are different from those formed in the highlands.

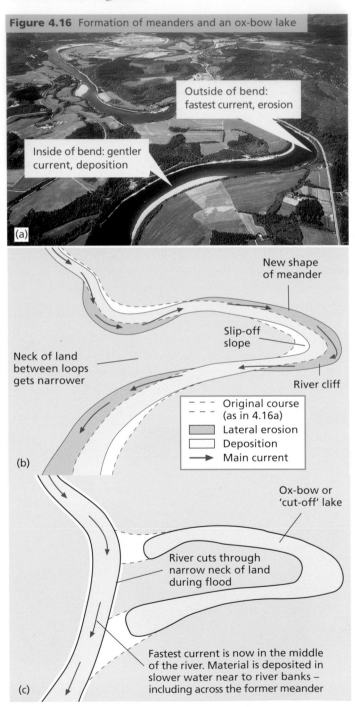

**Figure 4.16** Formation of meanders and an ox-bow lake

Outside of bend: fastest current, erosion

Inside of bend: gentler current, deposition

(a)

New shape of meander

Slip-off slope

Neck of land between loops gets narrower

River cliff

- - - Original course (as in 4.16a)
Lateral erosion
Deposition
→ Main current

(b)

Ox-bow or 'cut-off' lake

River cuts through narrow neck of land during flood

Fastest current is now in the middle of the river. Material is deposited in slower water near to river banks – including across the former meander

(c)

## *Meanders and ox-bow lakes*

When rivers flow over flatter land, they develop increasingly larger bends known as *meanders*. In a meander, most water is directed towards the outside of the bend (Figure 4.16a). This reduces friction and increases the speed of flow. As the river has more energy, it can transport material in suspension and so can erode the outside bank. As this bank is increasingly undercut, it will collapse and retreat to leave a small *river cliff*. The river is now wearing away the land by *lateral erosion*.

As there is less water on the inside of the bend, there is an increase in friction and a decrease in velocity. As the river loses energy it is unable to transport as much material and so some of its load is deposited. The material slowly builds up to form a *slip-off slope* (Figure 4.16b).

As erosion continues on the outside bends, the neck of land within the meander gets narrower (Figures 4.16b and 4.17). Eventually – and usually at a time of flood – the river cuts through the neck and takes the new and shorter route (Figure 4.16c). As the fastest current now flows in the centre of the channel, deposition is likely to occur next to the banks. The original meander is blocked off leaving a crescent-shaped ox-bow lake. This gradually dries up, only refilling after heavy rain or during a flood.

The OS map on page 206 shows a large meander on the River Tyne to the west of Newcastle, and the OS map on page 207 shows a smaller meander on the River Derwent just before it enters Derwentwater (grid square 2518).

**Figure 4.17** Meanders on the River Biebrza, Poland

## Flood plains and levées

As a river flows across a lowland area, it widens its valley through lateral erosion. During times of flood, it uses considerable amounts of energy to transport large amounts of material in suspension. Should the river overflow its banks, it spreads out over any surrounding flat land. The sudden increase in friction reduces the water's velocity and so much of the finer material (silt) is deposited. Each time the river floods, another layer of silt is added and a flat *flood plain* is formed (Figure 4.18

and, on page 207, the land between Derwentwater and Bassenthwaite lakes). The coarsest material is dropped first. This can form a natural embankment, called a *levée*, next to the river. As deposition also builds up the river's bed, these embankments have to be artificially strengthened because the river can flow at a height above its flood plain. If, at a later date, these embankments should break, then widespread flooding can result (see page 50).

## Deltas

Large rivers transport huge amounts of material in suspension down to their mouths. On reaching the sea the river current may suddenly be reduced and so the material is deposited. Deposition in the main channel causes the river to divide into a series of channels called *distributaries*. Over a period of time the deposited material builds upwards and outwards to form a *delta* (Figure 4.19). Deltas are common in the tideless Mediterranean Sea region, e.g. the Ebro (Spain), Rhône (France) and Po (Italy).

Deltas can also form when a river flowing in a highland area flows into the gentle waters of a lake, for example the River Derwent (see page 207) into Derwentwater (grid square 2619) and Bassenthwaite (grid square 2327).

**Figure 4.18** Cross-section of a river flood plain

Usually a gentle valley side

River flowing above height of flood plain

Gentle valley side

Levée artificially heightened and strengthened

Flat flood plain

Coarse material forms natural levées

Layers of silt deposited during several floods

Silt builds up on bed of river

**Figure 4.19** The Rhône delta

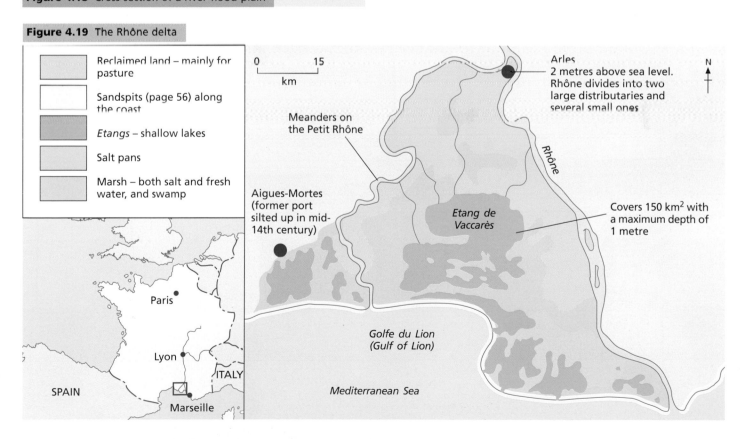

Reclaimed land – mainly for pasture

Sandspits (page 56) along the coast

*Etangs* – shallow lakes

Salt pans

Marsh – both salt and fresh water, and swamp

0    15
km

Meanders on the Petit Rhône

Aigues-Mortes (former port silted up in mid-14th century)

Arles
2 metres above sea level. Rhône divides into two large distributaries and several small ones

N

Rhône

Etang de Vaccarès

Covers 150 km² with a maximum depth of 1 metre

Golfe du Lion (Gulf of Lion)

Mediterranean Sea

Paris

Lyon

ITALY

SPAIN

Marseille

# River flooding – the UK

## The River Lavant (Chichester)

The River Lavant flows from the South Downs into the sea at Chichester (Figure 4.20). 'Flows' is not always an accurate description. The river often dries up during the summer months and under the extreme conditions of recent times it has sometimes failed to flow all year. Even during a wet winter, the river rarely fills its 2-metre-wide channel. To many people, the Lavant was not a real river – at least not until it flooded during January 1994.

### Effects

The first widespread flooding occurred on 3 January. It affected parts of Chichester (College Lane), the village of East Lavant and the A27 Chichester by-pass. By 5 January flood water was rising in the town's Hornet shopping area (Figure 4.21) and along the alternative flood route southwards from Westhampnett. An Emergency Control Centre was set up and some people were evacuated from highest-risk residential areas. The A27 by-pass was closed to traffic on 7 January (Figure 4.22). Flood levels continued to rise, with the two worst-affected areas being within and to the west of Chichester. It was not until 16 January that the flood waters showed the first signs of falling within Chichester – almost two weeks after the first report of flooding. The A27 did not re-open until 21 January. Flood damage was estimated to be £6 million.

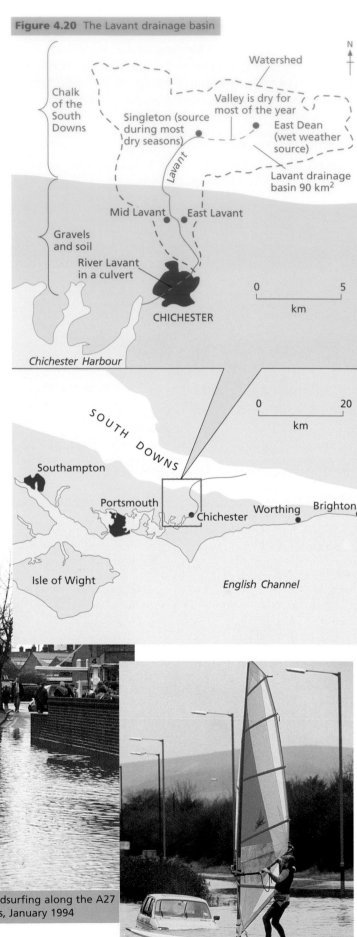

**Figure 4.20** The Lavant drainage basin

**Figure 4.21** Flooding in the Hornet shopping area

**Figure 4.22** Windsurfing along the A27 Chichester by-pass, January 1994

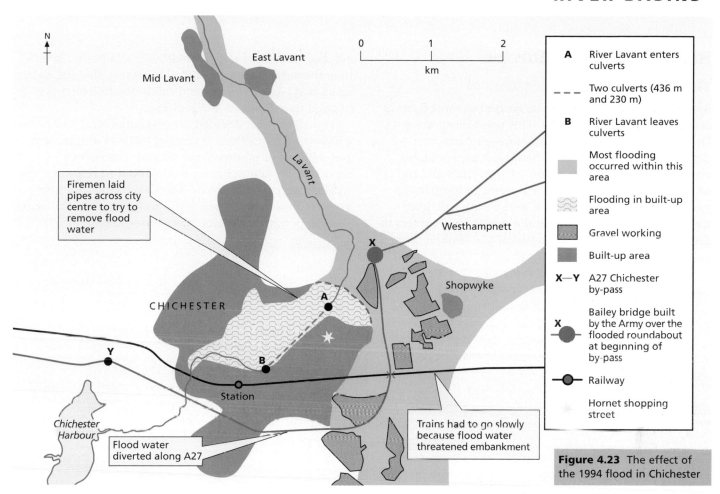

**Figure 4.23** The effect of the 1994 flood in Chichester

Map labels and legend:

East Lavant
Mid Lavant
La Vant
Westhampnett
Shopwyke
CHICHESTER
Chichester Harbour
Station

Firemen laid pipes across city centre to try to remove flood water

Flood water diverted along A27

Trains had to go slowly because flood water threatened embankment

A — River Lavant enters culverts
- - - Two culverts (436 m and 230 m)
B — River Lavant leaves culverts
Most flooding occurred within this area
Flooding in built-up area
Gravel working
Built-up area
X—Y A27 Chichester by-pass
X — Bailey bridge built by the Army over the flooded roundabout at beginning of by-pass
Railway
Hornet shopping street

## Causes

Although the physical causes were easy to explain, human causes were more controversial. Certainly the National Rivers Authority (NRA) blamed the exceptionally wet weather.

### Physical (natural)

- The upper drainage basin is on the chalk of the South Downs, a permeable rock which absorbs and stores water (Figure 4.20). This means that only a small amount of the total rainfall drains into the River Lavant – the majority percolates downwards and becomes groundwater (Figure 4.4).
- Above-average rainfall in the autumn and December of 1993 led to an increase in the amount of groundwater. More heavy rain fell from late December to mid-January due to a succession of depressions and their associated fronts moving across the region from the Atlantic (see page 8). This resulted in
  - the highest ever recorded water table (Figure 4.4)
  - a peak flow (Figure 4.7) of the Lavant of 7.9 cumecs on 10 January, which was nearly twice the previously recorded maximum flow.

### Human

- It is believed that the river was diverted from its natural course, possibly in Roman or medieval times, to act as a defensive moat around Chichester.
- During the 18th century the river was channelled under Chichester through a culvert (Figure 4.23). The culvert's capacity is 5 cumecs. If this capacity is reached, as it was on this occasion, water backs up behind it.
- Superstores, car parks, houses and roads have all been built on the flood plain. This has left less space for surplus water from the overflowing river, and provides an impermeable surface layer allowing faster run-off.
- The A27 was believed by some people to have acted as a dam across the flood plain.
- Several bridges impeded the river's flow, and a grill to the culvert trapped debris.
- Gravel excavations to the south and east of Chichester, into which surplus water from Chichester normally drains, could this time have delayed the speed of run-off from the town.

It was not so much the height or damage caused by the flood that made this a significant event but rather the length of time that it disrupted human activity.

# River flooding – Europe

## *The Rhine (1995)*

A wet end to 1994 had left the ground in most parts of north-west Europe saturated. This was followed, in January 1995, by a succession of fast-moving depressions which swept across the region bringing rain, gales and blizzards. Coupled with the rapid run-off of water into river channels was a rise in temperature which caused early snowmelt in the Alps and other highland areas. By the end of the month many rivers in the Rhine and Maas drainage basins had broken their banks (Figure 4.24).

The first settlements to be threatened by the rising Rhine were in Germany. Water levels at Koblenz reached their 1926 record. In Cologne, at the time of peak flow on 30 January, the city centre was flooded to a depth of 2 metres. It was several days before the waters receded and the Rhine could be re-opened to shipping.

In the Netherlands, the worst-affected areas were in the south of the country (Figure 4.24). At the Dutch–German border town of Lobith, water levels rose to 16.66 metres. This peak flow was the second highest ever recorded, falling just short of the 16.93 metres record of 1926 when hundreds of people drowned. In 1995 the greatest danger was around and to the west of Nijmegen where the rivers Maas and Rhine posed a double threat.

By 1 February, the water had reached the tops of the dykes (embankments) in many places (Figures 4.25 and 4.26). The longer the water level remained high, the greater the risk of subsidence as the dykes themselves

became saturated. The rivers flowed at a higher level than the surrounding countryside and so, had the dykes given way, many villages and fields would have been flooded to a depth of 4–6 metres.

The authorities decided on evacuation and some 250,000 people, 300,000 head of cattle, a million pigs and millions of poultry were moved. Emergency services and volunteers worked flat-out to reinforce the weakest parts of the dykes. The dykes held, but only just, until the water level began to fall in early February and the potential disaster was averted (Figure 4.27).

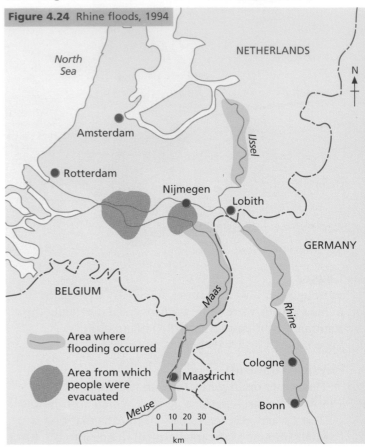

**Figure 4.24** Rhine floods, 1994

**Figure 4.26** Flooding in the Netherlands, 1995

**Figure 4.25** Water overtops a dyke in south Limburg

NEWSLETTER 1–1995

## THE DISASTER THAT NEVER HAPPENED

In early February 1995, newspapers and television stations around the world relayed images of the Netherlands facing another major flooding disaster. Fortunately, the reality was less dramatic. In Limburg province, parts of towns and villages were flooded by the Maas. But dykes along the Rhine, Waal and IJssel were just strong enough to avoid major flooding.

Much of the foreign media portrayed the situation as far more critical than it really was, even drawing parallels with the great flooding disaster in the south-west of the Netherlands in 1953. The comparison does not bear serious consideration, however, given the vastly different outcome. In 1995, not much land was flooded, no houses, roads or railway lines were destroyed, and – most important of all – there were no deaths. The 1953 floods, by contrast, cost more than 1,800 lives.

**Figure 4.27** From a Dutch geographical journal

### Difference between a Rhine flood and a flash flood

If there is rapid snowmelt or heavy rainfall in the upper Rhine drainage basin, it takes several days for the flood water to travel downriver to the Netherlands (see Figure 4.2). This gives the Dutch sufficient time to predict:

1 the maximum *height* to which the river is likely to rise, and
2 the actual *time* when the river will peak at that highest level.

This means that if it seems likely that the river will overflow its banks, there is time to alert the emergency services and to warn people in time to take preventive action.

With flash floods the situation is very different. Flash floods occur unexpectedly and have a short lag time (Figure 4.7). This means that there is less chance to warn people of the event, and so lives and property are at a much greater risk.

## An Italian flash flood – June 1996

Northern Italy experiences severe thunderstorms in most summers and autumns when hot air is pushed across the Gulf of Genoa and into the Alps or northern Apennines. On 20 June 1996, a ferocious storm struck the mountains to the north of Lucca, in Tuscany (Figure 4.28). Within minutes, rivers had swollen and burst their banks, sweeping away cars, flooding houses, destroying bridges, and cutting off villages. The main Genoa–Rome railway line was blocked by a huge mudslide (see page 31).

Worst hit were the villages of Montepania and Garfaguna (Figure 4.29) where raging rivers cut straight through houses (similar to Lynmouth during the north Devon flood of 1952). Twenty-four hours after the event, 11 bodies had been recovered and 30 people were still missing. It was the eleventh flash flood in the Lucca area in the last five years, and the worst in northern Italy since November 1994 when 59 people died and several thousand were made homeless in Piedmont.

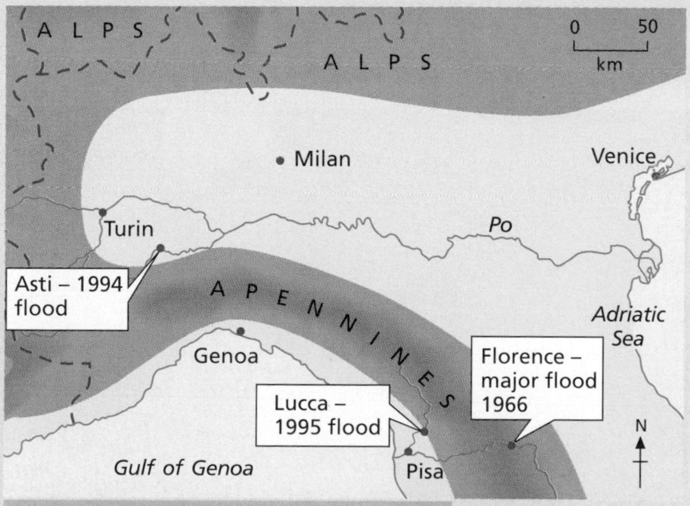

**Figure 4.28** Flash floods in northern Italy

**Figure 4.29** The village of Montepania, in Tuscany, after the 1996 flash flood

**1** *(Pages 40 and 41)*

Look at the diagram.

**a** Match the letters A, B, C and D to each of these terms:

- precipitation ● evaporation
- condensation ● transpiration.

**b** i) List four places on the diagram where water is stored.

ii) Give two ways, shown by arrows, in which water is transferred back to the sea.

**c** Explain what is meant by the terms *evapotranspiration* and *water table*.

**d** 'Interception varies from season to season and depends on the type of vegetation in an area.' Explain this statement.

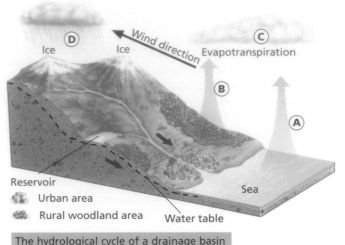

The hydrological cycle of a drainage basin

**2** *(Pages 42 and 43)*

Look at the map and graphs.

**a** i) How many hours after the start of the storm did most rain fall?

ii) How many hours after the start of the storm did the River Severn reach its peak discharge?

iii) Give a reason for the difference in these two times.

**b** i) Which river had the higher discharge?

ii) Which river had the shortest lag time?

iii) Which river had the most rapid increase in discharge after the storm?

**c** With help from the map, suggest reasons for these differences in discharge.

**d** Explain how the pattern of river discharge would be different if the River Severn drained a built-up area.

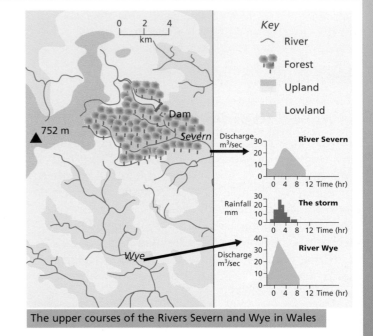

The upper courses of the Rivers Severn and Wye in Wales

**3** *(Pages 44 and 45)*

Look at the sketch of High Force, which is based on Figure 4.14.

**a** Match the letters A, B, C, D, E and F with the following:

- plunge pool ● steep-sided gorge
- Whin Sill ● undercutting
- rock collapse ● limestone and shale.

**b** With help from the diagram explain how the waterfall and gorge at High Force have been formed.

**4** *(Page 46)*

Look at the diagram, which shows some features of the river meander in grid square 2924 on page 207.

**a** i) What is a meander?
   ii) What is erosion?
   iii) What is deposition?

**b** Describe the variations in velocity of the river.

**c** i) Describe where, on the diagram, erosion and deposition are taking place.
   ii) Explain why erosion and deposition are taking place at those locations.

**d** Choose one of the following river landforms and describe how it was formed. Use labelled diagrams and name actual examples where possible.

   • Ox-bow lake   • Flood plain and levée   • Delta

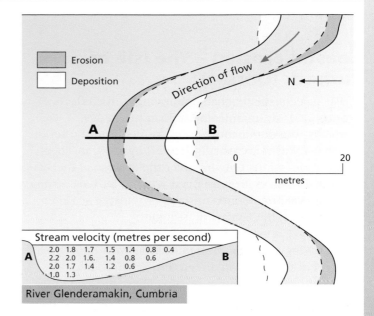

| Stream velocity (metres per second) | | | | | | |
|---|---|---|---|---|---|---|
| 2.0 | 1.8 | 1.7 | 1.5 | 1.4 | 0.8 | 0.4 |
| 2.2 | 2.0 | 1.6 | 1.4 | 0.8 | 0.6 | |
| 2.0 | 1.7 | 1.4 | 1.2 | 0.6 | | |
| 1.0 | 1.3 | | | | | |

River Glenderamakin, Cumbria

**5** *(Pages 42, 43, 50, 51)*

Study the hydrograph of the 1995 Rhine flood.

**a** i) When was the heaviest rain?
   ii) When was the peak discharge?
   iii) What was the lag time?

**b** Why is there such a long lag time on this hydrograph?

**c** How are the problems created by a flash flood different from those experienced on the Rhine?

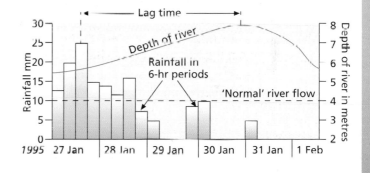

**6** *(Pages 47 and 50)*

The Rhine sometimes floods land in the Netherlands. Look at the flood prediction diagram showing what might happen there. Imagine that you are a planner and have to decide the type of land use for the area.

• For each zone choose two suitable land uses from the list below. In each case explain the reasons for your choice.

   * Sports fields              * Major roads
   * Old people's homes         * Hospitals
   * Low-cost rented housing     * Minor roads
   * Small factories            * Public parks

• All the land must be used, but safety should be a main concern.

**Zone A** Below normal river level • Likely to flood once in 5 years

**Zone B** Normal river level to 0.5 metres above normal • Likely to flood once in 20 years

**Zone C** More than 0.5 metres above normal river level • Likely to flood once in 50 years

**Zone D** Above flood level • Not likely to flood

Flood prediction zones in part of the Netherlands

# Coastal erosion – The Isle of Purbeck (Dorset)

Coasts are constantly changing owing to the effects of various land, air, marine and human processes. Normally, the dominant process results from the action of waves. Waves are usually created by the transfer of energy from winds blowing over the surface of the sea. The largest waves are produced when winds are strong, blow for lengthy periods of time, cross large sea areas and approach the land at right-angles.

As a wave approaches shallow water, its base reduces speed owing to an increase in friction with the sea-bed. The top of the wave, unaffected by friction, becomes higher and steeper until it breaks. There are two types:

1 **Constructive waves** use most of their limited energy in transporting material up the beach in the *swash*. Constructive waves are more likely to build up beaches and create deposition landforms (pages 56–57).

2 **Destructive waves** use most of their considerable energy in transporting material down the beach in the *backwash*. Destructive waves are more likely to erode the coastline.

## Processes of erosion

Waves, like rivers (Figure 4.12), can erode the land by one of four processes.
- **Corrasion** (abrasion) is caused by large waves hurling beach material against a cliff.
- **Attrition** is when waves cause rocks on the beach to bump into each other, making them break up into smaller particles.
- **Corrosion** (solution) is when salts and other acids in seawater slowly dissolve a cliff.
- **Hydraulic action** is the force of waves compressing air in cracks in a cliff.

## Landforms – the Isle of Purbeck

The Isle of Purbeck is a peninsula, not an island, located on the south coast of England (Figure 5.1). It consists of four main types of rock:
- chalk and limestone, which are harder, more resistant and permeable rocks
- clays and sands, which are softer and less resistant.

These differences in rock type have led to the formation of a range of erosion landforms.

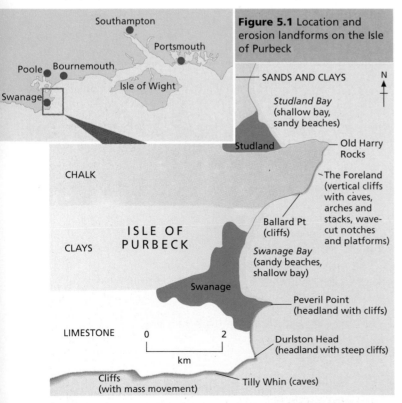

**Figure 5.1** Location and erosion landforms on the Isle of Purbeck

Southampton
Portsmouth
Poole, Bournemouth
Swanage
Isle of Wight

SANDS AND CLAYS
*Studland Bay* (shallow bay, sandy beaches)
Studland
Old Harry Rocks
CHALK
The Foreland (vertical cliffs with caves, arches and stacks, wave-cut notches and platforms)
Ballard Pt (cliffs)
ISLE OF PURBECK
*Swanage Bay* (sandy beaches, shallow bay)
CLAYS
Swanage
Peveril Point (headland with cliffs)
LIMESTONE
0        2
km
Durlston Head (headland with steep cliffs)
Cliffs (with mass movement)
Tilly Whin (caves)

**Figure 5.2** Formation of headlands and bays on the east coast of the Isle of Purbeck

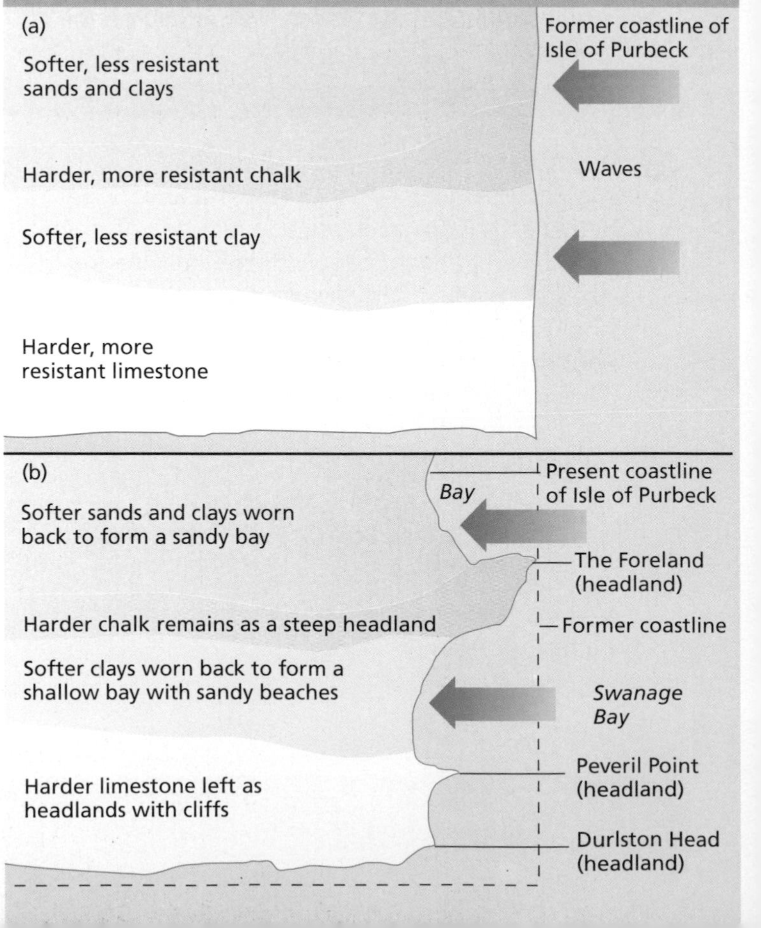

(a)
Softer, less resistant sands and clays
Harder, more resistant chalk
Softer, less resistant clay
Harder, more resistant limestone
Former coastline of Isle of Purbeck
Waves

(b)
Softer sands and clays worn back to form a sandy bay
Harder chalk remains as a steep headland
Softer clays worn back to form a shallow bay with sandy beaches
Harder limestone left as headlands with cliffs
Bay
Present coastline of Isle of Purbeck
The Foreland (headland)
Former coastline
*Swanage Bay*
Peveril Point (headland)
Durlston Head (headland)

## Headlands and bays

Headlands and bays have formed here due to the alternating outcrops of resistant and less resistant rock (Figure 5.2). Destructive waves have eroded the less resistant clays and sands to form the bays at Swanage and Studland. The waves have not, however, been able to wear away the more resistant chalk and limestone as quickly. As a result, headlands have been left protruding into the sea on either side of Swanage. As these headlands are now exposed to the full force of the waves, they have become vulnerable to erosion.

## Cliffs, wave-cut notches and wave-cut platforms

Erosion is most rapid when large waves break against the foot of a cliff. With wave energy at its maximum, the waves will undercut the cliff to form a wave-cut notch (Figure 5.3 and **X** on Figure 5.4). Over a period of time, the notch will enlarge and the cliff above it, now unsupported, will collapse. Where this process is repeated, as at The Foreland, the cliff will retreat leaving a wave-cut platform. This landform is a gently sloping area of bare rock marking the foot of the receding cliff. The wave-cut platform at Old Harry Rocks is exposed at low tide but covered at high tide (**Y** on Figure 5.4).

## Caves, arches and stacks

Although chalk and limestone are resistant rocks, they usually contain areas of weakness. The weaknesses may be in the form of cracks, known as *faults* (**A** on Figure 5.4), or as bedding planes and joints (page 29). Corrasion, corrosion and hydraulic action by the waves widen these weaknesses to form, initially, a *cave* (**B**), like the Tilly Whin Caves near Durlston Head. Where a

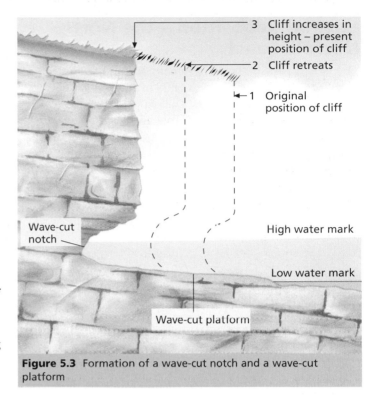

**Figure 5.3** Formation of a wave-cut notch and a wave-cut platform

cave forms in a headland, it may be widened and deepened until the sea cuts right through the headland to form an *arch* (**C**). If the waves continue to erode the foot of the arch, then the roof will eventually become too heavy to be supported and it will collapse leaving a detached column of rock known as a *stack* (**D**). At The Foreland (Figure 5.4), there are two stacks known as Old Harry Rocks. The stacks themselves are being undercut so that, in time, they will collapse to leave underwater stumps.

**Figure 5.4** Caves, arches and stacks at The Foreland, Dorset

## Coastal deposition – the North Norfolk coast

The North Norfolk coast between Sheringham and Overstrand consists of steep cliffs of easily eroded glacial deposits (Figure 5.5). During periods of heavy rainfall the cliffs become unstable and, as a result of mass movement, collapse (page 31). The most dramatic recent collapses have been near Overstrand. Here, despite the cliff being artificially protected by a sea-wall and groynes (Figure 5.6), the land retreated by 80 metres between 1990 and 1994. Later, and especially when the wind is in the north-east, waves will transport the collapsed material along the Norfolk coast. As shown on Figure 5.5, material is moved both to the west and the south. The material, as in a river, can be carried in solution and suspension or moved by traction (rolling) and saltation (Figure 4.11).

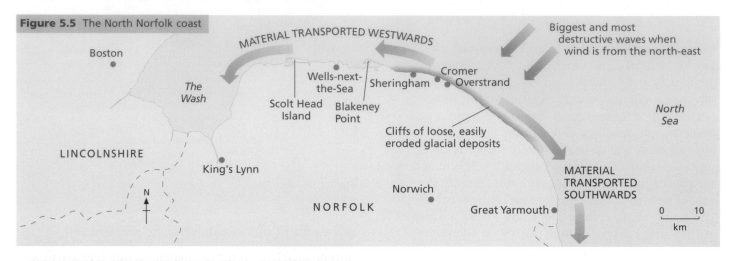

**Figure 5.5** The North Norfolk coast

**Figure 5.6** Groynes on the coast of East Anglia

### Transportation – longshore drift

The most important process of transportation by waves is longshore drift (Figure 5.7). Waves rarely approach a beach at right-angles, but rather from a direction similar to that from which the wind is blowing. When a wave breaks, the swash carries material up the beach at the same angle at which the wave approached the shore. As the swash dies away, the backwash returns material straight down the beach, at right-angles to the sea, under the influence of gravity. This means that material is slowly moved along the coast in a zig-zag course. The effect of longshore drift can best be seen when wooden groynes have been built to try to limit the movement of material along the beach (Figure 5.6).

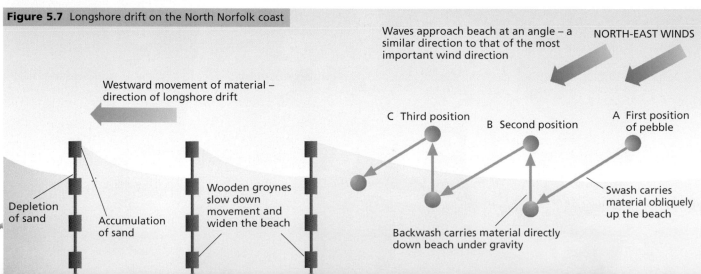

**Figure 5.7** Longshore drift on the North Norfolk coast

## Deposition landforms – spits

A spit, like the one at Blakeney Point (Figure 5.8), is a long, narrow accumulation of sand or shingle, with one end attached to the land and the other projecting at a narrow angle either into the sea or across a river estuary. Many spits have hooked or curved ends (Figure 5.8).

Blakeney Point has formed as a result of longshore drift carrying large amounts of material westwards along the North Norfolk coast (**A** on Figure 5.9). The supply of this material is guaranteed owing to the frequent collapse of the cliffs between Sheringham and Overstrand. At point **B** there was a gentle change in the direction of the former coastline. This allowed larger material, mainly pebbles, to be deposited in an area of slightly sheltered water. Further deposition, increasingly of smaller-sized shingle (**C**), enabled the feature to build up above sea level and to extend its length (**D**).

The Norfolk coast is protected by the land from the prevailing south-westerly winds. However, when these prevailing winds do blow, they cause the waves off Blakeney Point to change direction and to approach the land from the north-west. During these lengthy periods, some material at the end of the spit is pushed inland to form the curved end (**E**). When the next winter storms occur, the westward movement of material resumes and the spit continues to grow (**F**). Blakeney Point, with its numerous hooked ends, is evidence of the many changes in wind and therefore wave direction. The end

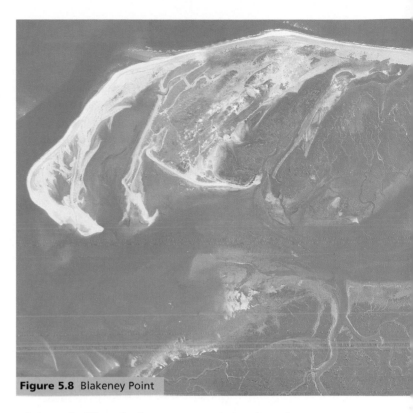

**Figure 5.8** Blakeney Point

of the spit (**G**), which consists mainly of sand, seems unable to extend any further owing to the strong river current which prevents deposition. A *bar* forms where a spit does extend across an estuary or bay.

Spits become permanent when sand is blown up the beach to form sand-dunes. Salt-marshes usually develop in the sheltered water behind the spit.

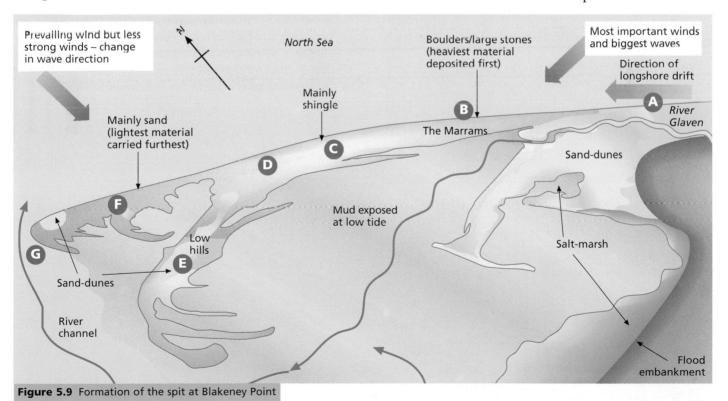

**Figure 5.9** Formation of the spit at Blakeney Point

# Coastal flooding – the southern North Sea

*Storm surges* are a major cause of coastal flooding. Where they occur in densely populated areas they can cause considerable loss of life, damage to property and disruption of everyday life. Two areas at risk from storm surges are the east coast of England, from the Humber to the Thames, and the coast of the Netherlands.

## Why are these areas at risk?

- Since the sixteenth century large parts of eastern England and the western Netherlands have been drained for farming. The result of this drainage was a shrinking in the level of the land so that the present-day English Fenlands and the Dutch Polders now lie below sea level.
- Elsewhere, flat areas behind the coast are protected either naturally by sand-dunes (Lincolnshire and the Dutch coast north of the Rhine) or artificially by sea-walls (East Anglia) and dykes (Netherlands).
- When northerly gale-force winds blow, they push water southwards into an area where the North Sea becomes both narrower and shallower. This surge of water can cause sea level to rise by over one metre.

## The 1953 storm surge

Storm surges occur in the southern North Sea three or four times a year. They result from the passing of a depression over the northern North Sea. As air pressure falls, the reduced pressure allows the level of the sea to rise.

On 31 January 1953 four factors became linked in a fateful combination.

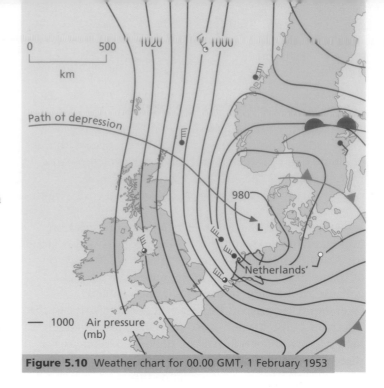

**Figure 5.10** Weather chart for 00.00 GMT, 1 February 1953

1 A very deep depression caused a larger than predicted rise in sea level (Figure 5.10).
2 Northerly storm-force winds (force 12) drove a wall of water down the North Sea and produced waves 6 metres high (Figure 5.11).
3 There was a full-moon spring tide (that is, the highest tide in a monthly cycle).
4 Rivers, especially in eastern England, were trying to discharge flood water into the sea.

The resultant surge of water was up to 3 metres higher than the predicted spring tide (Figure 5.12). The surge, coupled with the storm waves, broke through sea defences in eastern England (on the evening of 31 January) and the Netherlands (early morning of 1 February). The event caused the deaths of some 300 people in eastern England (Figure 5.13) and over 1,800 in the Netherlands (Figures 5.14, 5.15 and 5.16).

**Figure 5.11** Storm waves along the North Sea coast of East Anglia

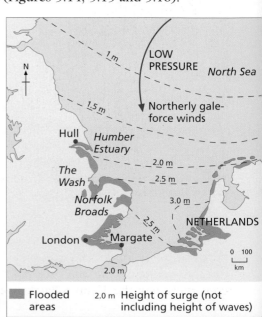

**Figure 5.12** The storm surge, 31 January to 1 February 1953

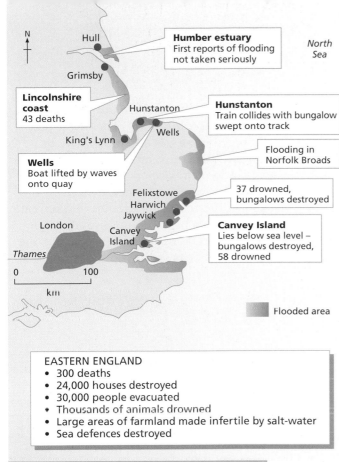

Humber estuary
First reports of flooding not taken seriously

North Sea

Hull

Grimsby

Lincolnshire coast
43 deaths

Hunstanton

Hunstanton
Train collides with bungalow swept onto track

King's Lynn

Wells

Flooding in Norfolk Broads

Wells
Boat lifted by waves onto quay

Felixstowe
Harwich
Jaywick

37 drowned, bungalows destroyed

London

Canvey Island

Thames

Canvey Island
Lies below sea level – bungalows destroyed, 58 drowned

0    100
km

Flooded area

EASTERN ENGLAND
• 300 deaths
• 24,000 houses destroyed
• 30,000 people evacuated
• Thousands of animals drowned
• Large areas of farmland made infertile by salt-water
• Sea defences destroyed

**Figure 5.13** The floods of 1953: eastern England

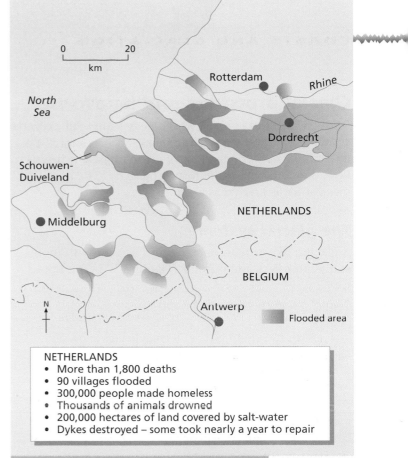

0    20
km

North Sea

Rotterdam

Rhine

Dordrecht

Schouwen-Duiveland

NETHERLANDS

Middelburg

BELGIUM

Antwerp

Flooded area

NETHERLANDS
• More than 1,800 deaths
• 90 villages flooded
• 300,000 people made homeless
• Thousands of animals drowned
• 200,000 hectares of land covered by salt-water
• Dykes destroyed – some took nearly a year to repair

**Figure 5.14** The floods of 1953: the Netherlands

**Figure 5.15** A breached dyke near Papendrecht, north of Dordrecht in the Netherlands

**Figure 5.16** The flooded village of Kerkwerve on the island of Schouwen-Duivelandnorth of Dordrecht in the Netherlands

Although 1953 may seem a long time ago, and a storm surge of this size may only occur once in every thousand years, both Britain and the Netherlands learnt from the disaster. One outcome in Britain was the construction of the Thames Barrage and in the Netherlands the Dutch Delta scheme (page 76). As a result of improvements in sea defences and early warning systems, flooding by the sea is now very rare . . . but the threat is always there!

## Glacial processes and landforms

Glaciers develop in areas where heavy snowfall exceeds snowmelt. As the snow accumulates, it is compressed into solid ice. As the weight of ice increases, it begins to flow downhill under the force of gravity. The moving mass of ice is known as a *glacier*.

### The glacial system

A glacier, like a river, operates as a system with inputs, stores, transfers and outputs (Figure 5.17). The upper part of a glacier, where inputs exceed outputs, is known as the *zone of accumulation*. The lower part, where outputs exceed inputs, is called the *zone of ablation* (Figure 5.18). In areas, or at times, when snowfall exceeds snowmelt, glaciers will advance. Conversely, where and when snowmelt exceeds snowfall, glaciers will retreat. This advance and retreat refers only to the position of the *snout* or end of a glacier. Even if a glacier is retreating, ice is still moving downhill. At present, glaciers in the Alps are retreating.

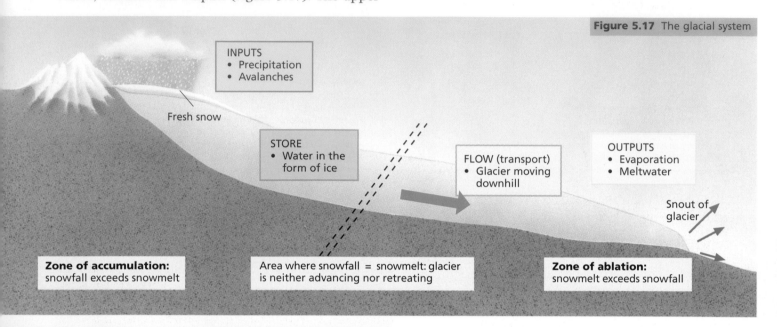

**Figure 5.17** The glacial system

INPUTS
- Precipitation
- Avalanches

Fresh snow

STORE
- Water in the form of ice

FLOW (transport)
- Glacier moving downhill

OUTPUTS
- Evaporation
- Meltwater

Snout of glacier

**Zone of accumulation:** snowfall exceeds snowmelt

Area where snowfall = snowmelt: glacier is neither advancing nor retreating

**Zone of ablation:** snowmelt exceeds snowfall

### Transportation by ice

Glaciers are capable of carrying large amounts of debris. They have been likened to huge conveyor belts which continually transport material from the highlands to the lowland (Figure 5.19). This rock debris, also known as *moraine*, can be transported either:

- on top of the glacier as *lateral* and *medial* moraine (Figures 5.20 and 5.23)
- within the glacier itself, or
- under the glacier and along the floor of the valley as ground or sub-glacial moraine.

## Bodies Recovered from Glacier

In 1820, members of a mountaineering expedition were swept away by an avalanche when they were within 300 metres of the summit of Mont Blanc. In 1861 their bodies emerged from the snout of the Glacier des Bossons. They had descended 3,200 metres in 41 years – a rate of 21.5 cm a day.

**Figure 5.19** A long journey

**Figure 5.18** A glacier showing the zone of accumulation (white snow) and the zone of ablation (darker-coloured ice)

## Erosion by ice

As glaciers can carry greater quantities of material than rivers, they are also capable of eroding the land far more quickly and effectively. The main source of material for a glacier results from *freeze-thaw weathering* (page 30). The glacier uses the frost-shattered material to widen and deepen its valley. There are two main processes of glacial erosion:

1 **Abrasion** is when the transported material rubs against, and wears away, the sides and floor of the valley. This sandpapering effect is similar to corrasion by a river (page 44) but on a much larger scale.

2 **Plucking** results from ice freezing onto the solid rock. As a glacier moves downhill, the ice pulls with it large pieces of rock.

## Deposition by ice

Material transported by a glacier is deposited at the snout. If the position of the snout does not change for a long time, the material will build up to form a *terminal moraine* (Figure 5.21). Terminal moraines extend across valleys. If the glacier retreats, then the material is spread more evenly over a wide area.

**Figure 5.21** Terminal moraine at the snout of a glacier in Greenland

**Figure 5.20** Moraines on the Aletsch Glacier, Switzerland

Lateral moraine

Lateral moraine

Medial moraine

## A glaciated landscape

During the last Ice Age, the Alps were a major centre of ice accumulation. Although today's glaciers are small by comparison, the spectacular scenery which attracts so many tourists to these mountains owes its origin to freeze-thaw weathering and glacial erosion (page 172).

Page 62 describes the major landforms found in a glaciated area such as the Alps (Figure 5.22) and pages 64 and 65 explain, with reference to the English Lake District, how these landforms were produced.

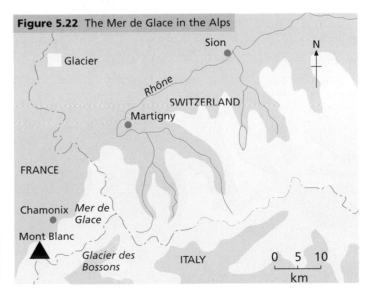

**Figure 5.22** The Mer de Glace in the Alps

Sion

Glacier

N

Rhône

SWITZERLAND

Martigny

FRANCE

Chamonix  *Mer de Glace*

Mont Blanc

*Glacier des Bossons*

ITALY

0  5  10

km

# A glaciated landscape – the Alps

Figure 5.23 shows the Mer de Glace (Sea of Ice) which is a 14 km long *valley glacier* in the French Alps. In the distance are the frost-shattered peaks of the Mont Blanc range. Many of these peaks have a pyramidal shape known as a *horn* (the classic example of this landform is the Matterhorn which is located in Switzerland – Figure 5.24). From these peaks radiate narrow, steep-sided ridges called *arêtes*. Between arêtes are deep snow-filled hollows (*cirques*), many of which contain small glaciers.

Erosion by the Mer de Glace has produced a deep, steep-sided valley known as a *glacial trough*. At the sides of the glacier are *lateral moraines* which have formed as a result of freeze–thaw weathering on the valley sides. *Medial moraines*, seen in the centre of the glacier, result from the merging of two lateral moraines where two smaller glaciers join. Notice the piles of rock debris near the snout of the glacier which indicate that the Mer de Glace is retreating.

The landforms of alpine valleys where glaciers have completely melted are a contrast to the river valleys which preceded the Ice Age (Figure 5.25). The V-shaped valleys have become U-shaped, interlocking spurs have had their ends removed to give *truncated spurs*, and tributary valleys now descend, often as impressive waterfalls, down *hanging valleys*. The flat floor of many of the valleys contain long, narrow *ribbon lakes*.

**Figure 5.23** The Mer de Glace, France

Frost-shattered peaks

Horn (pyramidal peak)

Cirque glacier

Arête

Hanging valley

Glacial trough

Truncated spur

Mer de Glace

Medial moraine

Lateral moraine

Snout

**Figure 5.24** The Matterhorn, Switzerland

**Figure 5.25** Lauterbrunnen, Switzerland

# Avalanches

An avalanche is a sudden downhill movement of snow or rock which may, on its way, pick up trees, boulders and other debris. Usually everything in its path is destroyed (Figure 5.26).

## Conditions favouring avalanches

- Heavy snowfalls compress and add weight to existing snow. Many alpine areas receive over 10 metres of snow during an average winter.
- Stability rapidly decreases on steep, non-vegetated mountainsides where the angle of slope exceeds 30°. Instability has been increased near winter sports resorts where forests have been cleared to make ski-runs.
- A sudden rise in temperature can be dangerous, especially on sunny, south-facing slopes.
- Vibrations can be caused by earth tremors, passing heavy traffic and, increasingly, off-piste skiers.
- In spring, heavy rain adds weight to existing snow.

## Movement

At first only a small amount of snow is likely to slip forward. This soon 'snowballs' in amount and speed. Usually a cloud of powdery snow is pushed ahead of, and often conceals, the main mass. Avalanches can travel at speeds of more than 200 km/hour.

## Consequences

There are, on average, 25 deaths a year caused by avalanches in Switzerland alone. Most of these

**Figure 5.26** An avalanche

(89 per cent) are off-piste skiers. Less frequently avalanches hit buildings. In 1965 a Swiss dam construction site was buried, killing 88 workers, while 50 French children died in 1950 when the hospital in which they were convalescing was hit. Avalanches can block roads and railways, pull down telephone wires and electricity cables and destroy forests and farmland.

## Prediction and prevention

Although 80 per cent of avalanches in the Alps occur between January and March and during certain weather conditions, it is still impossible to predict the exact time or the precise place where an avalanche may occur. Alpine countries have taken some measures to try to protect people and their property (Figures 5.27 and 5.28) as well as issuing avalanche warnings and alerting rescue teams.

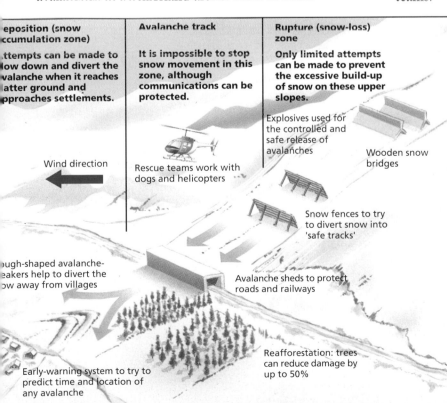

**Deposition (snow accumulation zone)**

Attempts can be made to slow down and divert the avalanche when it reaches flatter ground and approaches settlements.

**Avalanche track**

It is impossible to stop snow movement in this zone, although communications can be protected.

**Rupture (snow-loss) zone**

Only limited attempts can be made to prevent the excessive build-up of snow on these upper slopes.

Explosives used for the controlled and safe release of avalanches

Wooden snow bridges

Wind direction

Rescue teams work with dogs and helicopters

Snow fences to try to divert snow into 'safe tracks'

Trough-shaped avalanche-breakers help to divert the snow away from villages

Avalanche sheds to protect roads and railways

Reafforestation: trees can reduce damage by up to 50%

Early-warning system to try to predict time and location of any avalanche

**Figure 5.28** Avalanche shed protecting a road

**Figure 5.27** Avalanche protection schemes

# The formation of glacial landforms – the Lake District

Although it is too warm for glaciers to be found in Britain today, much of the scenery of the English Lake District, as well as in highland areas of Scotland and Wales, owes its attractiveness to the work of ice. During the last Ice Age much of northern Britain was covered by a large ice-sheet with glaciers which, like the Mer de Glace, extended down valleys (Figure 5.23).

## Cirques, arêtes and pyramidal peaks (horns)

Red Tarn is one of many cirque lakes found in the Lake District (Figure 5.29). Cirques, also referred to as *corries* and *cwms*, are deep, rounded hollows with a steep back wall and a rock basin. Red Tarn began to form when snow accumulated in hollows on the eastern side of Helvellyn (Figure 5.30a). Snow is more likely to lie on north and east-facing slopes in Britain as these receive less sunlight (page 5) and are less affected by the moderating influence of the sea (page 4) than slopes facing south and west. As the snow turned to ice it flowed downhill as a glacier.

Freeze–thaw weathering and plucking loosened and removed material from the back of the hollow, creating a steep, jagged back wall (Figure 5.30b) which, today, rises over 200 metres above Red Tarn. Ground moraine, dragged along the base of the glacier, deepened the floor of the hollow by abrasion. A rock lip was left where the power of the glacier declined, and its height was increased by the deposition of moraine. Towards the end of the Ice Age the rock lip and moraine acted as a natural dam to meltwater, forming Red Tarn (Figure 5.30c).

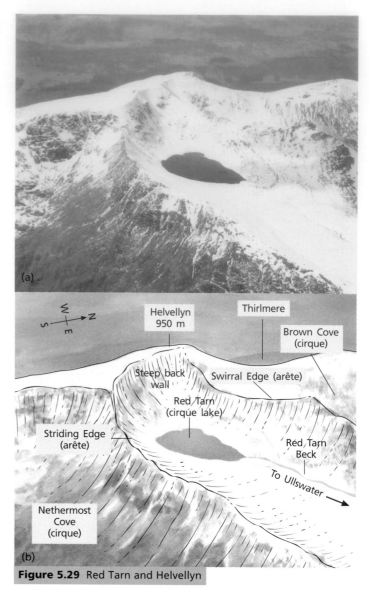
(a)
(b)

**Figure 5.29** Red Tarn and Helvellyn

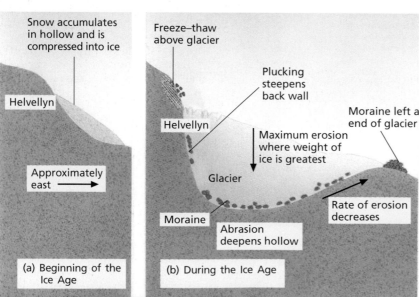

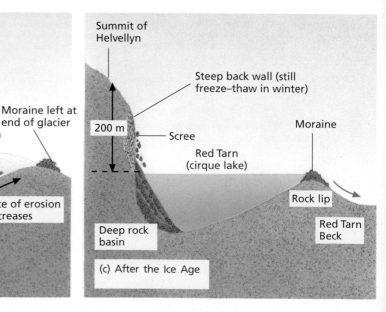

**Figure 5.30** Formation of Red Tarn, a cirque lake

Figure 5.29 also shows two *arêtes* – Striding Edge and Swirral Edge. These were formed when cirque glaciers to either side eroded the intervening hillside. The land between them became increasingly narrower until a knife-edged ridge was formed. A landform typical of most glaciated areas, but usually absent or poorly formed in Britain, is the *pyramidal peak or horn* (Figure 5.24). This feature forms when three or more cirque glaciers cut backwards into the same mountain creating a central peak with radiating arêtes (Figure 5.31).

## Glacial troughs, ribbon lakes, truncated spurs and hanging valleys

Figure 5.32 shows Wasdale, which is in the south-west of the Lake District. During the Ice Age a glacier widened, deepened and straightened a former river valley, mainly through abrasion. In doing so, the glacier converted the original V shape of the river valley (page 45) into the equally characteristic U shape of a glacial trough. The glacier in Wasdale overdeepened the valley floor. When the ice melted, a long, narrow and, in the case of Wastwater, deep ribbon lake formed (Wastwater is over 250 metres deep). The glacier also removed the ends of interlocking spurs (page 45) to leave steep, cliff-like truncated spurs (to the right of the photo). These non-vegetated valley sides are still subject to intensive

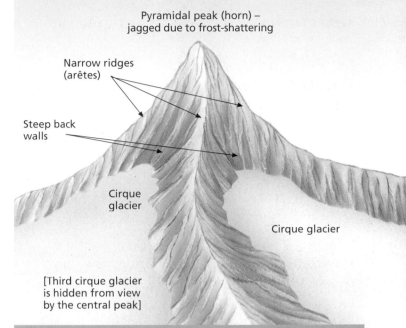

**Figure 5.31** Formation of a pyramidal peak and its radiating arêtes

freeze–thaw weathering – as witnessed by the famous Wastwater screes.

Two small rivers, the Mosedale Beck (**A**) and Lingmell Beck (**B**), can be seen flowing into Wastwater. Lingmell Beck is a fine example of a hanging valley. It formed because the glacier moving down its valley was smaller than the one which moved down Wasdale. As the smaller glacier could not erode downwards so quickly, when the ice melted its valley was left 'hanging' above the main valley. The Lingmell Beck now has to descend into Wasdale by a series of rapids and small waterfalls.

**Figure 5.32** Wastwater

**1** *(Pages 54 and 55)*

Study the sketch, which shows coastal scenery near Etretat on the Normandy coast of north-west France.

**a** Answer A, B, C, D or E to the following.
  i) This feature is called a stack.
  ii) Sand deposited by wave action.
  iii) Rocks fallen from the cliff.
  iv) Remains of a collapsed arch.
  v) Crack or weakness in the cliff.

**b** Explain with the help of diagrams how feature C may have been formed.

**2** *(Pages 56 and 57)*

Look at the sketch which shows Hurst Castle spit at the mouth of the Solent in southern England.

**a** What is longshore drift?
**b** What is a prevailing wind?
**c** How do sand-dunes form? How do they help spit development?
**d** What are groynes for?
**e** Explain with the help of diagrams how Hurst Castle spit may have been formed.

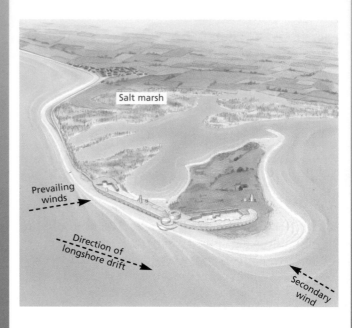

**3** *(Pages 58 and 59)*

**a** The 1953 storm surge in the North Sea is an example of a natural hazard. Describe its effects on people, property and farming by writing a sentence for each of the headlines below.

> **Death toll soars as evacuations continue**

> **Property hit in Europe's worst flood**

> **Farming devastated by storm surge floods**

**b** Look at Figures 5.11 and 5.12 on page 58 which show conditions at the time of the storm surge. (For weather map symbols look back at page 9.)
  i) What was the direction of the wind along England's east coast?
  ii) What was the average wind speed in the North Sea?
  iii) What was the height of the greatest storm surge?
  iv) Whereabouts was the greatest storm surge?

**c** i) Given the weather conditions, explain why the English and Dutch coasts were flooded.
  ii) What other factors helped cause the flood?

**4** *(Pages 60 and 61)*
  **a** Write clues to each of the answers given in the crossword.
  **b** Complete the crossword using these clues:
   • Material transported by a glacier.
   • The lower end of a glacier.
  **c** Describe in detail how a glacier is able to transport large amounts of material. Try to include a labelled sketch in your description.

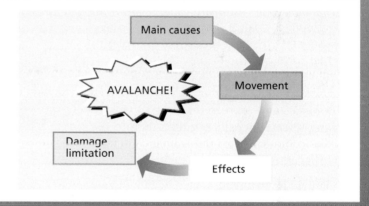

**5** *(Page 63)*
An avalanche is an example of a natural hazard.
  **a** i)  What is a natural hazard?
    ii)  Give three other examples of natural hazards.
    (Refer to Chapters 2, 3 and 4.)
  **b** Using the headings show in this diagram, explain how avalanches happen, their effects, and how the damage they cause can be reduced. Write no more than four lines for each heading.

Main causes

Movement

AVALANCHE!

Damage limitation

Effects

**6** *(Pages 62, 64, 65)*
Look at the sketch showing a glaciated landscape.
  **a** Name the features at A, B, C, D, E, F and G.
  **b** Choose **either** a cirque (cwm or corrie) **or** a pyramidal peak. For your chosen landform:
    i)  name an example
    ii)  describe its appearance
    iii)  explain its formation.

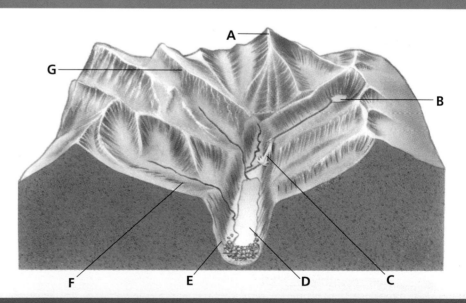

## River pollution – the Rother

The River Rother flows northwards through Derbyshire. Although several headstreams of the river rise in the Peak District National Park, the Rother flows for much of its course through urban and industrial areas before joining the Don at Rotherham (Figure 6.1).

### The Rother in 1992

In 1992, the Rother was described as 'Britain's dirtiest river'. The river had had a long history of damage caused by channel modification, mineral extraction and industrial development. Its poor water quality resulted from:

- untreated or inadequately treated waste released from more than 30 sewage works
- sewers overflowing at times of high river discharge (Shire Brook)
- coalmining, coking (Orgreave) and associated chemical industries (Staveley) which polluted the Rother (below Chesterfield) and the Doe Lea (near Bolsover)
- chemicals and untreated industrial waste being released legally but directly into the rivers (chlorine from the Staveley chemical works, chloroform from Coalite at Bolsover and ammonia from Orgreave – Figure 6.2)
- illegal industrial discharges of oil, mercury and pesticides
- leaching of wastes from landfill disposal sites (Shire Brook and Doe Lea)
- polluted water seeping through abandoned coalmines
- farm fertiliser and slurry seeping into rivers by throughflow.

The poor water quality meant that large sections of the Rother and its tributaries were lacking in fish, deficient in wildlife and failed to generate recreational activity or interest.

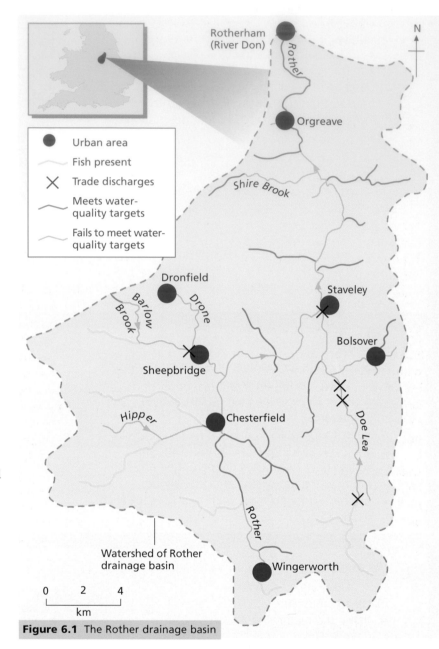

**Figure 6.1** The Rother drainage basin

**Figure 6.2** Industrial pollution on the Rother

## The National Rivers Authority and the Environment Agency

The National Rivers Authority (NRA) was established in 1989 as 'the Guardian of the Water Environment in England and Wales'. It was a non-departmental government organisation whose main responsibilities included regulation and management of water resources, water quality, flood defence, freshwater fisheries, water recreation and navigation. In April 1996 the NRA became part of a newly created Environment Agency (Figure 6.3).

The role of the NRA was:
- to protect and improve the water environment through effective management of water resources and by substantial reduction in pollution
- to provide effective defence for people and property against flooding from rivers and the sea
- to operate openly and balance the interests of all who benefit from and use rivers, groundwaters, estuaries and coastal waters.

## The NRA and the Rother

Since 1992 there have been several improvements within the Rother drainage basin. Water quality has begun to improve, although it still discourages the development of aquatic life. Flooding remains a problem in several parts of the basin although recent flood prevention schemes have included channel widening, the construction of flood banks and providing washlands (places where the river can flood without affecting people). The Rother Valley Country Park now provides a range of water sports, although these are not on the river itself.

# ENVIRONMENT AGENCY

On 1 April 1996, the National Rivers Authority (NRA), Her Majesty's Inspectorate of Pollution (HMIP), Waste Regulation Authorities (WRAs) and units from the Department of the Environment combined to form the Environment Agency. By combining the regulation of land, air and water, the Agency offers a comprehensive approach to environmental protection and improvement in England and Wales.

**Figure 6.3** The Environment Agency

By the turn of the century the Environment Agency hopes to:
- improve water quality by:
  - improving water treatment works and so reducing the discharge of sewage
  - reducing the amount of contaminated land and clearing disused industrial sites
  - reducing and controlling effluent from existing industries
  - controlling more effectively discharge from waste disposal sites pumping water from abandoned coalmines
  - reducing agricultural pollution in order to protect supplies of drinking water
- improve physical habitats to allow the development of sustainable fish populations
- continue to improve flood defences and to provide a flood warning system
- consider promoting navigation on the Chesterfield Canal and a riverside walk (the 'Cuckoo Trail') from Chesterfield to north of Staveley.

**Figure 6.4** Improvements in the Rother drainage basin

(a)

(b)

## River management – the Rhine

The Rhine is an international river. It receives water from Switzerland, France, Germany, Luxembourg, the Netherlands and even part of Austria. Over 50 million people live and work within its drainage basin, and no other river in the world flows through as many heavy industrialised centres (Figure 6.5).

In the early 1970s the river acted as a major form of transport and a source of drinking water for 20 million people. It was used by industry for cooling purposes, for the discharge of waste and as a source of energy. The river, despite beginning as melting alpine snow, was so polluted by the time it flowed into the North Sea that it became known as 'the sewer of Europe'.

In 1971 the river almost suffocated. Exceptionally low levels of dissolved oxygen in the water meant that water life became almost non-existent. The early 1970s was also a time when water pollution reached a peak. Pollution came from industries (mainly chemicals and paper pulp), municipal waste and, increasingly, from the air and from agriculture. Salmon, regarded as a measure of water quality, had not been seen in the river for over 35 years (Figure 6.7).

As early as 1950, five countries grouped together to form the International Commission for the Protection of the Rhine (ICPR). Of these, Switzerland used the river least, France and Luxembourg extracted little water from it but discharged into it, Germany was the heaviest industrial user, and the Netherlands extracted most for domestic use and received the waste of the other countries. Providing the countries could agree on how to reduce pollution, they then had to decide who paid for the schemes and to trust each other to keep any agreement.

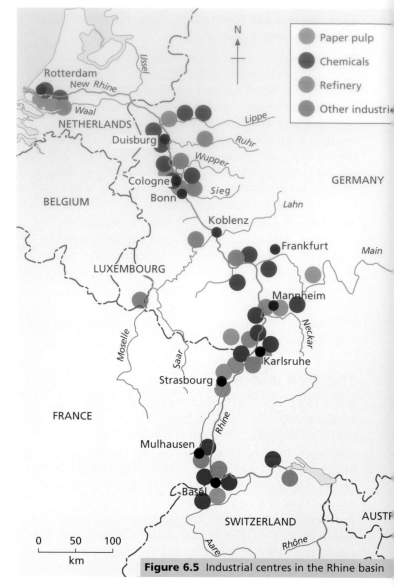

**Figure 6.5** Industrial centres in the Rhine basin

**Figure 6.6** A healthy river salmon

**Figure 6.7** Number of salmon caught in the Rhine, 1895–1995

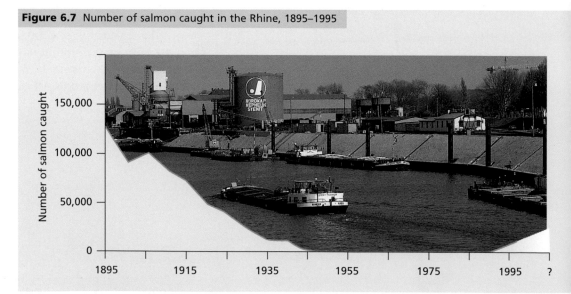

So far there have been three phases of co-operation.

1 *From 1950 to the mid-1970s* – the ICPR investigated the origins, types and extent of pollution.

2 *From 1976 to November 1986* – Convention on chemical pollution in 1976, to the fire at the agrochemicals warehouse at Sandoz, Basel in 1986. During the fire, large quantities of toxic chemicals were washed into the Rhine in water used to extinguish the fire. The result was large-scale death of fish in the river, the closure of riverside factories, and the prohibition of water extracted for domestic use, all highlighting the vulnerability of the Rhine ecosystem.

3 *The Rhine Action Plan (RAP) of 1987 to 1999* – its targets are:

- To improve the ecosystem in and around the Rhine, and so allow higher species to return to the river. The salmon was chosen as the symbol for the plan (Figure 6.6). The concept was that if water quality could be improved enough to allow salmon to be re-introduced, then other forms of aquatic life, such as sea trout, insect larvae and water snails, would also return. Fish ladders have had to be built to let migrating salmon by-pass various barrages built across the river (Figure 6.8).
- To achieve a sufficiently high water quality that drinking water can be prepared from the river at all times with the help only of natural purifying agents.
- To reduce substantially the risk of water pollution by accidents.
- To reduce pollution from all sources, e.g. the chemical industry, raw sewage, agriculture, and salt from potassium mines. A list of 45 pollutants was drawn up for which discharges had to be reduced by at least 50 per cent between 1985 and 1995 (Figure 6.9).

**Figure 6.8** The weirs of the Iffezheim barrage and Gambsheim power plant are now equipped with fish passages for salmon and other migrants

Two further additions were later added to the plan: to reduce the level of pollutants discharged into the North Sea, and to improve flood control schemes following the events of the winters of 1993–94 and 1994–95 (page 50).

Water quality, as shown by the increase in oxygen (Figure 6.10), has improved appreciably. Salmon were initially released into the River Sieg in 1988, and were caught in the same river in 1990 (Figure 6.6). In 1995 a salmon was caught 40 km north of Strasbourg – 700 km from the estuary. Hopes are high that salmon may indeed reach Basel by the year 2000. Meanwhile the number of species of water life recorded in the Rhine, which had fallen from 151 in 1900 to only 27 in the early 1970s, had risen to 103 by 1990.

**Figure 6.9** Concentrations of selected pollutants in the Rhine at the Dutch/German border (mg per litre)

|  | 1980 | 1990 | 1993 |
|---|---|---|---|
| Chloride | 168 | 187 | 144 |
| Organic carbon | 8.5 | 5.6 | 4.2 |
| Phosphate | 0.6 | 0.3 | 0.2 |
| Mercury | 0.18 | 0.05 | 0.04 |
| Cadmium | 1.58 | 0.11 | 0.06 |
| Lead | 14.7 | 5.1 | 4.6 |

**Figure 6.10** Oxygen saturation in the Rhine

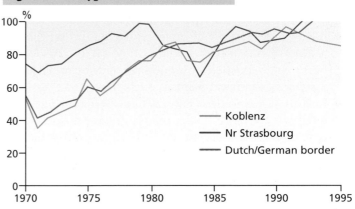

Koblenz
Nr Strasbourg
Dutch/German border

## River flood management

In the UK, since the passing of the Land Drainage Act (1930), the aim has been to prevent rivers flooding. This policy, as in other west European countries, has increasingly put rivers in both rural and urban areas into artificial channels.

In rural areas (Figure 6.11):
- River courses have been straightened – by increasing a river's gradient, water is able to drain away more quickly.
- River channels have been deepened and widened so as to transport more water at times of flood.
- Flood banks (artificial levées – see page 47) have been built to try to prevent rivers from overflowing.
- Flood plains, which used to take surplus water, have been drained for farming.

In urban areas (Figure 6.12):
- Rivers have been straightened and their banks and beds lined with concrete to prevent erosion and, by reducing friction, to speed up discharge.
- Rivers have been diverted and channelled by culverts under buildings (River Lavant, page 49).
- Drains and sewers carry excess rainfall as quickly as possible to rivers.
- Flood plains have been drained and built upon.

Recent floods have led many experts to realise that complete river taming and flood control is impossible. Although the frequency of flooding may be reduced, when the event does occur following extreme weather conditions, the effects are likely to be much greater. Flood control schemes, despite their often high installation and maintenance costs, cannot guarantee protection. Perhaps of greater importance is the realisation that flood control schemes are environmentally damaging. Plants, fish and insects, all forming part of a river ecosystem (page 80), may be removed during dredging, or the diversity of species and numbers reduced following the change to or destruction of their natural habitats.

Now there is a new approach:
- Allow rivers to flow more freely than at present, and to flood – but in places where they will do least harm. Silt deposited by a flooding river maintains the fertility of the flood plain.
- Restore rivers to their natural state. Meandering channels are more stable, offer a greater range of habitat and are more attractive than those that have been straightened.
- River banks must allow diverse plant and animal populations to develop.

**Figure 6.11** The straightened River Skjern Å in Jutland, Denmark

**Figure 6.12** An urban river

### Denmark

In the 1950s and 1960s, meandering rivers such as the Skjern Å and Brede (Figure 6.13), were altered into ruler-straight canals, and thousands of hectares of land were drained for agriculture. In the early 1990s, by which time 97.8 per cent of Danish rivers had been straightened, it was decided to return the two rivers to their former courses.

**Figure 6.13** Location of rivers Skjern Å and Brede

0    50
km

N

Jutland

DENMARK

Skjern Å

Brede

Zealand

GERMANY

The three photos in Figure 6.14 show how the River Brede in South Jutland was restored from a drainage ditch to an eco-friendly river. The river was dredged and straightened in the 1950s to create a deep, narrow channel (a). Farmers benefited but flora and fauna became poorer in the channel and in the valley. Artificial fertiliser was carried to the sea. In the period 1991–96 the County Council of South Jutland reinstated meanders on a 17 km long stretch and raised the river bed by half a metre. Natural flooding (c) is expected to increase the deposition of silt and nutrients over the flood plain and to reduce the amount of fertiliser needed. The scheme has also improved the Brede as a sport fishery and as a habitat for birds. The project was funded by the County of South Jutland and partly supported by Danish EPA and EU Life funds.

**Figure 6.14** The River Brede, Jutland

(a)

(b)

(c)

## The UK

The River Cole (Figure 6.15) and the Skerne, in Darlington, are the first full-scale practical examples in Britain of the new thinking in river management which is being adopted in western Europe and the USA.

**Figure 6.15** The River Cole, near Swindon

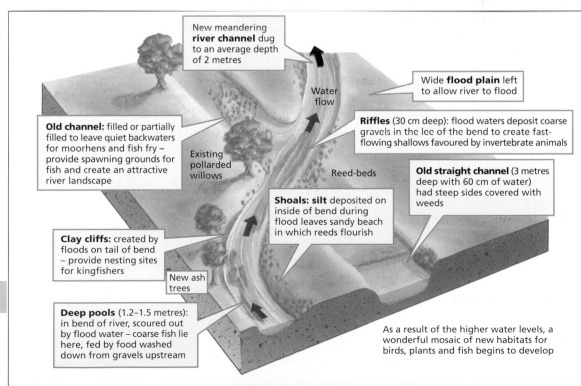

New meandering **river channel** dug to an average depth of 2 metres

Wide **flood plain** left to allow river to flood

Water flow

**Old channel:** filled or partially filled to leave quiet backwaters for moorhens and fish fry – provide spawning grounds for fish and create an attractive river landscape

Existing pollarded willows

Reed-beds

**Riffles** (30 cm deep): flood waters deposit coarse gravels in the lee of the bend to create fast-flowing shallows favoured by invertebrate animals

**Old straight channel** (3 metres deep with 60 cm of water) had steep sides covered with weeds

**Shoals: silt** deposited on inside of bend during flood leaves sandy beach in which reeds flourish

**Clay cliffs:** created by floods on tail of bend – provide nesting sites for kingfishers

New ash trees

**Deep pools** (1.2–1.5 metres): in bend of river, scoured out by flood water – coarse fish lie here, fed by food washed down from gravels upstream

As a result of the higher water levels, a wonderful mosaic of new habitats for birds, plants and fish begins to develop

# Coastal management – protection against erosion

'In the past we have tried to manage the coast by resisting the power of the sea – with sea defences of various kinds. Only recently have we begun to realise that not only is this extremely costly but also that in many cases it merely increases the risks both to ourselves and our ecological heritage. We are now entering a new phase of coastal management in which we attempt to understand and work with the natural forces of the coast rather than to resist them.'

*Humber Estuary & Coast. Management Issues,* University of Hull & Humberside County Council, November 1994

## *Holderness*

### Coastal problems

Holderness did not exist until the end of the last Ice Age when a retreating ice-sheet deposited large amounts of mud and sand. Since then, waves and rain have eroded the new coast at a rate among the fastest in Europe (Figure 6.16). Since Roman times alone, the coastline has receded by an estimated 5.6 km causing the loss of farmland and over 30 villages (Figure 6.17). Recent measurements show that the average rate of recession is 2 m a year. Although erosion is a natural process, it has been accelerated by human activity.

Figure 6.16 Cliff erosion on the Holderness coast

Figure 6.17 Changes in the coastline of Holderness

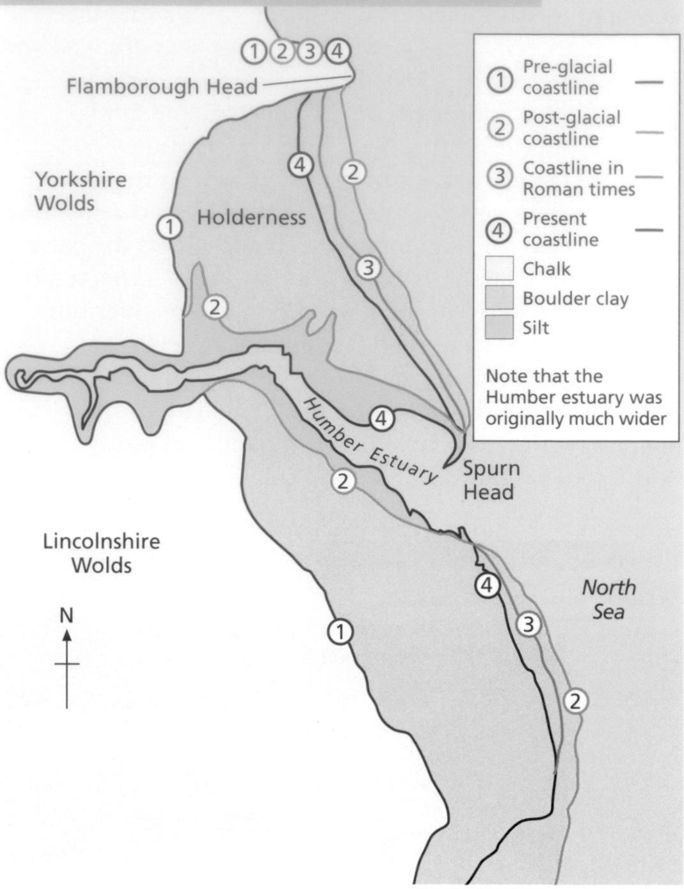

### What attempts have been made to protect the coast?

The towns of Hornsea and Withernsea have been protected by the building of concrete sea-walls. Here, and elsewhere along the coast, wooden groynes (Figure 5.6) have been constructed partly to reduce the effect of breaking waves but mainly to trap material moving along the beach. Groynes help to widen beaches and protect cliffs.

### How do sea defences create problems?

While cliff erosion has been halted at Hornsea, it has continued on either side of the town. Hornsea now projects into the sea on an artificial headland. It is realised that:

1 The cost of constructing new sea defences and maintaining existing ones is becoming too great to sustain.
2 While the protection of the Holderness coast is seen by those who live or work there as essential, it may be viewed entirely differently by those who live and work on adjacent coasts. In other words, preventing erosion on one stretch of coastline only shifts the problem elsewhere.

## Spurn Head – a test case for coastal management

Spurn Head is an 8 km long spit curving out into the mouth of the River Humber. At its landward end, where it is narrowest, it is a thin strip of land only a few metres in width and height (Figure 6.18). Towards its southern end it consists of a sandy beach capped with sand-dunes which rise to a height of 15 m. Spurn was formed by material eroded from the cliffs of Holderness being carried southwards by longshore drift and deposited in gentler waters.

It appears that Spurn has been breached by the waves several times in its known history – the last time around 1850. To prevent further erosion and future breaches, wooden groynes and sea walls were constructed. These defences have been allowed to deteriorate with the result that once again the sea is threatening to break through and possibly even to destroy the feature.

A report by the University of Hull for the Humberside County Council (November 1994) suggests that the current Spurn, far from being a natural feature, is largely artificial, relying on wooden groynes and concrete walls for its survival. It states: 'The question facing the Yorkshire Wildlife Trust, who currently own the peninsula, is whether the original natural processes can be restored or whether they must simply accept the changes that are now taking place on Spurn. One thing is clear: any attempt to protect the present peninsula with artificial defences would not only be prohibitively expensive but must lead to its ultimate destruction – Spurn cannot be tied down but must be free to move as the Holderness coast retreats.'

During the high tides of February 1996, Spurn Head nearly became an island as storms threatened to breach the spit once again. Although 300 m of road were washed away, Spurn lived to fight another day . . . but the question remains: 'How long can it exist?'. While some groups of people fight for its continued protection, others argue that it would be better to let nature take its own course. There is a growing acceptance that so long as the southern end of the spit, with its important lifeboat station and lighthouse, remains stable, then the rest of the spit should be allowed to move westwards as the Holderness coast to the north of it recedes.

**Figure 6.18** Spurn Head, looking north towards Holderness

# Coastal management – protection against flooding

## The Delta project

Although one small dam had been completed by 1950 (number 9 on Figure 6.19), it was the storm surge of 1953 (Figure 5.14) that led to the Delta project in the Netherlands being extended in scale and brought forward in time. The first work to be completed after 1953 was a storm surge barrier in the Hollandse IJssel (1). Its purpose was to protect polder land in the west Netherlands.

In the next 30 years, nine dams were built – four 'primary' dams to the seaward side (2, 4, 5 and 10) and five 'secondary' dams inland (6, 7, 8, 11 and 12). The dams were built at least one metre higher than the level of the 1953 flood – the highest recorded so far. Smaller dams were built first to allow the Dutch to develop the technology and expertise needed for the larger, more difficult dams. Figure 6.19 shows three types of dam.

1. The Eastern Scheldt was closed to the sea by a storm surge barrier, with 62 steel gates (Figure 6.20) – unlike the barrier on the New Waterway which is mobile.
2. Two of the primary dams have sluice gates to allow water from rivers such as the Rhine and Maas to discharge into the North Sea.
3. Three of the secondary dams are equipped with locks for shipping.

Figure 6.20 The Eastern Scheldt storm barrier

### Impact of the project

- An enormous effect on the safety of the area by virtually eliminating flooding.
- Improved water management schemes with fresh water available for domestic and industrial uses.
- New opportunities for outdoor leisure pursuits and the creation of nature reserves.
- The dams have shortened the coastline (from 800 km to 80 km between **A** and **B** on Figure 6.19) and reduced distances between places (from 150 km to 100 km between Rotterdam and Vlissingen).
- A new freshwater canal linking the rivers Scheldt and Rhine.
- Improved inland fishing areas.

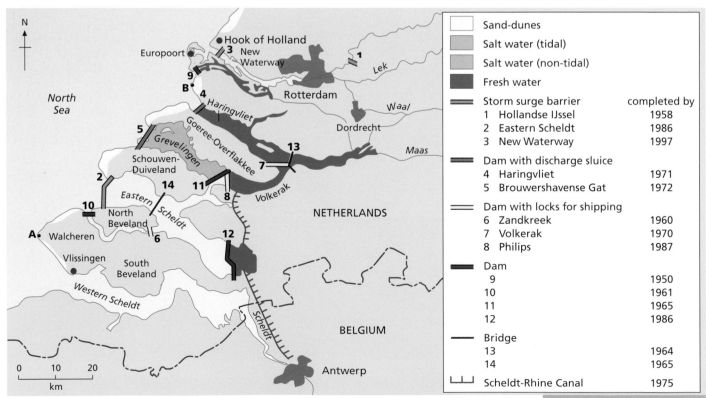

| Legend | | completed by |
|---|---|---|
| Sand-dunes | | |
| Salt water (tidal) | | |
| Salt water (non-tidal) | | |
| Fresh water | | |
| **Storm surge barrier** | | |
| 1 | Hollandse IJssel | 1958 |
| 2 | Eastern Scheldt | 1986 |
| 3 | New Waterway | 1997 |
| **Dam with discharge sluice** | | |
| 4 | Haringvliet | 1971 |
| 5 | Brouwershavense Gat | 1972 |
| **Dam with locks for shipping** | | |
| 6 | Zandkreek | 1960 |
| 7 | Volkerak | 1970 |
| 8 | Philips | 1987 |
| **Dam** | | |
| 9 | | 1950 |
| 10 | | 1961 |
| 11 | | 1965 |
| 12 | | 1986 |
| **Bridge** | | |
| 13 | | 1964 |
| 14 | | 1965 |
| Scheldt-Rhine Canal | | 1975 |

Figure 6.19 The Delta project

# Protection against people – North Norfolk

An area of 451 square km of the North Norfolk coast was designated as an Area of Outstanding Natural Beauty (AONB) by the Countryside Commission in 1968. It contains over 30 sites of national importance and two larger sites of international significance for wildlife. The increasing number of visitors can bring many benefits such as income and jobs. However, the area needs to be carefully managed so that the natural beauty and the wildlife which attract those visitors are protected.

The Norfolk Coast project (1995) has identified several visitor management zones within the Norfolk Coast AONB (Figure 6.21). These zones range from extremely fragile environments with considerable visitor pressures to more robust environments with limited visitor pressure. The project recognises the need to overcome problems in the threatened Red Zone, to maintain the delicate balance in the Orange and Yellow zones, and to develop quiet recreation and tourism opportunities in the Green zones.

The main aims of the project have been identified as:
- to increase the involvement of local communities
- to discourage the use of the car and to reduce all forms of pollution
- to ensure that various wildlife habitats, landscapes and archaeological features are protected and, where possible, enhanced
- to use information to increase awareness, enjoyment and respect for the AONB
- to achieve mutual respect between existing and new recreation activities, and between them and the AONB.

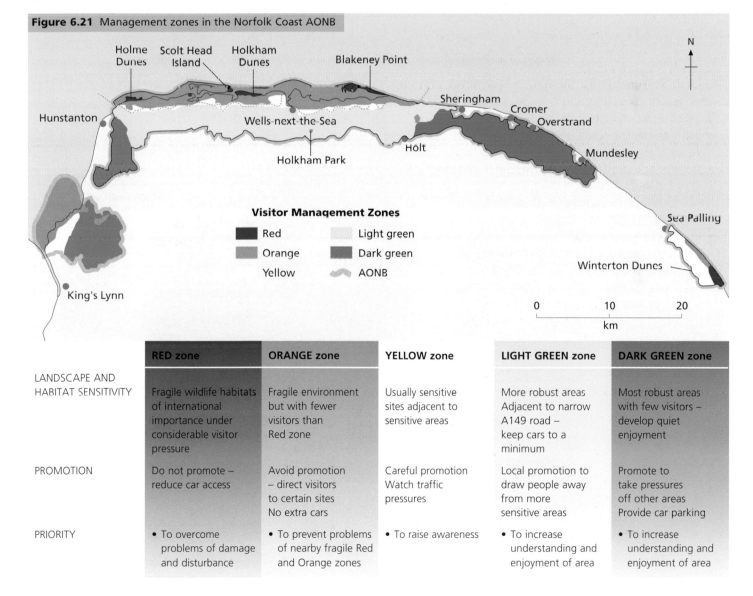

**Figure 6.21** Management zones in the Norfolk Coast AONB

Visitor Management Zones
- Red
- Orange
- Yellow
- Light green
- Dark green
- AONB

|  | RED zone | ORANGE zone | YELLOW zone | LIGHT GREEN zone | DARK GREEN zone |
|---|---|---|---|---|---|
| LANDSCAPE AND HABITAT SENSITIVITY | Fragile wildlife habitats of international importance under considerable visitor pressure | Fragile environment but with fewer visitors than Red zone | Usually sensitive sites adjacent to sensitive areas | More robust areas Adjacent to narrow A149 road – keep cars to a minimum | Most robust areas with few visitors – develop quiet enjoyment |
| PROMOTION | Do not promote – reduce car access | Avoid promotion – direct visitors to certain sites No extra cars | Careful promotion Watch traffic pressures | Local promotion to draw people away from more sensitive areas | Promote to take pressures off other areas Provide car parking |
| PRIORITY | • To overcome problems of damage and disturbance | • To prevent problems of nearby fragile Red and Orange zones | • To raise awareness | • To increase understanding and enjoyment of area | • To increase understanding and enjoyment of area |

**1** *(Pages 68 and 69)*

Look at the map.

**a** i) Describe the water quality near Rotherham and Chesterfield.

ii) Which part of the river system has the cleanest water?

iii) Describe the quality of water for most of the River Rother.

**b** i) Describe the type and cause of pollution on the Rother.

ii) State what problems have been caused by pollution.

iii) Describe some of the steps that can be taken to reduce the levels of pollution.

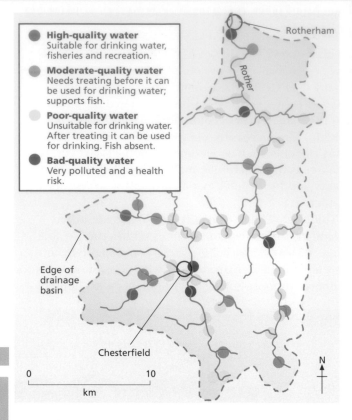

● **High-quality water**
Suitable for drinking water, fisheries and recreation.

● **Moderate-quality water**
Needs treating before it can be used for drinking water; supports fish.

● **Poor-quality water**
Unsuitable for drinking water. After treating it can be used for drinking. Fish absent.

● **Bad-quality water**
Very polluted and a health risk.

Rotherham

Rother

Edge of drainage basin

Chesterfield

0    10
km

N

*The River Rother – pollution levels*

**2** *(Pages 70 and 71)*

**a** Look at the block diagram of the Rhine basin.

i) In which country is the source of the Rhine?

ii) Name the countries through which the Rhine flows.

iii) Give six sources of Rhine pollution.

**b** Suggest why the Rhine has been called 'Europe's sewer'.

**c** Describe the steps that have been taken to reduce pollution on the Rhine.

**d** To what extent has the clean-up scheme been successful?

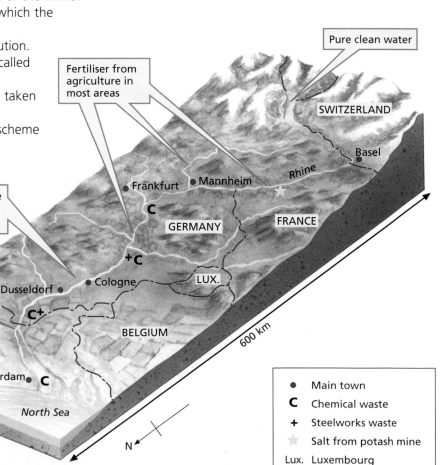

Pure clean water

Fertiliser from agriculture in most areas

SWITZERLAND

Basel

Rhine

Frankfurt   Mannheim

Untreated sewage from many large urban areas

C

GERMANY        FRANCE

Oil and waste from ships

+C

Cologne        LUX.

Dusseldorf

C+

BELGIUM

600 km

NETHERLANDS

Rotterdam  C

North Sea

N

*River Rhine pollution*

● Main town
**C** Chemical waste
**+** Steelworks waste
★ Salt from potash mine
Lux. Luxembourg

**3** (Pages 72 and 73)

a Look at the map of the River Ouse, which shows York, a city that frequently has a flooding problem.

   i) How many stations recorded more than average rainfall?

   ii) What was the greatest rainfall recorded?

   iii) Where was the greatest rainfall?

   iv) Suggest why the Ouse flooded at York.

b During the last 50 years many sections of river in this area have been changed by people. Describe how each of the following changes may reduce flooding:

   • straightening        • deepening
   • levée building       • concrete lining
   • culverting           • drain construction

c Modern methods of river management are aimed at retaining the natural form of a river.

   i) Describe the main features of this approach.

   ii) Explain the advantages.

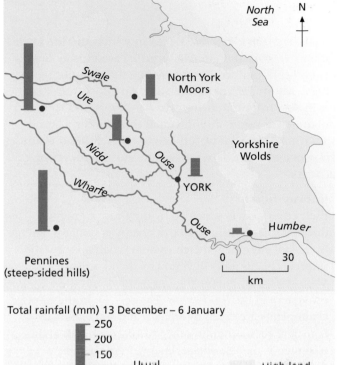

Total rainfall (mm) 13 December – 6 January

Usual average ● ■ 45

High land

Low land

River Ouse and its tributaries

**4** (Pages 74 and 75)

a Look at the newspaper item about the Holderness coast.

   i) What has been Mappleton's problem?

   ii) How can places like Mappleton be protected from the sea?

   iii) How can a beach provide 'natural protection'?

   iv) How can sea defences cause problems?

b Are sea defences 'friend' or 'foe'? Should a coast be protected, or should it be left to natural forces? Give reasons for your answer.

## New sea wall – friend or foe?

Since 1991, Mappleton residents have celebrated their newly completed £2 million sea defence scheme which has saved their village from being washed into the sea. Only 3 km down the coast, however, cliff-top residents are furious as their homes teeter on the rapidly eroding cliff edge. They say that the new scheme has caused a loss of beach deposits which has left their bit of coast with no natural protection and at the mercy of the sea.

April 1995

**5** (Pages 58, 59, 76)

The Delta project in the Netherlands is an example of a coastal management scheme designed to give protection against flooding. Briefly describe the scheme as follows.

a What was the problem?

b What was done to protect the area?

c What were the main effects of the project?

**6** (Page 77)

The Norfolk Coast project is an example of a coastal management scheme designed to protect natural beauty and wildlife of an area from over-use. Briefly describe the scheme as follows.

a What was the problem?

b What are the aims of the scheme?

c How does the project protect but at the same time allow visitor use?

# 7 ECOSYSTEMS

An *ecosystem* is a natural system in which the life cycles of plants (*flora*) and animals (*fauna*) are closely linked to each other and to the non-living environment (solar energy, water, air, rocks and soil). An ecosystem can vary in size from extensive areas of desert and forest to sand-dunes, a pond, an individual tree, under a stone and within a drop of water. Ecosystems depend upon two processes: the flow of energy and the recycling of nutrients.

## 1 Energy flows

Each ecosystem is sustained by the flow of energy through it. The main source of energy is sunlight. Energy from sunlight enters the ecosystem when it is absorbed by green plants and converted by the process of *photosynthesis*. Energy then passes through the ecosystem in the *food chain* (Figure 7.1). In the food chain plants are eaten by animals and some animals consume each other. In other words, each link in the chain feeds on and obtains energy from the link preceding it. In turn it is consumed by and provides energy for the link that follows it. As energy only passes one way, the ecosystem is an open system with inputs, flows, stores and outputs (page 41).

## 2 Recycling of nutrients

Certain nutrients are continually circulated within the ecosystem. Each cycle consists of plants taking up nutrients from the soil. The nutrients are then used by the plants or by animals which consume the plants. When the plants or animals die, they decompose and the nutrients are returned to the soil ready for future use (Figure 7.2).

A typical ecosystem for a deciduous woodland in Britain is shown in Figure 7.3. It shows both the flow of energy in an open system and the recycling of nutrients in a closed system. This particular ecosystem is said to be in balance with nature. Unfortunately human interference often alters, and even destroys, ecosystems through activities such as deforestation, draining wetlands, ploughing grasslands and polluting rivers. A vital issue for future human generations is: 'How to gain most benefit from an ecosystem without damaging or destroying it' – the concept of *sustainable development* (page 200).

**Figure 7.1** Transfers of energy in an ecosystem

| NON-LIVING ENVIRONMENT | PRODUCERS | CONSUMERS | CONSUMERS | DECOMPOSERS |
|---|---|---|---|---|
| – obtaining solar energy | – green plants which convert this energy by photosynthesis | – herbivores which eat green plants | – carnivores which consume herbivores | – e.g. bacteria which break down dead matter |

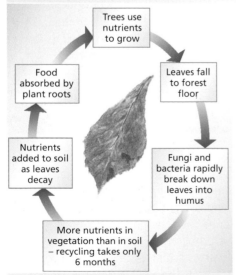

**Figure 7.2** Recycling in a British woodland – the nutrient cycle

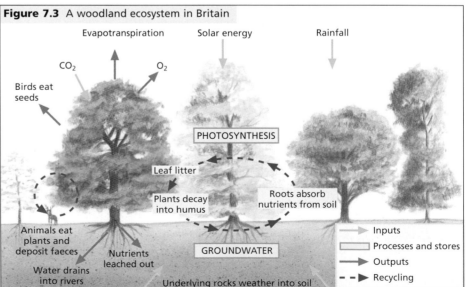

**Figure 7.3** A woodland ecosystem in Britain

80

# Sand-dunes – a fragile ecosystem

Sand-dunes provide a unique and a fragile ecosystem (Figure 7.4). Where the dunes are left in their natural state, there is a balance between the non-living and the living environment. Figure 7.5 shows how, as sand-dunes develop, they pass through several stages and how at each stage there is a corresponding development in vegetation and fauna.

**Figure 7.4** Sand-dunes at Bamburgh, Northumberland

However, human influence can easily upset this balance and can damage the ecosystem. Local people and visitors (including school parties!) can create ever widening footpaths, leave litter and disturb wildlife, while construction companies may extract sand. If the influence is limited, then the ecosystem may be able to repair itself naturally. If the influence is severe, then irreversible damage can result and the habitats for numerous plants and wildlife will be destroyed. This is why many sand-dune areas, including those on the North Norfolk coast (page 77) and at Spurn Head (page 75), have become protected and are now carefully managed.

| | BEACH | STRAND LINE (high tide) | EMBRYO DUNES | FORE DUNES | MAIN RIDGES | OLDER DUNES |
|---|---|---|---|---|---|---|
| NON-LIVING ENVIRONMENT | Sand with shells 1 Constructive waves and 2 prevailing winds move sand up beach | Seaweed and driftwood trap sand | Sand: • very dry as water sinks through it rapidly • alkaline because of shells | Grasses bind soil together, and as they die add humus to the soil | Humus increases – reduces alkaline content and retains water | Too far from source of sand – signs of erosion  Paths cut by animals |
| FLORA | None | Sea-couch | Some lyme, marram and sea-couch grasses | Marram grass dominates – long roots to get water, protection against wind | Greater variety of plants: bracken, gorse, heather | Small trees, tall shrubs, bracken |
| FAUNA | Sea birds, lugworms | Insects | Insects | Insects, worms | Butterflies, toads and frogs, rabbits, reptiles | Nesting birds, hedgehogs, foxes |

**Figure 7.5** Transect across a sand-dune area showing the relationship between the non-living environment and flora-fauna

# Afforestation – an ecosystem changed by human activity

In prehistoric times much of Britain was covered by deciduous trees such as oak, ash, birch and beech. As Britain's population began to increase, forests were cleared for farmland or for wood which was needed as a fuel or a building material. Later, at the start of the Industrial Revolution, and before coal was used, further clearances were made to provide wood for charcoal, to provide more farmland to feed the growing population and for urban growth. By 1919, after further clearances made during the First World War, only 4 per cent of Britain was classified as forest. It was then that the Forestry Commission was set up to begin a controlled replanting scheme. Later, in 1968, the Forestry Commissioners were given the duties of:

- developing areas of afforestation, maintaining adequate reserves of growing trees and providing a supply of timber and other forest products
- controlling timber pests and diseases
- providing tourist and recreational facilities
- ensuring that forestry formed part of an integral pattern of rural land use, harmonising with farming and the environment.

Figure 7.6 shows what a typical afforested area in Britain looked like in the 1970s. Such a landscape was not appreciated by everybody. Many people were not in favour of the mass re-clothing of upland valleys and moorlands with conifers, and felt that the planting of row upon row of uniform trees (i.e. all the same type, age and size) spoilt the 'natural' landscape. They argued that although conifers grew more quickly, they were visually less attractive and more monotonous than deciduous trees and, by limiting the amount of light reaching the forest floor, they discouraged plant, bird and animal life.

**Figure 7.6** Planning the landscape in an afforested area in the 1970s

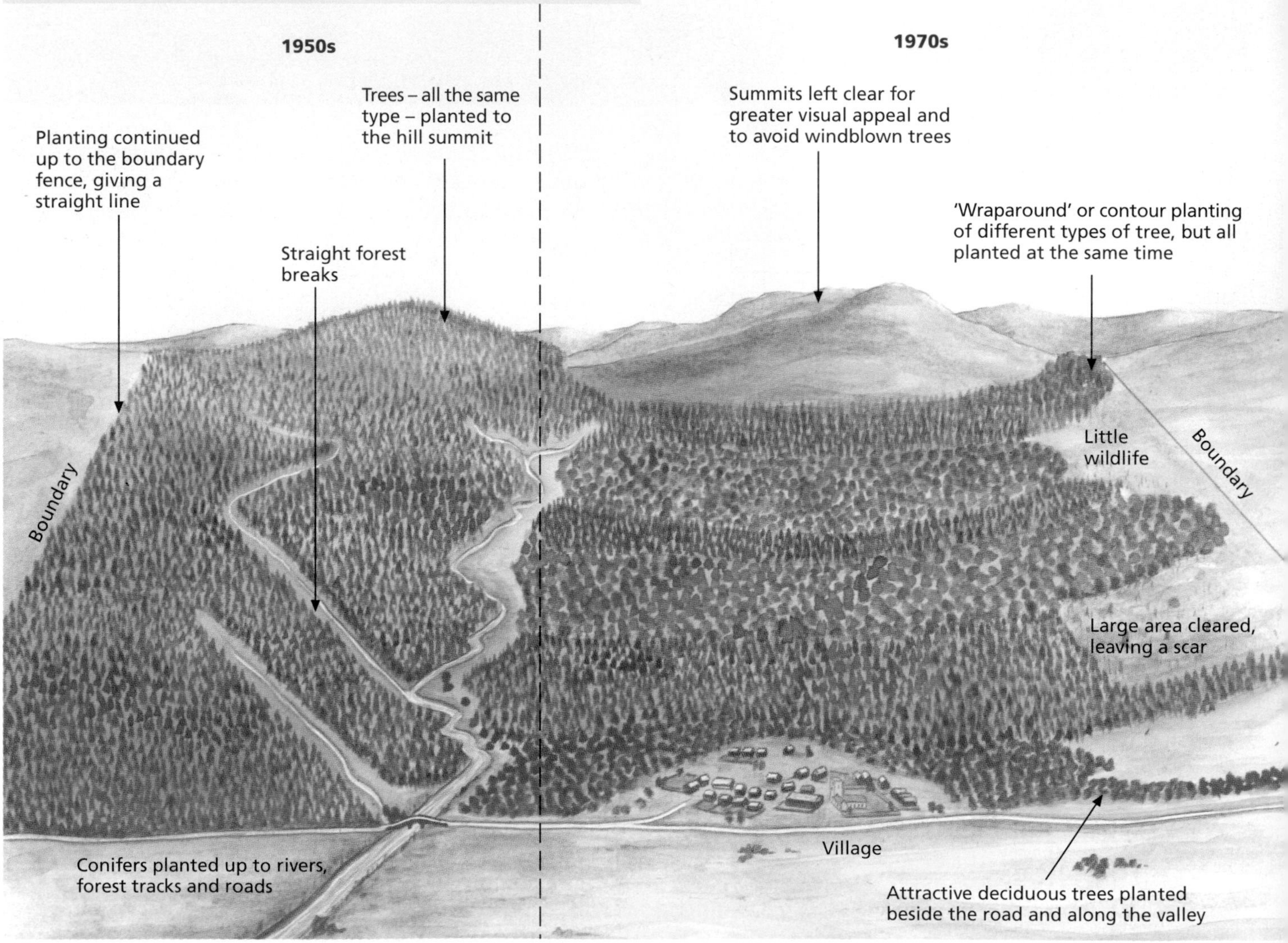

1950s

1970s

Trees – all the same type – planted to the hill summit

Summits left clear for greater visual appeal and to avoid windblown trees

Planting continued up to the boundary fence, giving a straight line

'Wraparound' or contour planting of different types of tree, but all planted at the same time

Straight forest breaks

Boundary

Little wildlife

Boundary

Large area cleared, leaving a scar

Conifers planted up to rivers, forest tracks and roads

Village

Attractive deciduous trees planted beside the road and along the valley

Since the 1970s there has been a growing demand in Britain for recreational opportunities, an increase in the cost of spraying trees to rid them of insect pests, and a change in people's perception of the environment. As a result the Forestry Commission has adopted new approaches in an attempt to recreate a balanced woodland ecosystem. Some of these measures are shown in Figure 7.7. Here, in the Kielder Forest of Northumberland, the Commission has tried to improve the whole ecosystem rather than, as earlier, concentrating solely on the landscaping of trees. The overall result is shown in Figure 7.8.

By 1996, the amount of Britain covered in forest had risen to 10 per cent.

**Figure 7.8** Landscaping in the Kielder Forest

**Figure 7.7** An improved woodland ecosystem – Kielder Forest in the late 1990s

Trees planted at different times – the differences in height are scenically more attractive

Summits left clear for heather moorlands – a habitat for grouse and golden eagles

Trees of different types and with a lower density encourage more birds, which feed on and reduce the number of insects – less need to spray pesticides

Native Scots pine planted – favoured habitat for the threatened red squirrel

Forest trails encourage visitors

Mature woodland forms a habitat for tawny owls and provides food for short-eared owls

Only small areas are cleared at a time, to reduce 'scars' on the landscape

Cleared forest – branches left to rot – it takes 10 years for nutrients to be returned to the soil

Grassland forms a habitat for short-eared owls and provides food for tawny owls

Winding forest road

Picnic areas for visitors

Land beside roads/tracks cleared to width of 100 m and left as grass or planted with attractive deciduous trees

Ponds created

North Tyne

Land next to river left clear for migrating animals, e.g. deer

## Wetlands – a threatened ecosystem

The term *wetland* is applied to landscapes where water – which may be fresh, brackish or salt – plays a key role. Wetlands form transition zones between sea or lake and dry land – sometimes being inhospitable, sometimes highly productive. At all times, however, they produce an environment that is a haven for special kinds of plants, birds and animals. Wetlands, which may include fen, marsh and swamp, are fragile places whose existence, especially in the last few decades, has become increasingly under threat. This threat was recognised internationally when, in 1971, representatives from many countries met at Ramsar, in Iran. Members at this convention agreed to:

- identify wetlands of international importance
- plan for the sustainable development of these wetlands
- establish nature reserves on wetlands, train people in wetland studies and management, and encourage wetland research.

### The Norfolk Broads

The Broads, which are shallow lakes, did not form naturally. They result from the time when, in the medieval period (ninth to thirteenth centuries), peat was dug as a fuel for heating and cooking. Since that time, water levels have risen. The peat diggings have become flooded and shallow lakes or 'broads' have formed (Figure 7.10).

The Broads today are a mosaic of four main types of landscape and habitat.

1 **Waterways** are a habitat for birds, fish and water plants. They also used to provide the main form of transport for local people.
2 **Fens** surround several rivers and broads. They consist mainly of reeds, which used to be cut for thatching, and sedges. Well-maintained fens offer shelter for numerous birds and animals, and are the only British habitat for the swallowtail butterfly.
3 **Wet woodlands** form where the fens have not been maintained in their traditional way.
4 **Marshes** were initially a habitat for fish, eels, ducks and other waterfowl. Later, as at Halvergate Marshes, they were drained to provide grazing marshes – that is, open fields divided by dykes (Figure 7.9). The marsh environment is the preferred home for certain types of birds, animals and insects.

**Figure 7.9** The Halvergate Marshes, drained for grazing

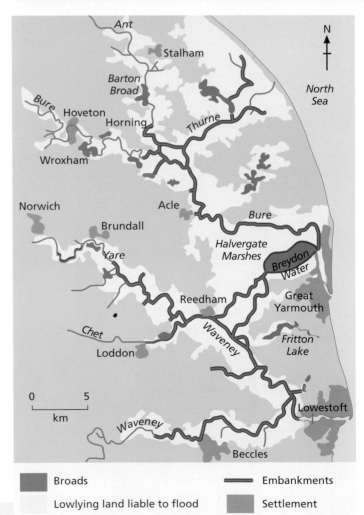

**Figure 7.10** The Norfolk Broads

| Broads | | Embankments |
| Lowlying land liable to flood | | Settlement |

Plant and animal communities developed alongside, and at times were even sustained by, traditional methods of farming and wetland management practices (Figure 7.11). Recently, however, the delicate balance between people and nature has been increasingly upset. The international importance of the area was eventually recognised, and in 1987 the Broads became Britain's first Environmentally Sensitive Area (ESA – see page 135).

When the Broads Authority was set up in 1978, only three of the 33 broads had clear water and a healthy plant and animal life. In contrast, 20 broads had algae-covered water and a decreasing plant and animal life.

**Figure 7.11** A balanced wetland ecosystem

## Problems

- The water table has been lowered rapidly as modern pumps are more efficient than the traditional windmills. The land has sunk below river levels and so has to be protected by flood banks (page 47), many of which need urgent, expensive repairs.
- Many areas are also below the height of the highest tides (pages 58–59). This puts them at risk of flooding by salt water which ruins the soil.
- Reeds along river banks have been cleared or are dying. This leaves fewer habitats for birds, animals and insects and exposes more of the bank to waves created by passing pleasure boats. The waves increase the rate of erosion and wash more soil into river channels.
- The water has become increasingly polluted by phosphate-rich sewage effluent from the growing human population living in the Broads, and by nitrogen-rich run-off from farmland.

- The increase in nitrates has led to eutrophication and the growth of algae. The resultant depletion in oxygen supplies has led to a decrease in the number of fish and wildfowl.
- An estimated 300,000 motorboats, carrying over half a million tourists each year, cause congestion, noise and oil pollution (Figure 7.12).

**Figure 7.12** Human activities upsetting a wetland ecosystem

## Solutions

These include strengthening flood banks, imposing speed limits on motorboats, and opening up the quieter southern Broads in order to reduce pressure on the busier northern ones. Some schemes are very ambitious, such as building a flood barrier across the River Yare to prevent flooding. Others, like the Barton Broad 'Clear Water 2000' project, are more practical. The 'Clear Water 2000' project began in 1995. Its aims are to restore Barton Broad, already a nature reserve, a Site of Special Scientific Interest (SSSI) and a Ramsar site, to a healthy and attractive state, to benefit wildlife and to increase public enjoyment. In order to restore clear water and wildlife, the work at present being done at Barton aims to:

- suction-dredge the whole lake to remove the nutrient-rich (mainly phosphates) mud – the mud will be deposited on nearby arable land where it should do little harm
- restore the reed swamp fringe to the edge of the broad – the reeds form the habitat for water fleas which thrive on algae
- re-create a small island, once used for picnics, which had been eroded.

# The Camargue – a wetland ecosystem under pressure

The Camargue lies in the delta of the River Rhône (Figure 7.13 and page 47). Along with the Coto Doñana (south-west Spain) and the Danube delta, it is one of only three large expanses of marshland still surviving in Europe.

To the newcomer it is a flat bleak expanse of reed beds, salt-marshes and shallow étangs (lakes). The monotony is one of pale greens and greys of grass and scrub. Vegetation gives way to water and sky. The largest étang covers 150 square km yet is no deeper than one metre. There are few trees in this battlefield between fresh and salt water. Some étangs have formed behind coastal spits.

To someone familiar to the area, the water means the land is not dead. There are colours here, the ever changing blues and greys of the wind-rippled water, the faded yellows of the marsh beds lining the étangs, the near blackness of smooth crowned cypresses, the dark green of windbreak pines, the startling bright green of occasional lush grazing pastures, striking vivid against the brown and harsh aridity of the tough, sparse vegetation and salt flats baked hard under the sun. And, above all, there is life here – birds in great number, very occasional small groups of black cattle and, even more rarely, white horses

Adapted from Alistair Maclean, *Caravan to Vaccarès*

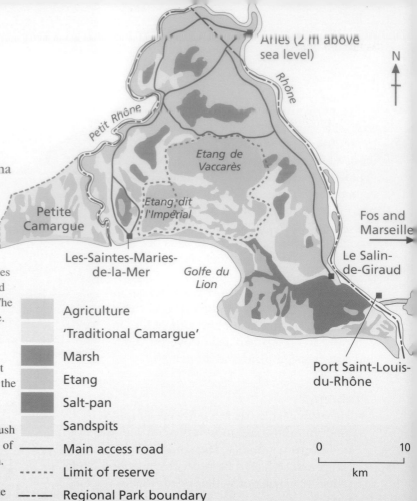

**Figure 7.13** The Camargue Regional Park

To some people it is *inhospitable* because:
- rivers flood after spring snowmelt in the Alps or heavy storms in summer
- the cold, strong mistral wind blows down the Rhône valley, especially in autumn and winter
- mosquitoes breed between June and September
- the summer drought creates an arid, salty environment.

It is a *living environment* for:
- black bulls and white horses (Figure 7.14)
- pink flamingos (Figure 7.15), egrets, herons and numerous migratory birds
- a variety of marsh plants, fish and animals, both fresh and saltwater.

The environment is *under pressure* due to:
- the encroachment by urban areas, such as Arles, and second homes
- the growth of tourism along the coast
- the expansion of farming and the increasing amount of chemical fertiliser and pesticides reaching rivers and étangs; although fewer vines and less rice are grown, land is being continually drained for wheat cultivation
- the threat of industrial pollution from the nearby Fos industrial complex
- the expansion of the largest area of salt production in Europe.

It is estimated that over half of the Carmargue's wild landscape has been lost since 1945.

**Figure 7.14** Wild white horses in the Camargue

**Figure 7.15** Flamingos in the Camargue

**1** *(Page 80)*

  **a** From the ecosystem diagram below give an example of each of the following:
    i) the non-living environment
    ii) a producer
    iii) a carnivore consumer
    iv) a herbivore consumer.

  **b** i) Which letter represents the decomposers?
    ii) What part do decomposers play in this ecosystem?

  **c** Describe how nutrients are recycled in a simple woodland ecosystem.

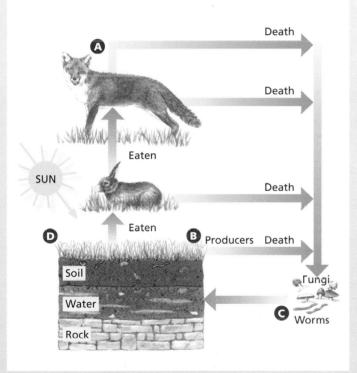

**2** *(Pages 77, 80, 81)*

  **a** Look at the diagrams below.
    i) Describe where there is most litter and erosion.
    ii) Describe where there are most paths.
    iii) What is the link between the number of paths and the amount of litter and erosion?

  **b** Using an ecosystem approach, describe the likely effects of visitors to the area.

  **c** Suggest how an area like this might best be protected.

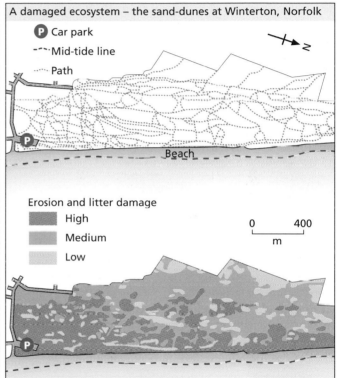

A damaged ecosystem – the sand-dunes at Winterton, Norfolk

**P** Car park
---- Mid-tide line
···· Path

Beach

Erosion and litter damage
High
Medium
Low

0     400
m

**3** *(Pages 84 and 85)*

The Norfolk Broads is an example of a fragile and threatened environment.

  **a** i) Describe the main features of the Norfolk Broads ecosystem.
    ii) Explain the problems that have arisen.
    iii) Suggest how these problems may be overcome.

  **b** For each of the people shown here, suggest the benefits that careful management of the Broads ecosystem might bring. Give reasons for your answers.

Birdwatcher      Farmer

Tourist with a yacht      Owner of local shop

## Population distribution and density

The distribution of people in Europe is uneven and there are considerable variations in population density.

*Distribution* describes the way in which people are spread out across the earth's surface. This distribution is uneven and changes over periods of time. Notice how people are concentrated into certain parts of Europe, making them very crowded (Figure 8.1). In contrast, other parts are sparsely populated, with very few people living there.

*Density* describes the number of people living in a given area, usually a square kilometre. Density is found by dividing the total population of a place by its area. Population density is usually shown by a choropleth map (Figure 8.2). Some parts of the European Union (EU) have a very high population density while others have a very low density.

On global and continental scales, patterns of distribution and density are mainly affected by *physical* factors such as relief, climate, vegetation, soil, natural resources and water supply. At regional and more local scales, patterns are more likely to be influenced by economic, political and social factors – that is, *human* factors.

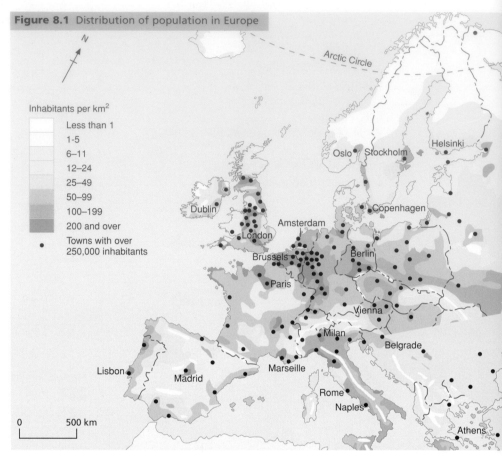

**Figure 8.1** Distribution of population in Europe

Inhabitants per km²

- Less than 1
- 1–5
- 6–11
- 12–24
- 25–49
- 50–99
- 100–199
- 200 and over
- Towns with over 250,000 inhabitants

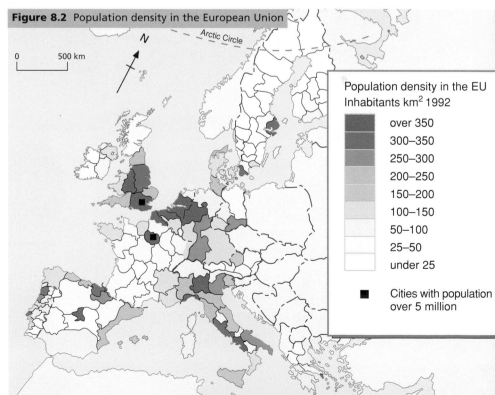

**Figure 8.2** Population density in the European Union

Population density in the EU
Inhabitants km² 1992

- over 350
- 300–350
- 250–300
- 200–250
- 150–200
- 100–150
- 50–100
- 25–50
- under 25
- Cities with population over 5 million

Figure 8.3 gives reasons, with specific examples, why some parts of Europe are crowded and have a high population density and why others are sparsely populated and have a much lower population density. You should, however, be aware that:
- there are usually several reasons why an area is either densely populated (e.g. the Netherlands which has the highest density in Europe) or sparsely populated (e.g. northern Scandinavia)
- within areas there are usually variations in density (e.g. in areas where the overall population density is relatively low there may be places with a higher density, e.g. ski-resorts in the Alps and market towns in East Anglia)
- factors which initially influenced population patterns may no longer apply today (e.g. a coalfield closes but the mining towns remain).

**Figure 8.3** Factors affecting the distribution and density of population in Europe

| | Densely populated areas | Examples | Sparsely populated areas | Examples |
|---|---|---|---|---|
| **Physical** | | | | |
| Relief | Flat and lowlying | Netherlands | High, rugged mountains | Norway, Pyrenees |
| | Broad river valleys | Paris Basin | Worn-down shield lands (Figure 3.15) | Scandinavia |
| Climate | Warm throughout the year and a long growing season | French Riviera, Spanish costas | Cold and a short growing season | Northern Scandinavia, Iceland |
| | Reliable rainfall spread evenly throughout the year | Western UK, Netherlands | Unreliable rainfall and/or a seasonal drought | Central Spain |
| Vegetation | Grasslands easy to clear/farm | Paris Region | Coniferous forest | Scandinavia |
| Soil | Deep fertile silt left by rivers | Po Valley (Italy) | Thin soils due to removal by glaciers | Central Scandinavia |
| | Volcanic soils | Mount Etna | Lacking humus, eroded | Apennines |
| Natural resources | Minerals, e.g. coal, iron ore | Ruhr (Germany), Kiruna (Sweden) | Lack of minerals and/or energy supplies | Republic of Ireland |
| | Energy supplies, e.g. HEP | North Italian Plain | | |
| Water supply | Reliable supplies | Northern UK | Seasonal drought | Central Spain |
| **Human** | | | | |
| Economic | Ports | Rotterdam, Marseille | Limited facilities for ports | South-west France |
| | Good roads, railways, airports | Germany, Paris Basin | Poor transport links | Scandinavia |
| | Industrial areas (traditional) | Ruhr, Tyneside | Lack of industrial development | Finland |
| | Development of tourism | Mediterranean coasts and Alpine areas | Lack of tourist developments | Northern Scandinavia |
| | Money available for non-high-tech industries | South of France, M4 Corridor | Lack of money for new investments | Belgian coalfield |
| Political | Government investment | North Italy | Lack of government investment | Scottish Highlands |
| | New towns Creation of a capital city | Around London and Paris Madrid | Depopulation of rural and old industrial areas | Massif Central (France) |
| | Reclamation of land | Dutch polders | Loss of land, e.g. deforestation, and soil erosion | Apennines |
| Social | Better housing opportunities | London Docklands | Poor housing opportunities | Isolated highland areas, e.g. Massif Central, Ardennes (Belgium) |
| | Education, health facilities and entertainment | Milan | Limited education, health facilities and entertainment | |
| | Retirement areas | Spanish costas, south coast of England | Poor facilities for retirement | |

## Population changes

The total population of an area depends upon changes in the *natural increase* and *migration* (Figure 8.4). The *natural increase* (or *decrease*) is the difference between the birth rate and the death rate. The *birth rate* is the number of live births in a year for every 1,000 people in the total population. The *death rate* is the number of people in every 1,000 who die in a year. If the birth rate is higher then the total population will increase. If the death rate is higher then the total population will decrease.

Throughout history birth rates have usually exceeded death rates. Exceptions have occurred during major outbreaks of disease (bubonic plague), wars (former Yugoslavia) and in the present decade in one or two western European countries (Germany and Italy).

## The demographic transition model

The demographic transition model describes a sequence of changes in the relationship between birth rates and death rates (Figure 8.5). The model was produced using changes in the natural increase in several industrialised countries in western Europe and in North America. It suggests that the population (or demographic) growth rates for *all* countries can be divided into four stages.

It should be noted that this model, like any other model, has its limitations. While several western European countries appear to be entering a fifth stage (not predicted by the model), many economically less developed countries, especially those in Africa, are still at stage 2.

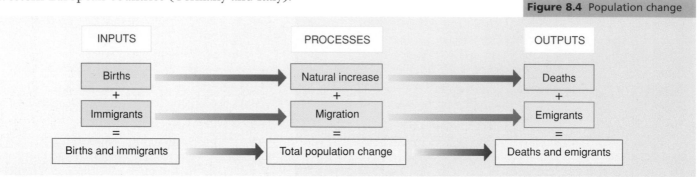

**Figure 8.4** Population change

**Figure 8.5** The demographic transition model

| | Stage 1 | Stage 2 | Stage 3 | Stage 4 | Stage 5 |
|---|---|---|---|---|---|
| | High fluctuating | Early expanding | Late expanding | Low fluctuating | ? |
| | Birth rates and death rates are both high | Birth rates remain high but death rates fall rapidly | Birth rates now fall rapidly, death rates fall less quickly | Birth rates and death rates are low | Birth rates fall below death rates |
| **Model as applied to UK** | Pre-1780 | 1780–1880 | 1880–1940 | 1940– | – |
| World examples | Isolated rainforest tribes | Bangladesh, Kenya | Brazil, China | USA, Japan | – |
| European examples | – | – | Republic of Ireland | France, Spain | Italy, Germany |

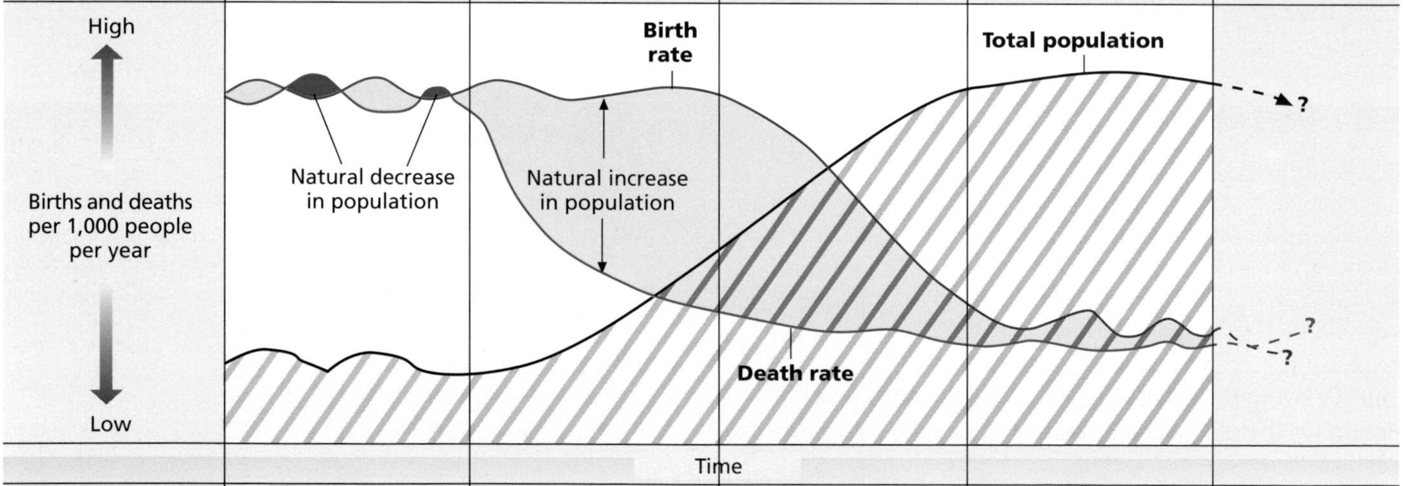

**Figure 8.6** Birth rates, death rates and natural increase in western Europe

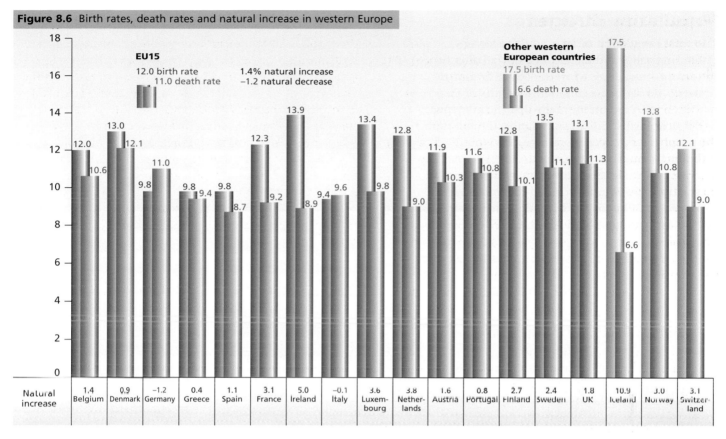

**Natural increase in western Europe (1993)**

- The average birth rate for the 15 countries of the EU was 11.1 (which was much lower than the world figure of 25.0).
- The average death rate for the EU was 10.1 (which was slightly higher than the world figure of 9.0).
- The natural increase for the EU was, therefore, 1.0 (compared with that of 16.0 for the world).

As with population distribution and density (pages 88 and 89), the natural increase is not even across western Europe. Figure 8.6 gives the natural increase for the 15 EU countries together with the remaining three that make up western Europe. Notice that Germany and Italy had a natural decrease (page 95). Figure 8.7 shows how the natural increase varies not only between countries but also within countries.

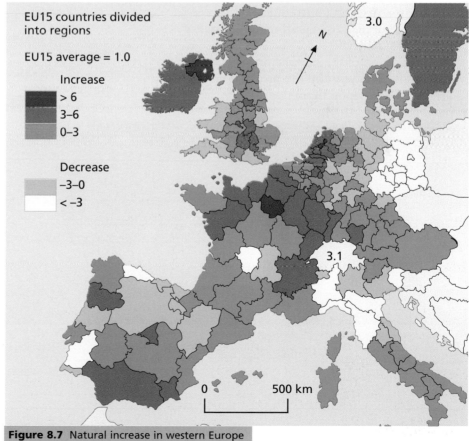

**Figure 8.7** Natural increase in western Europe

# Population structures

The rates of natural increase, births, deaths, infant mortality and life expectancy all affect the population structure of a country. (The *infant mortality rate* is the number of deaths of children who die before their first birthday per 1,000 live births. *Life expectancy* is the number of years that the average person born in a particular country can expect to live.)

The population structure of a country can be shown by a *population* or *age-sex pyramid* (Figure 8.8). Population pyramids show:

- the total population divided into five-year age groups
- the percentage of people in each of those age groups
- the percentage of males and females in each age group.

Population pyramids are useful because they show:

- trends in the birth rate, death rate, infant mortality rate and life expectancy – these trends can help a country to plan its future services, e.g. more homes for the elderly if there is an ageing population or fewer schools if there is a declining birth rate
- the effects of people migrating into or out of a region or country
- the proportion of the population who are economically active and the proportion who are dependent upon them.

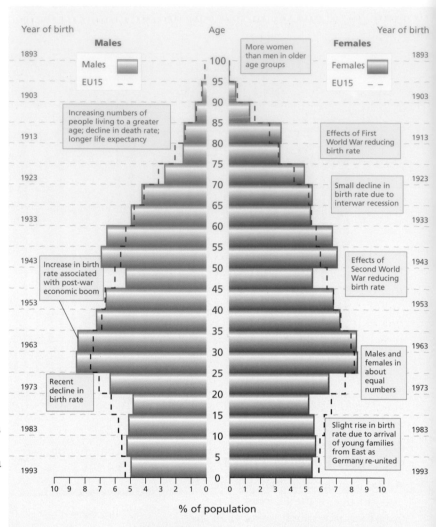

**Figure 8.8** Population pyramid for Germany, 1994

**Figure 8.9** Population pyramids showing different stages of development

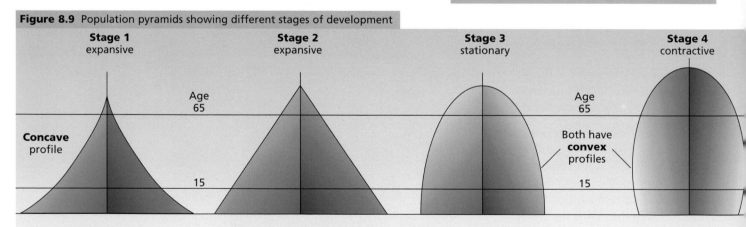

| Stage 1 expansive | Stage 2 expansive | Stage 3 stationary | Stage 4 contractive |
|---|---|---|---|
| High birth rate; rapid fall in each upward age group due to high death rate; short life expectancy | Still a high birth rate; fall in death rate as more living in middle age; slightly longer life expectancy | Declining birth rate; low death rate; more people living to a greater age | Low birth rate; low death rate; higher dependency ratio; longer life expectancy |
| Typical of economically less developed countries | | Typical of economically more developed countries | |

The last feature can be shown as the *dependency ratio* which can be expressed as:

$$\frac{\text{Non-economically active (children + retired people)}}{\text{Economically active (those of working age)}} \times 100$$

In Germany, for example, the dependency ratio in 1994 was:

$$\frac{13{,}911 + 12{,}044}{55{,}309} \times 100 = 46.92$$

This meant that for every 100 people of working age there were 46.92 people dependent upon them.

Population pyramids allow comparisons to be made between countries. Unlike the demographic transition model (Figure 8.5), population pyramids include immigrants, but like that model they can be shown as one of four idealised types of graph with each graph representing a different stage of development (Figure 8.9). As with most models, many countries show an individual shape which does not fit precisely into any pattern.

Most western European countries do, however, show many of the characteristics associated with stage 4. The population pyramid for the Netherlands (Figure 8.10) shows a relatively small proportion of its population in the pre-reproductive age groups (18 per cent under 15). This indicates that the Netherlands, like Germany (Figure 8.8), has low birth and infant mortality rates. Although the proportion in the retired/post-reproductive age groups appears small (16 per cent over 65), this proportion is growing steadily as the death rate falls and life expectancy increases. As the numbers entering the reproductive age groups decline there is likely to be a fall, in time, in the total population.

The population pyramids for the Republic of Ireland (Figure 8.11) and Iceland both differ slightly from those of other western European countries. Both have higher birth rates, so a relatively higher proportion of their population is in the under-15 age groups.

**Figure 8.10** Population pyramid for the Netherlands, 1994

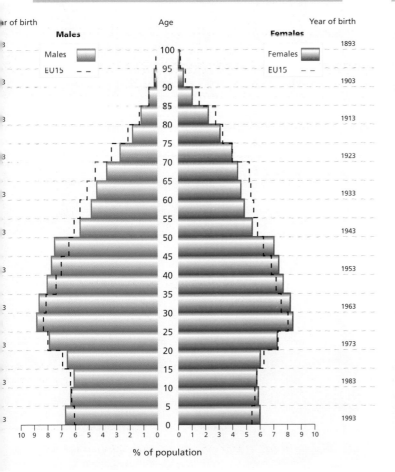

**Figure 8.11** Population pyramid for Ireland, 1994

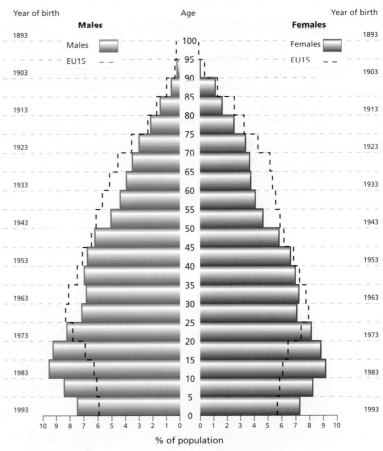

# Future population trends

## Birth rates and population growth

To maintain a stable population within the EU, without growth or decline, each woman needs to have, on average, 2.1 children. In the UK and several other western European countries, birth rates have for over twenty years fallen below those needed for the natural replacement of the population. Recent figures (Figure 8.12) claim that British and German women are only averaging 1.8 and 1.7 children respectively, although this is relatively healthy when measured against the forecast of 1.3 children early next century in Italy and Spain. Countries failing to reach the *replacement rate* fear a reduction in their competitive advantage in science and technology, insufficient unskilled labour and a lack of security in providing pensions.

The decline in the birth rate and natural increase in the EU (Figure 8.13a and b) means that the total population is predicted to peak early next century and, by 2025, to have begun to fall. It also means that as the population living in economically less developed countries continues to grow rapidly, the proportion of the world's population living in the EU15 will continue to shrink (Figure 8.13c).

# Fall in British births

FALLING fertility rates are expected to lead to an historic fall in Britain's population by the year 2025, experts warned yesterday.

The move, which marks the reversal of a trend, will be the first since records began.

Government population experts expect almost one in five of today's 25 to 19-year-olds will remain childless – a move that will have repercussions next century. The figure compares with just 10% of the women born in 1944.

The last time deaths outnumbered births probably happened after the Black Death in 1347–51 and the Great Plague in 1665.

In the UK, fertility has been at a level below that needed for the natural replacement of the population for 20 years. Women are having 1.8 children compared to the 2.1 needed.

Childlessness is on the increase. We are likely to have a population heavily weighted towards the elderly and with few workers in it.

Part of the reason for women opting for childlessness could be due to an increase in employment opportunities. However, a study of women born between 1924 and 1969 showed that while some may delay childbirth, others are putting it off altogether.

*Newcastle Journal, 14 June 1996*

**Figure 8.12** Decline in the UK birth rate

**Figure 8.13** Population in the EU

| Year | Live births | Deaths | Natural increase | Total population ('000s) |
|------|-------------|--------|------------------|--------------------------|
| 1960 | 18.3 | 10.7 | 7.6 | 314,826 |
| 1970 | 16.2 | 10.8 | 5.3 | 339,974 |
| 1980 | 13.0 | 10.5 | 2.5 | 354,571 |
| 1990 | 12.0 | 10.2 | 1.8 | 363,714 |
| 1994 | 11.1 | 10.1 | 1.0 | 370,392 |

(a) Population change in the EU, 1960–94

Italian deaths outnumbered births in 1995 for a third successive year, with Italy more than ever a country of one-child families, the government's annual population report said yesterday. The trend to small families has mainly been blamed on financial constraints. In 1995 there were 526,064 births and 555,203 deaths. But because of an influx of immigrants, Italy's population increased by 55,000 last year to 57,333,996.

*AP, Rome*

(b) Population changes in Italy, 1995

(c) Proportion of the world's population living in the EU15, 1950–2025

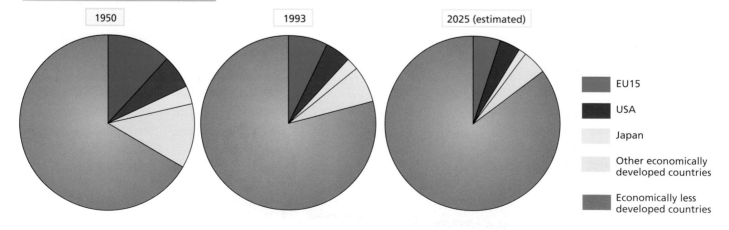

1950    1993    2025 (estimated)

- EU15
- USA
- Japan
- Other economically developed countries
- Economically less developed countries

## An ageing population

Due to improvements in medical facilities, hygiene and vaccines, the death rate in western Europe has continued to decline and life expectancy to increase. In the UK in 1966, the Office of Population Censuses and Surveys forecast that the 15.8 per cent of the British population aged over 65 in 1993 was likely to rise to 24.1 per cent by the middle of next century (Figure 8.14). With growing numbers of elderly people, Britain will be faced with increased demands for more pensions, more money for the National Health for medical care, and more residential homes and other social services. As Britain's population continues to age, there will be fewer people in the economically active age groups to support them. A major political problem facing most governments in western Europe in the next few years will be how to provide sufficient money to support the growth of their ageing populations (Figure 8.15).

## Overpopulation and underpopulation

The term *overpopulation* is applied to a country or region where the number of people living there is too many for the resources available (food, energy, minerals, technology). In contrast, *underpopulation* is when there are far more resources available in a country or region than can be used by the people living there.

The Netherlands, with 448 people per km², has one of the highest population densities in the world. However, it is not considered to be overpopulated as, under normal circumstances, there are enough houses and jobs, and sufficient food and energy supplies to maintain both a high standard of living and a good quality of life (page 200).

There is a fear in several western European countries that, if their total population does decrease, they may become relatively underpopulated and their standard of living might fall.

# Ageing trend as population grows older

THE number of people aged 75 and over will increase by 70 per cent during the next 40 years, predicts the Office of Population Censuses and Surveys.

It forecasts that the number of pensioners – men over 65 and women over 60 – will only increase slowly to reach 9.6 million in 2003 but will then rise to 14.8 million in 2034 – an increase of 54 per cent in just over 30 years.

While the number of over 75-year-olds will rise by 70 per cent between now and 2034, the number of children under 16 will fall from the present total of 10.6 million to 9.1 million in 2034.

The consequence of this is that there will be fewer people of working age paying taxes to support the growing number of pensioners.

The number of children and pensioners as a proportion of the number of workers will stay near its present level of 64 per 100 people of working age for the next 20 years, then rise to reach 80 per 100 by 2034.

| | Under 16 | 16–39 | 40–64 | 65–79 | 80 and over |
|---|---|---|---|---|---|
| **Mid-year** | | | | | |
| 1971 | 25.5 | 31.3 | 29.9 | 10.9 | 2.3 |
| 1981 | 22.3 | 34.9 | 27.8 | 12.2 | 2.8 |
| 1991 | 20.3 | 35.3 | 28.6 | 12.0 | 3.7 |
| 1993 | 20.6 | 34.9 | 28.8 | 11.9 | 3.9 |
| Males | 21.6 | 36.3 | 29.2 | 10.6 | 2.4 |
| Females | 19.6 | 33.5 | 28.4 | 13.1 | 5.4 |
| **Mid-year projections** | | | | | |
| 2001 | 20.7 | 32.9 | 30.6 | 11.4 | 4.3 |
| 2011 | 19.2 | 30.0 | 34.1 | 11.9 | 4.7 |
| 2021 | 18.3 | 29.7 | 32.7 | 14.3 | 5.1 |
| 2031 | 18.2 | 28.4 | 30.5 | 16.3 | 6.6 |
| 2041 | 17.6 | 27.8 | 30.1 | 16.8 | 7.8 |
| 2051 | 17.6 | 28.0 | 30.3 | 14.9 | 9.2 |
| Males | 18.2 | 28.9 | 30.9 | 14.5 | 7.5 |
| Females | 17.0 | 27.2 | 29.7 | 15.2 | 10.9 |

**Figure 8.14** Britain's ageing population

**Figure 8.15** An ageing Greek Lady

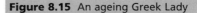

# Migration

Migration is a movement which, in human terms, usually involves a permanent change of home. Although migration can take place either within a country or between countries, the term can be applied more widely to include temporary, seasonal and daily movements of people (Figure 8.16). *Internal migration* affects the distribution of people within a country. *External migration* affects the total population (Figure 8.1) and the population structure of a region or country.

- The *migration balance* is the difference between the number of emigrants (people who leave a country) and the number of immigrants (people who enter a country).
- Countries with a *net migration loss* lose more people through emigration than they gain by immigration. Depending upon their natural increase (the balance between the birth rate and the death rate) these countries may have a declining population (the former Yugoslavia in the early 1990s).
- Countries with a *net migration gain* receive more immigrants than they lose emigrants and so, assuming birth and death rates are evenly balanced, they are likely to have a population increase (France). In some cases (Italy – Figure 8.13b), a net migration gain offsets a natural decrease. In others (Ireland), the natural increase is greater than the net migration loss (Figure 8.17).

Migration may be either voluntary or forced. *Voluntary migration* is when migrants choose to move. This is usually:

- to improve their standard of living, e.g. more and better-paid jobs
- to improve their quality of life, e.g. retiring to a warmer climate, working in a more pleasant environment or where there are better services (schools, hospitals)
- for increased personal freedom, e.g. greater religious or political tolerance.

*Forced migration* is when migrants have no personal choice. This may result from:

- natural disasters, e.g. earthquakes, volcanic eruptions and floods
- economic and social impositions, e.g. wars, famine, forced labour, inner-city redevelopment, religious or political persecution.

| Permanent | External (international) | Figure 8.16 Types of migration |
|---|---|---|
| | 1 voluntary | |
| | 2 forced (refugees) | |
| | **Internal** | |
| | 1 rural population | |
| | 2 urban depopulation | |
| | 3 regional | |
| **Semi-permanent** | for several years | |
| **Seasonal** | for several months or several weeks | |
| **Daily** | commuters | |

**Figure 8.17** Migration into Europe showing (a) movements since 1945 and (b) net balance in 1993

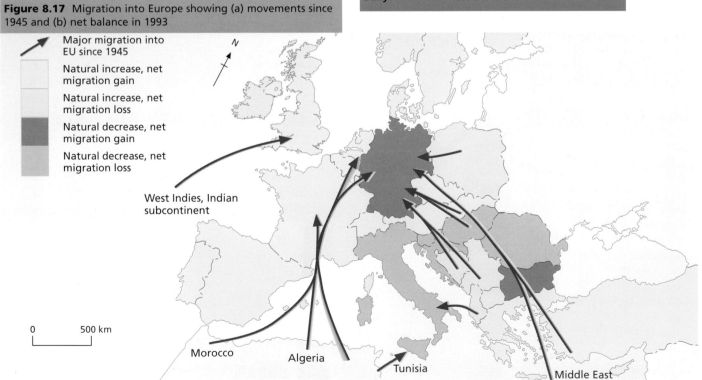

Legend:
- Major migration into EU since 1945
- Natural increase, net migration gain
- Natural increase, net migration loss
- Natural decrease, net migration gain
- Natural decrease, net migration loss

West Indies, Indian subcontinent

0    500 km

Morocco   Algeria   Tunisia   Middle East

## Migration into and within the EU

Most early arrivals were *economic migrants*. These were people looking for work in order to improve their standard of living. They included people from North Africa moving into France, from Turkey into the then West Germany, and from the West Indies and Indian subcontinent into the UK (Figure 8.18). These early migrants were later joined by their families. More recently, and especially during the break-up of the former Yugoslavia, many would-be immigrants have sought asylum (safety). If asylum-seekers can prove that they are escaping from political, racial or religious persecution then they are granted the status of being *refugees* (Figure 8.19). The United Nations define people who are forced to move within their own country as *displaced persons*. The greatest concern at present to EU countries is the increasing number of illegal immigrants who try to enter a country without seeking permission.

On 1 January 1994, it was estimated that of the 367 million inhabitants living in the EU (Figure 8.20):

- 5.3 million were Community citizens living in a member state other than their country of origin (e.g. Portuguese living in France)
- 11.6 million were classified by the EU as 'foreign population originating from non-member countries' (e.g. North Africans living in France).

Most of the foreign population (72 per cent) lived in either Germany, France or the UK (Figure 8.20). The majority of these immigrants came from Turkey, the former Yugoslavia, North Africa and eastern Europe (Figure 8.21).

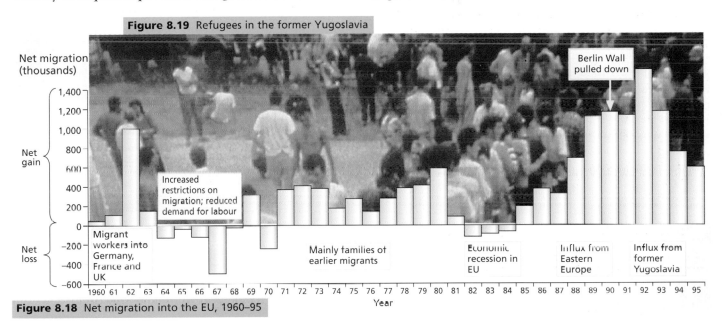

**Figure 8.19** Refugees in the former Yugoslavia

**Figure 8.18** Net migration into the EU, 1960–95

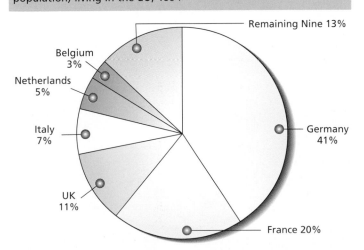

**Figure 8.20** Proportion of non-Community members (foreign population) living in the EU, 1994

- Remaining Nine 13%
- Belgium 3%
- Netherlands 5%
- Italy 7%
- UK 11%
- France 20%
- Germany 41%

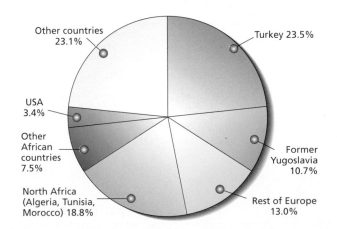

**Figure 8.21** Country of origin of non-Community foreigners, 1994

- Other countries 23.1%
- Turkey 23.5%
- USA 3.4%
- Other African countries 7.5%
- North Africa (Algeria, Tunisia, Morocco) 18.8%
- Former Yugoslavia 10.7%
- Rest of Europe 13.0%

# Foreign residents in the EU

## North Africans into France

Like several other western European countries in the late 1940s, France had many more job vacancies than it had workers. This was partly due to the higher than average death rate experienced during the Second World War and partly due to the need to rebuild the country after that war. Later, as France became increasingly prosperous, it attracted workers from the poorer parts of Europe (notably Portugal) and from North Africa (especially from its colonies, as they were then, of Algeria and Morocco).

Initially many migrants either went into farming or found unskilled jobs in Marseille – the port of entry into France. As these immigrants became more settled, they turned to relatively better-paid jobs in factories and the construction industry. Even so, the majority of immigrants were forced to take jobs which the French themselves did not want, i.e. when the work was dirty, unskilled, poorly paid or demanded long and unsociable hours (Figure 8.25). Although some of the immigrants eventually took out French citizenship, many have not. Figure 8.22 gives the 1993 breakdown of the resident French population and the country of origin of the non-nationals.

The population pyramid for non-national residents of France (Figure 8.23) shows several features which are characteristic for most countries with a significant number of immigrants.

- The largest numbers are in the economically active age groups as these are people who have come to find work.
- The large number of young children is a result of the economically active age groups coinciding with the reproductively active age groups.
- There is a relatively small proportion of elderly people as these are the least likely to migrate.
- There are more males than females. This is because it is usually the male who moves first to seek work with the intention later of either returning home or being joined by his family.

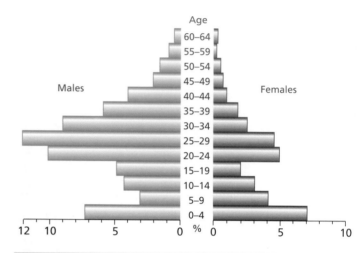

**Figure 8.23** Population pyramid for non-Community foreigners in France, 1994

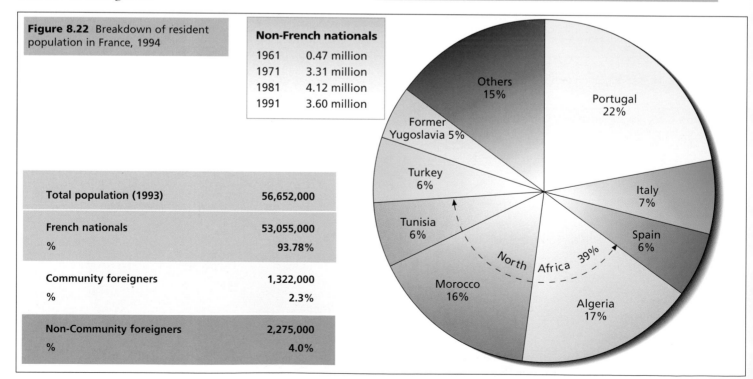

**Figure 8.22** Breakdown of resident population in France, 1994

| Non-French nationals | |
|---|---|
| 1961 | 0.47 million |
| 1971 | 3.31 million |
| 1981 | 4.12 million |
| 1991 | 3.60 million |

| | |
|---|---|
| Total population (1993) | 56,652,000 |
| French nationals | 53,055,000 |
| % | 93.78% |
| Community foreigners | 1,322,000 |
| % | 2.3% |
| Non-Community foreigners | 2,275,000 |
| % | 4.0% |

## Problems facing the immigrants

### Housing

Many of the early immigrants into Marseille and Paris were forced to live in shanty settlements known as 'bidonvilles' (*bidon* is French for a petrol can). Houses in 'bidonvilles' were made from flattened cans, strips of plastic, planks of wood and any other loose material. The settlements, which were illegal, often lacked electricity, sewerage and clean water. Although 'bidonvilles' have now been replaced by large blocks of government-built high-rise flats (Figure 8.24), the flats are often overcrowded and of poor quality.

### Education and health

Children of illegal immigrants, the majority arriving from North Africa, are unlikely to attend school and so are illiterate, unable to speak French and lacking in work skills. Differences in language, religion and culture leave them isolated and this increases racial tension. Poor nutrition and a lack of access to health care have marked effects on infant mortality and child illnesses.

### Jobs

Some immigrants have become very successful, especially in sport, but many still have to accept unskilled, poorer-paid jobs (Figure 8.25). Most come from rural areas, and are unfamiliar with industrial work. In times of unemployment, they are the first to be laid off. Many have to find work in the informal sector.

## The situation today

Post-war migration into countries such as France has presented problems as well as having advantages (Figure 8.26). Recently levels of immigration have led to increasing concerns among French nationals.

- North African immigrants, although never encouraged to integrate socially, existed relatively peacefully with French nationals until the early 1990s. Since then, however, a growth in unemployment among French people has caused increased resentment against those North Africans still in work.
- The growth in Islamic fundamentalism in the early 1990s encouraged strikes by Arab workers and discouraged Arab women from adopting French customs.
- French fears, caused by the increase in illegal immigrants from North Africa and the high birth rate of legal immigrants, has led to the growth of an extreme political party – a party favouring the expulsion of all non-EU foreigners.

**Figure 8.24** Housing for non-Community foreigners in Marseille

**Figure 8.25** Jobs for non-Community foreigners in Paris

| Advantages | Disadvantages |
|---|---|
| • Overcomes labour shortage | • Pressure on jobs but most likely to be the first unemployed in a recession |
| • Prepared to do dirty, unskilled jobs | • Low-quality, overcrowded housing lacking in basic amenities |
| • Prepared to work long hours for low salaries | • Ethnic groups tend not to integrate |
| • Cultural advantages and links | • Racial tension |
| • Some highly skilled immigrants | • Limited skills/education |
| • In a developing country these migrants could increase the number of skilled workers | • Lack of opportunities to practise their own religion, culture, etc. |
| | • Language difficulties |
| | • Often less healthy |

**Figure 8.26** Effects of immigration into France

**1** *(Pages 88 and 89)*

Look at the population density map.

**a** i) Give the meaning of the term *densely populated*.

ii) Name two countries that are densely populated.

iii) Name two countries that are sparsely populated.

**b** Describe and suggest reasons for the population density at A. Use the following headings:

\* Relief \* Climate \* Soils
\* Transport

**c** London is one of the most densely populated areas in Europe. Suggest reasons for this.

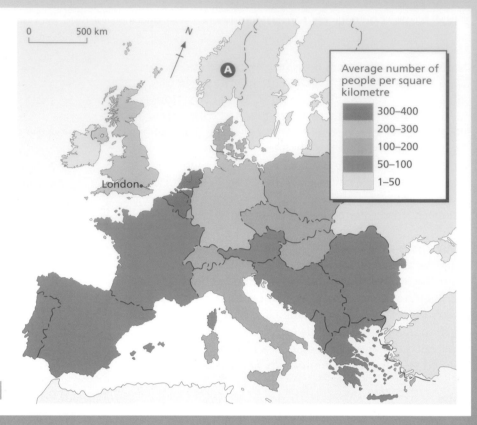

0    500 km

N

Average number of people per square kilometre

300–400
200–300
100–200
50–100
1–50

London

Population density – Europe

---

**2** *(Pages 90 and 91)*

Look at the graph.

**a** i) What is meant by *birth rate*?

ii) What is meant by *death rate*?

**b** i) What is meant by *natural increase*?

ii) Which letter, A, B, C or D, represents the natural increase?

iii) What was the rate of natural increase in England and Wales in 1995?

**c** Using the graph, suggest in which year England and Wales had the most rapid population growth? Give reasons for your answer.

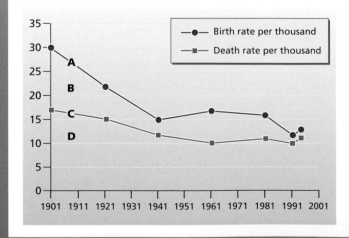

Birth rate per thousand
Death rate per thousand

A
B
C
D

1901 1911 1921 1931 1941 1951 1961 1971 1981 1991 2001

---

**3** *(Pages 90 and 91)*

Study the graph which shows population change in four stages.

**a** At which stage are both birth **and** death rates i) high and ii) low?

**b** Which stage does the following description fit?

\* Falling birth rate \* Low death rate
\* Rapid population increase

**c** Describe and give reasons for the population change in stage 2.

**d** i) At which stage will the population have the highest proportion of older people? Give reasons for your answer.

ii) Name three countries that are at this stage.

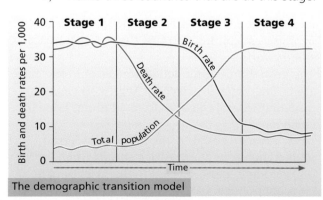

Stage 1    Stage 2    Stage 3    Stage 4

Birth and death rates per 1,000

Birth rate
Death rate
Total population

Time

The demographic transition model

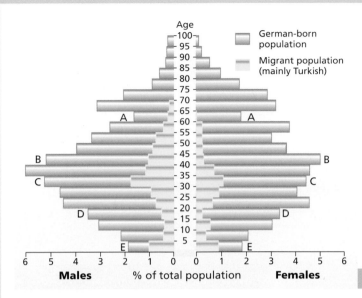

German-born population

Migrant population (mainly Turkish)

Munich, Germany, in 1980 (after a period of migration)

**4** *(Pages 92 and 93)*

**a** Study the population pyramid and answer A, B, C, D or E to the following. Which age group shows:

i) young people starting employment
ii) older people requiring care
iii) the effect of high death rates and low birth rates during the Second World War
iv) the biggest influx of migrant workers
v) that migrant workers were starting families?

**b** In the future, will Munich need to provide more homes for the elderly, or increase the number of schools? Give reasons for your answer.

**5** *(Pages 94 and 95)*

Look at the sketches which show the balance between population and resources.

**a** i) Which diagram represents overpopulation? Give reasons for your answer.
ii) Give four examples of important resources needed to support a population.

**b** i) Which diagram represents underpopulation? Give reasons for your answer.
ii) How can underpopulation cause problems for a country?

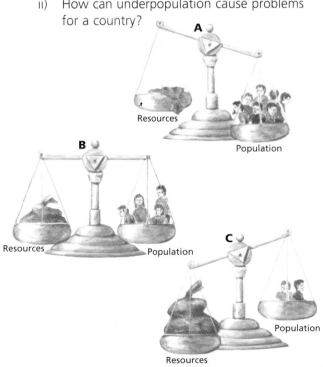

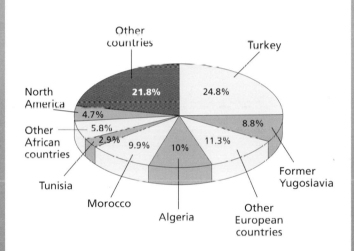

Origin of non-EU migrants into Germany, 1992

**6** *(Pages 96 and 97)*

**a** Study the diagram which shows the migration of people to Germany from non-EU countries.
i) What is the meaning of the term *migration*?
ii) From which country did most people migrate to Germany?

**b** Suggest four reasons why people might migrate from one country to another.

**c** i) Why have some countries such as Germany encouraged inward migration in the past?
ii) What problems might develop in a country that has encouraged inward migration?

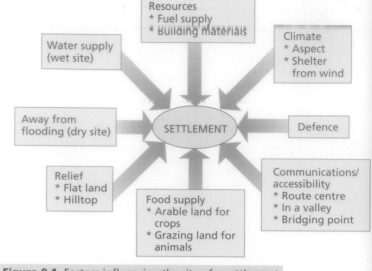

**Figure 9.1** Factors influencing the site of a settlement

## Settlement sites and hierarchies

*Site* describes the characteristics of the actual place where people decided to locate a settlement. It was of major importance in the initial growth of a town or village. The most important factors in determining the site of a settlement are shown in Figure 9.1. You should be aware, however, that often several of these factors operated together in influencing the choice of a specific site.

| Site | | A HAMLET<br>Stair, Cumbria | B VILLAGE<br>Corfe Castle, Dorset |
|---|---|---|---|
| | Photo to show physical appearance | | |
| | Site and services as shown on a 1:50 000 OS map | | |
| | Site factors | • Water supply – wet site<br>• Local stone and slate for building materials<br>• In a valley sheltered by mountains<br>• On flat land above level of flooding<br>• Grazing land for animals | • Dry site but small river nearby<br>• Local stone for building<br>• Castle on a chalk ridge for defence<br>• Route through the ridge<br>• Grazing and arable land nearby<br>• Lowland nearby was originally wooded – fuel supply |
| **Settlement hierarchy** | Approximate population size | 50 | 1,400 |
| | Approximate sphere of influence | Just the hamlet – about 1 km | 2–3 km |
| | Services/ provision of goods | Telephone box | Post office, small shops, church and chapel, village hall, main road, inn/public house, access to railway, facilities at National Trust property (Corfe Castle), junior school |

*Situation* describes the location of a place in relation to surrounding features such as neighbouring settlements, river valleys and high land. Situation becomes the most important factor in the continued growth and development of a settlement.

A *settlement hierarchy* is when settlements are arranged in an order of importance. Three different methods may be used to produce a settlement hierarchy:

1 The *population size* of each settlement.

2 The *sphere of influence* of each settlement – that is, the area served by a particular settlement.

3 The type and number of *services* provided by each settlement.

Figure 9.2 shows four settlements at different levels of the hierarchy. For each settlement the table:
- lists the major factors that determined the original site
- applies the three different methods of producing a hierarchy.

**Figure 9.2** Settlement hierarchy

| C TOWN<br>Keswick, Cumbria | D CITY<br>Durham, County Durham |
|---|---|
|  |  |
| 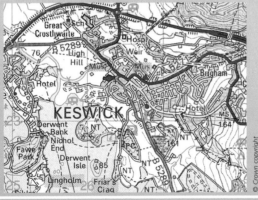 | 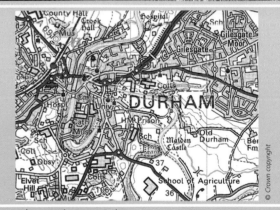 |
| • Water supply from river and nearby lake – wet site<br>• On gentle hillsides – dry site<br>• Local stone and slate for building materials<br>• Meeting-point of valleys – easier communications<br>• Grazing land for animals<br>• Bridging point<br>• Aspect facing south-west | • Water supply on a river – wet site<br>• Within a meander which acted as a natural defence<br>• Above level of flooding – dry site<br>• Nearby stone for building materials<br>• Routeway along river valley<br>• Bridging point<br>• Lowlying farmland for crops and animals |
| 5,700 | 41,500 |
| 10–20 km | 20–50 km |
| Shops, churches, cafés and restaurants, town hall, bus station, hotels, small hospital, small theatre, museums, doctors, youth hostel, junior and senior schools | County hall, hotels, large hospital, several secondary schools, university, bus and rail stations, cinemas, castle, cathedral, many churches, large city centre shopping complex, prison, museums |

## Urban land use

The increase in the proportion of people who live in towns and cities is called *urbanisation*. Although the first sizeable settlements in Europe developed during Greek and, later, Roman times, the real period of urbanisation only began with the growth of industry in the nineteenth century. In the UK, where the Industrial Revolution began, only 10 per cent of the population were living in towns in 1801. Now, as Figure 9.3 shows, over 90 per cent live in towns of over 10,000.

Urban growth has continued throughout this century in most parts of Europe (Figure 9.4). This is mainly because urban areas:

- provide more jobs, many of which are better-paid, cleaner, and demand more skill than those in rural areas
- are nearer to places of work, reducing distance, time, and cost of travel from home
- have better housing, schools and hospitals, shopping and transport facilities, and a wider range of entertainment.

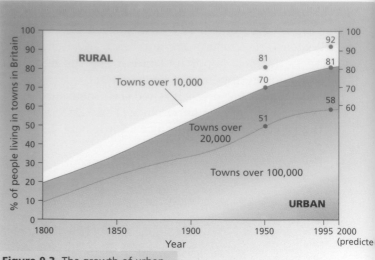

**Figure 9.3** The growth of urban population in the UK, 1800–2000

## Urban land use models

You should already be aware that a *model* is a theoretical framework. Although it may not actually exist, the model should help to explain the reality. It has been suggested that urban areas do not grow in a haphazard way but tend to develop with recognisable shapes and patterns. Although each town or city has its own distinctive pattern, it is likely to share certain characteristics with other urban settlements.

Two land use models, which were among the first to be put forward and which are still the easiest to apply, are shown in Figure 9.5.

1 **Burgess** claimed that in the centre of all towns and cities there was a *central business district (CBD)*. This CBD was surrounded by a zone which contained industry and poor-quality housing. Burgess then suggested that towns grew outwards in a concentric pattern, shown on his model as four circles (Figure 9.5a). These were based on the age of houses and the wealth of their occupants.

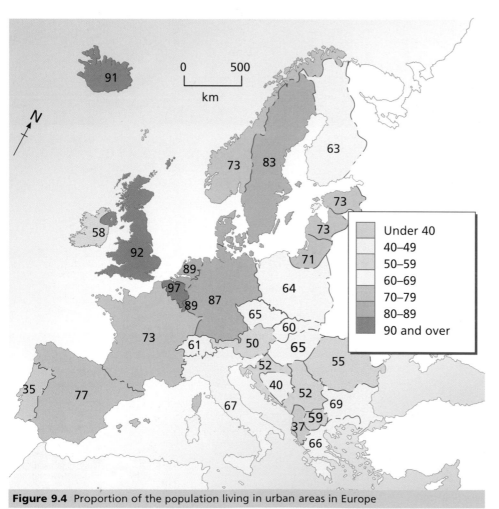

**Figure 9.4** Proportion of the population living in urban areas in Europe

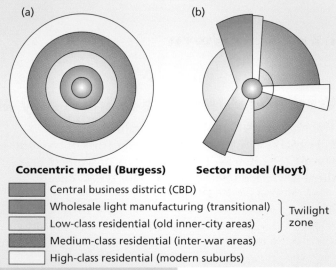

**Concentric model (Burgess)**   **Sector model (Hoyt)**

- Central business district (CBD)
- Wholesale light manufacturing (transitional) } Twilight zone
- Low-class residential (old inner-city areas) } Twilight zone
- Medium-class residential (inter-war areas)
- High-class residential (modern suburbs)

**Figure 9.5** Urban land use models

2 **Hoyt** put forward his model after the development of public transport in cities. He suggested that towns developed in *sectors*, or wedges, alongside main roads (Figure 9.5b). This meant that if industry and low-cost housing developed in one part of a town in the nineteenth century, then newer industry and modern low-cost housing would also develop within that same sector.

## Functional zones in a city

Each of the zones shown in Figure 9.5 has a special function or purpose. The four main types of function are shops and offices, industry, housing, and open space. The location of each functional zone and the distribution of land use in a city are related to three factors:

1 **Accessibility** The CBD, where the main routes from the suburbs and surrounding towns meet, is the easiest to reach from all parts of the city.

2 **Land values** Land values are highest in the CBD because for several types of land use this is the 'prime site'. The resultant competition, together with the lack of available space, pushes up land prices. Land values decrease rapidly towards the edge of the city.

3 **Changes in demand** The main demand for land use in most nineteenth-century cities was for industry and low-quality housing. Today the demand is for industry, shops and better-quality housing – all in a more pleasant environment – and open space.

Figure 9.6 is a more realistic model showing land use patterns and functional zones in a British city. Figure 9.7 is a transect showing changes in land use across a typical German city.

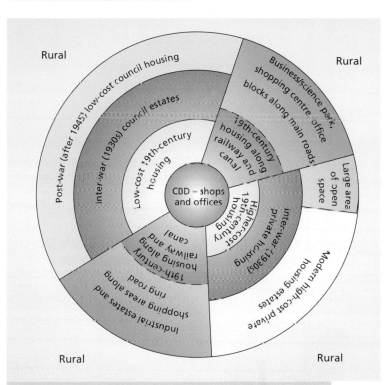

**Figure 9.6** Land use patterns and functional zones in a UK city

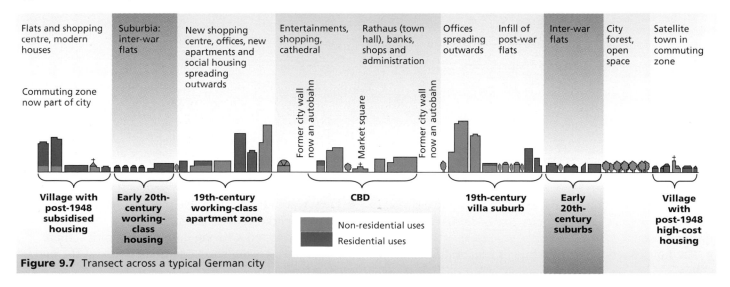

| Flats and shopping centre, modern houses | Suburbia: inter-war flats | New shopping centre, offices, new apartments and social housing spreading outwards | Entertainments, shopping, cathedral | Rathaus (town hall), banks, shops and administration | Offices spreading outwards | Infill of post-war flats | Inter-war flats | City forest, open space | Satellite town in commuting zone |

Commuting zone now part of city

**Village with post-1948 subsidised housing** | **Early 20th-century working-class housing** | **19th-century working-class apartment zone** | **CBD** | **19th-century villa suburb** | **Early 20th-century suburbs** | **Village with post-1948 high-cost housing**

Former city wall now an autobahn
Market square
Former city wall now an autobahn

- Non-residential uses
- Residential uses

**Figure 9.7** Transect across a typical German city

## Traditional land use in inner-city areas

The nineteenth century saw the rapid growth of industrial towns in the UK and other parts of western Europe (Figure 9.8). The huge influx of workers into these towns led to a big demand for quick, cheap housing. Builders constructed as many houses as possible on a small area of land. The result was a high density of housing and an overcrowded population.

**Figure 9.8** An industrial scene in the nineteenth century

### Housing

The houses were built in long straight rows and in terraces (Figure 9.9). The streets themselves were in a grid-iron pattern (see grid square 2264 on page 206). In those days of non-planning, few amenities were provided either in the house (no indoor toilet, bathroom, running water, sewerage or electricity) or around it (no gardens or open space). The worst kind of houses were the so-called 'back-to-back' houses in northern England and the tenement blocks in Scotland. These were built around a central courtyard in which there were one or two outdoor WCs and cold-water taps (Figure 9.10). The dampness of the houses, the lack of sanitation and clean water, the closeness of the people and the smoke from the nearby factories all combined to ruin people's health and reduce their life expectancy.

**Figure 9.9** Terraced housing

**Figure 9.10** Back-to-back/ housing in London

Yet despite these conditions, living in what have become known as *old inner-city areas* did have advantages.

- The houses were cheap to buy or rent and rates were low.
- They were near to people's place of work (there was no public transport in those days).
- They developed a strong community spirit – there was often a corner shop or public house at the end of each road.

## Industry

Many of the factories and mills that were built during the Industrial Revolution were located (Figure 9.11):

- on the nearest available land to the town centre where there was plenty of space for the large buildings
- next to canals and, after the 1840s, railways which were needed to transport the heavy and bulky raw materials and manufactured goods
- beside rivers which, initially used as a source of power, provided water for washing and cooling and a means of disposing waste
- next to the new low-cost housing developments, which provided the large numbers of workers that were needed, and near to the shops and banks of the town centre.

Later urban growth has surrounded these early factories leaving them in what is now an inner-city location.

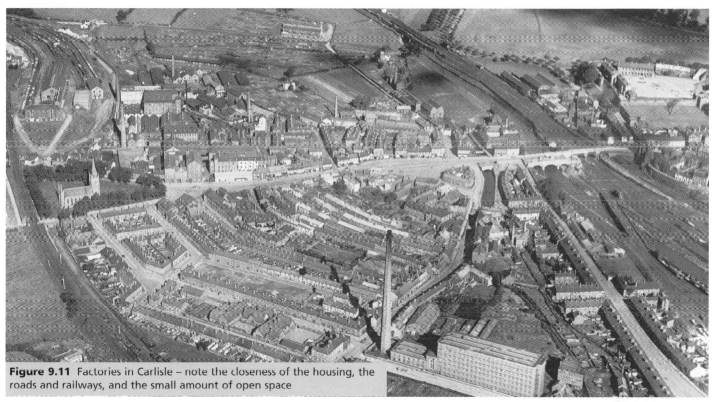

**Figure 9.11** Factories in Carlisle – note the closeness of the housing, the roads and railways, and the small amount of open space

## Shops

In those days most people shopped at corner shops (Figure 9.12). People worked long hours and had little spare time to walk to shops, as there were neither cars nor public transport. Corner shops served a small area, no more than a few streets, and were visited frequently. They sold everyday necessities (that is, low-order convenience goods). These shops were open for long and irregular hours and were a social meeting-point for local people.

## Open space

Open space was extremely limited in inner cities. This was because land close to the CBD was very expensive, and these areas were developed long before cities had planning policies. Also, the long working hours meant that city residents had little time for recreation.

**Figure 9.12** The corner shop

## Traditional land use on the edge of cities

The rapid outward growth of cities began with the introduction of public transport, and accelerated in the 1930s with the increased popularity of the private car and, in London, the extension of the Underground. This outward growth, known as *urban sprawl*, led to the construction of numerous private, car-based suburbs (*suburbia*). The inter-war houses, which corresponded with Burgess's zone of medium-cost housing, were mainly semi-detached. They are characterised by their front and back gardens, garages and bay windows (Figure 9.13).

**Figure 9.13** Inter-war semi-detached housing

### Housing

After the Second World War, urban sprawl continued, with land on the fringes of towns being used, mainly, for one of two types of housing: private estates and outer-city council estates.

1 **Private estates** with low-density, high-quality housing (Figure 9.14). These houses, many of which are large and detached, are likely to have modern amenities both indoors (central heating, double-glazing and deluxe bathrooms) and outside (large gardens and even double garages). The many culs-de-sac and winding roads are often tree-lined and relatively free of traffic (grid reference 1867 on page 206).

**Figure 9.14** A house on a modern private estate

**Figure 9.15** An edge-of-city council estate

2 **Outer-city council estates** on former 'greenfield' sites (Figure 9.15). These were created in the 1950s and 1960s when local councils cleared the worst of the slums from the inner-city areas and rehoused the evicted residents on large edge-of-city estates (Kenton Estate, grid reference 2268 on page 206). Accommodation usually included high-rise tower blocks, low-rise flats and single-storey terraces. Although the density of housing was higher than on the private estates, it was lower than in the inner-city areas which they replaced. Although most homes were small and lacked gardens and garages, they did have modern bathrooms, kitchens and other indoor amenities.

## Shops

As cities expanded between the wars and during the post-war years, each new housing estate was located increasingly further from the shops in the CBD. Consequently small parades of shops were built within each housing estate (Figure 9.16). These shops, which local residents would use several times a week, saved people travelling-time and money. Each parade was likely to include a sub-post office, a small chain store (which provided mainly low-order, convenience goods), several specialist shops (butchers and chemists) and one or two supplying non-essential services (hairdressers and launderette). Most of these shopping parades, especially those in the private estates, had space for limited car parking.

## Open space

Apart from larger gardens in private estates and grassy areas in council estates, the amount of public open space is also much greater towards the edges of a town or city (Figure 9.17). This is mainly because more land becomes available and land is cheaper towards the outskirts. More recently, town planning has taken into account people's needs for recreation and a more pleasant environment in which to live. The OS map on page 206 shows, on the fringes of Newcastle, a large park with woodland and a lake (2570), three golf courses (e.g. 2369) and a specialist attraction, the race course (2570).

## Industry

At the time when many edge-of-city housing estates were built, in the 1950s and 1960s, most shops and offices were still located in the CBD and industry in inner-city areas. Local residents had, therefore, to travel long distances, as commuters, in order to reach their places of work.

## Green belts

The outer edge of the city, the so-called urban–rural fringe, became an attractive place for development following the increase in car ownership and public transport systems. Uncontrolled development, however, caused urban growth and the loss of farmland. The Green Belt Policy was introduced in 1947, in an attempt to prevent urban sprawl. A green belt is an area of land around an urban area where the development of houses and other buildings is severely restricted and the open character of the countryside is preserved for farming and recreation. By controlling the outward growth of

**Figure 9.16** A suburban shopping parade

**Figure 9.17** Open space on the edge of a British city

urban areas, adjacent towns were prevented from merging to form any more conurbations. Most British conurbations are now surrounded by a green belt, and in some instances large areas of open space within cities are also protected, for example Hampstead Heath in London, and Town Moor in Newcastle upon Tyne. Green belts are, however, under constant pressure from developers.

# Concentrations and segregation in UK cities

## Population density

The population of large urban areas is not distributed evenly. The greatest concentrations are in the old inner-city areas with their high-density housing (page 106). The concentration becomes less dense towards the edge of the city, with the sparsest population in the modern low-density private estates (page 108).

## Social and economic groupings

Burgess suggested, in his urban model (Figure 9.5a), that the areas of lowest-cost housing were in the inner city nearest to the CBD. He claimed that the cost of housing rose with distance from the city centre, so the most expensive properties would be those nearest to the city boundary. This difference in the cost of housing has led to two distinctive groupings, both socially and economically, of people. As Figure 9.18 shows, those on low incomes tend to concentrate within the inner-city areas and those on higher incomes group together towards the edge of the city.

## Ethnic concentrations

Figure 9.18 lists immigrants as one of the groups more likely to live in the lower-cost housing areas. Questions on the ethnic origins of people living in Britain were first asked in the 1991 Census (Figure 9.19).

In this census people were asked if they considered themselves to be white, black Caribbean, Black African, Indian, Pakistani, Bangladeshi, Chinese or from another ethnic group. The census showed that 5.5 per cent of the UK population was non-white: 2.7 per cent south-east Asian, 1.6 per cent black and 1.2 per cent Chinese. It also revealed that nearly 50 per cent of that non-white population had been born in the UK.

With the exception of the Chinese, the 1991 Census confirmed that over two-thirds of each of the major ethnic groups were living in the major conurbations in England. Indeed, the proportion living in conurbations, especially that of Greater London, was continuing to rise (Figure 9.20).

**WHO MOVES INTO THE INNER CITY?**

Elderly living on low income, no longer with family, looking for cheaper housing near to CBD and other services (shops, library, hospital)

Young married couples with little capital and no family – first-time buyers

Poor families with limited resources

Immigrants from overseas, especially those with limited money, education and skills

**WHO MOVES TOWARDS THE EDGE OF THE CITY?**

Those with higher income now capable of buying their own home in suburbia

Those with higher skills and qualifications

Parents with a young family wishing for garden, open space and larger house

Immigrants who have established themselves over a period of time

**Figure 9.18** Movement into and within a British city

According to the Office of Population Censuses and Surveys (now merged with the Central Statistical Office to form the Office for National Statistics), 'One of the most striking new developments in British society since the census began in 1801 has been the rise of substantial populations of non-European ethnic and racial origin through post-war immigration, mostly from the New Commonwealth'. This office suggests that 'An ethnic group is a collectivity within a larger population having real or putative (i.e. supposed) common ancestry, memories of a shared past, and a cultural focus upon one or more symbolic elements which define the group's identity, such as kinship, religion, language, shared territory, nationality or physical appearance.' The 1991 Census was aimed at 'identifying the size and distribution of the main visible ethnic minority groups in Britain, distinguishable in terms of skin colour from the majority population'.

**Figure 9.19** The ethnic question in the 1991 Census

The census also confirmed that even within conurbations, most ethnic groups were concentrated in inner-city areas. (Note the location of the Sikh temple [2364] and mosque [2363] on the map of Newcastle upon Tyne on page 206.) However, different ethnic groups tended to concentrate in different parts of the inner city; e.g. in London, Sikhs concentrate in Southall, Jamaicans (black Caribbeans) in Brixton, Indians in Camden and Bengalis in East London. In other words, each ethnic group segregates itself from other ethnic groups (Figure 9.21).

An ethnic group will concentrate in an area that it finds to be attractive; that is, where there is affordable housing available, and where there are jobs that suit their skills and culture. Later migrants are likely to join people of their own ethnic group because they share a similar background, e.g. language, colour, religion, customs, diet, education and dress.

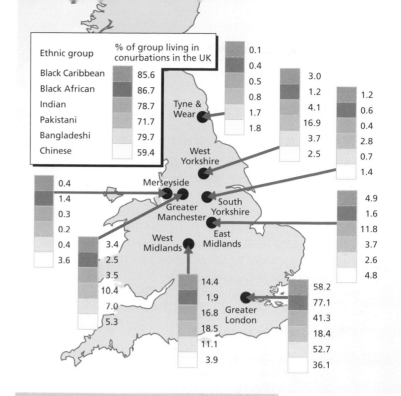

| Ethnic group | % of group living in conurbations in the UK |
|---|---|
| Black Caribbean | 85.6 |
| Black African | 86.7 |
| Indian | 78.7 |
| Pakistani | 71.7 |
| Bangladeshi | 79.7 |
| Chinese | 59.4 |

**Figure 9.20** Concentration of ethnic minorities in conurbations (1991 Census)

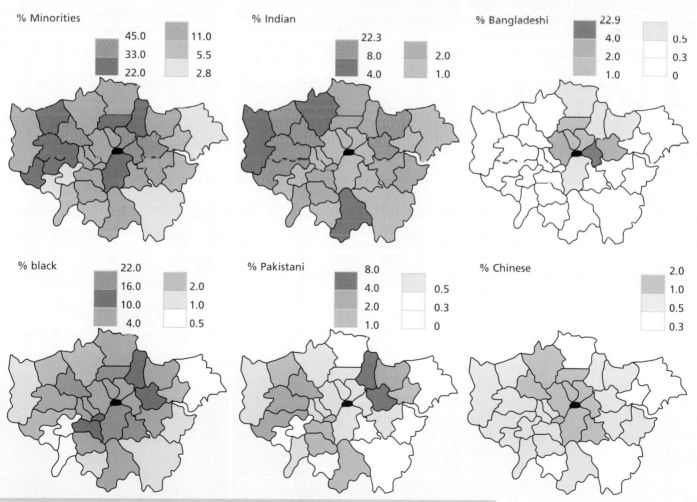

**Figure 9.21** Concentrations of different ethnic minority groups in Greater London (1991 Census)

## Transport

### Travel into and within urban areas

In most urban areas, traffic systems have developed piecemeal as the city has grown and as new forms of transport have been introduced. Most people now use one form of transport or another every day. Transport allows people to become more mobile and gives them greater accessibility to places where they work, shop and are educated, or where they can find health provision and recreation (Figure 9.22). It also allows people to receive visitors and trades-people.

### Choice of transport

When choosing the most appropriate type of transport, whether for the movement of people or goods, the following factors should be considered:

- **Time** – How long will the journey take? Which form of transport is likely to be the quickest? How important is speed?
- **Distance** – How far is the journey?
- **Cost** – How much will the journey cost? Which form of transport will be the cheapest?
- **Convenience** – Which is the easiest way to travel?
- **Frequency** – How often is the journey to be made?

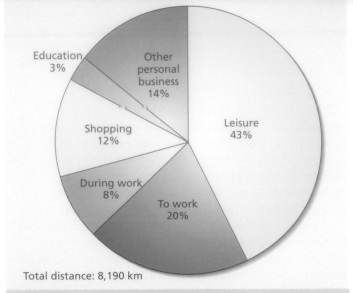

**Figure 9.22** Distance travelled per person per year in Greater London (1992–94)

- **Safety** – What is the risk of an accident to people or damage to goods?
- **Volume** – How many people will be travelling at one time? What is the size and weight of the goods to be sent?

Most people in the UK make two journeys in every three by car (Figure 9.23a). An exception is in Greater London where less than half the total journeys are by car (Figure 9.23b).

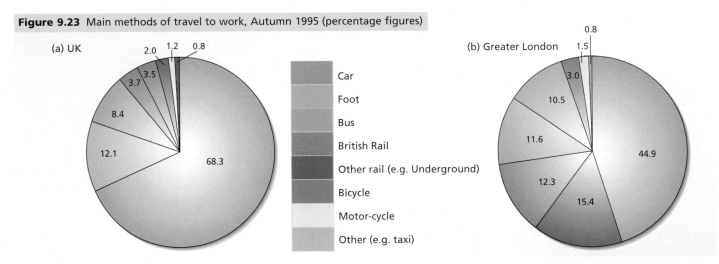

**Figure 9.23** Main methods of travel to work, Autumn 1995 (percentage figures)

### Traffic problems

Traffic in general and the car in particular are the cause of many problems within urban areas. The car has become an important possession of most families in western Europe. Few people who have a car want to go back to using a bicycle or public transport. Yet in many cities the widespread use of the car is bringing traffic to a standstill (Figure 9.24) and is a major cause of environmental, economic and social problems. (Figure 9.25).

**Figure 9.24** Traffic congestion

| Numbers | Rapid increase in number of cars. In the UK there were 4.5 million in 1955, 14.8 million in 1975 and 21.7 million in 1995. Congestion and, under extreme conditions, gridlock (traffic at a standstill). |
|---|---|
| Commuters | Twice-daily peak (rush hour) of people travelling to and from work. |
| Pollution | Visual, noise and atmospheric. Emission of carbon dioxide and nitrous oxides (greenhouse gases). Lead, if added to petrol, a health hazard. |
| Pedestrians | Risk of accidents. Stress caused by noise. |
| Health | Exhaust fumes cause respiratory illnesses and can create low-level ozone which causes asthma (page 25). Leaded petrol can cause brain damage and mental retardation. |
| Economy | High costs of building and maintaining roads and by using petrol and diesel fuel. Time wasted in traffic hold-ups, finding parking spaces, and avoiding parked cars and unloading lorries and buses. Average speed in Greater London (1994) was 20 km/hour (12 mph). Delays due to repairs to roads or to underground utilities. |
| Land | Taken up by car parks and road-widening schemes. |
| Buildings | Older town centres where buildings give narrow streets and newer city centres where buildings have been demolished. Traffic vibrations damage buildings. |
| Repairs | Either to roads themselves or to underground utilities. |

**Figure 9.25** Traffic problems in urban areas

## Commuting

Daily movement in all urban areas shows a distinctive pattern with two peaks a day. The first is when most people travel to work (the morning rush hour), and the second is when they travel home (the evening rush hour).

A *commuter* is a person who lives in a small town or village in the area surrounding a larger town or city, and who travels to that larger town or city for work. The term is now also applied to residents living in the suburbs of a large city such as Greater London. The increase in car ownership means that more commuters live further from their place of work, often in a pleasant environment. This has led to increasingly large commuter 'hinterlands' (the areas around large cities) where commuters live. A recent trend is a reversal in the movement of some commuters as firms close in inner-city areas and re-locate on the edges of cities.

Figure 9.26 is a flow-line map showing the number of commuters into and out of the German town of Mulheim. The flow lines show directions of movement of, in this case, people. The wider the line, or arrow, the greater the number of commuters. Notice that:

● the greater the distance to travel the fewer the number of commuters
● smaller settlements have a net loss of commuters to surrounding larger settlements; larger towns have a net gain from places which are smaller
● people will commute further if there are good communication links.

**Figure 9.26** Commuters into and out of Mulheim, in Germany

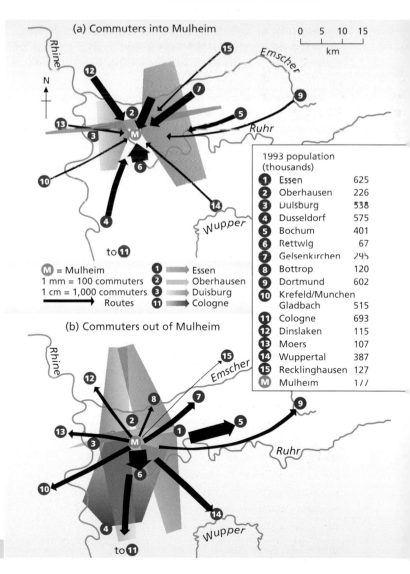

(a) Commuters into Mulheim

0  5  10  15
km

| 1993 population (thousands) | | |
|---|---|---|
| ① Essen | 625 |
| ② Oberhausen | 226 |
| ③ Duisburg | 538 |
| ④ Dusseldorf | 575 |
| ⑤ Bochum | 401 |
| ⑥ Rettwig | 67 |
| ⑦ Gelsenkirchen | 295 |
| ⑧ Bottrop | 120 |
| ⑨ Dortmund | 602 |
| ⑩ Krefeld/Munchen Gladbach | 515 |
| ⑪ Cologne | 693 |
| ⑫ Dinslaken | 115 |
| ⑬ Moers | 107 |
| ⑭ Wuppertal | 387 |
| ⑮ Recklinghausen | 127 |
| Ⓜ Mulheim | 177 |

Ⓜ = Mulheim
1 mm = 100 commuters
1 cm = 1,000 commuters
→ Routes

① ➡ Essen
② ➡ Oberhausen
③ ➡ Duisburg
⑪ ➡ Cologne

(b) Commuters out of Mulheim

## Urban decay and deprivation

In most large urban areas it is usually the inner cities where the economic, social and environmental conditions pose the biggest problems. Although local residents may find many positive reasons for living there, the more likely perception of these areas to non-residents is negative. To them, inner cities present an image of poverty, dirt, crime, overcrowding, unemployment, poor housing conditions and racial tension.

There is a danger, when describing some of the problems facing inner-city residents, that we are reinforcing these negative images. However, it is often only by identifying problems that we can begin to understand the difficulties and offer workable solutions.

### The 1971 Census

One of the consequences of the 1971 Census was the highlighting of urban decay in the inner cities. It was the result of specific questions asked in that census on basic housing amenities, overcrowding, employment and population structure that the size of the problem became apparent. The problem was most noticeable in the conurbations, with Clydeside topping the national urban deprivation league (Figure 9.27). Deprivation is defined by the Department of the Environment as when 'an individual's well-being falls below a level generally regarded as a reasonable minimum for Britain today' – that is, they had a low quality of life.

## What were the problems?

**Housing** Large numbers of houses were identified as lacking the basic amenities such as hot water, baths and indoor toilets. Other properties were without a bathroom, a proper kitchen or electricity. Many suffered from damp because they were built before the introduction of damp courses.

**Population structure** The relatively high proportion of pensioners and children aged under 15 gave a high dependency ratio (page 93). As people who could afford to move did so, only the disadvantaged and those who were discriminated against remained (Figure 9.28). Ethnic minorities (page 111) were disadvantaged in employment, housing and education.

### Who has remained?

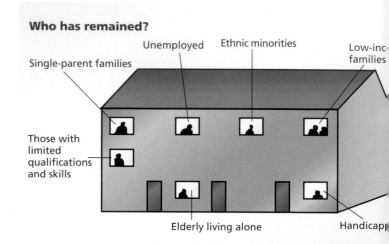

**Figure 9.28** Who is left living in the inner cities?

| Conurbation | Clydeside | West Midlands | Greater Manchester | Merseyside | West Yorkshire | Inner London | Tyne & Wear |
|---|---|---|---|---|---|---|---|
| Sharing or lacking hot water | 15.5 | 7.5 | 4.8 | 5.2 | 1.7 | 27.7 | 2.7 |
| Sharing or lacking a bath | 15.6 | 3.9 | 6.0 | 5.0 | 1.9 | 28.2 | 3.1 |
| Lacking inside WC | 5.9 | 6.2 | 13.6 | 6.8 | 3.6 | 7.0 | 6.0 |
| Without exclusive use of all basic amenities | 13.5 | 4.7 | 9.6 | 5.4 | 2.6 | 21.7 | 4.2 |
| Houses with over 1.5 persons per room | 37.3 | 5.6 | 1.9 | 1.5 | 3.0 | 21.8 | 1.3 |
| Households with car | 25.7 | 2.9 | 8.9 | 5.0 | 8.5 | 12.9 | 7.2 |
| Males unemployed | 23.1 | 2.8 | 6.1 | 9.0 | 4.2 | 2.9 | 6.7 |
| Females unemployed | 13.7 | 3.8 | 5.4 | 6.2 | 3.5 | 6.3 | 2.9 |
| Population aged 0–14 | 12.8 | 5.5 | 4.3 | 3.4 | 3.3 | 3.5 | 1.9 |
| Pensioner households | 4.8 | 1.4 | 3.8 | 0.9 | 5.3 | 4.3 | 1.4 |

**Figure 9.27** Major areas of urban deprivation, 1971 Census (percentage figures)

**Overcrowding** Overcrowding is defined as when a house has 'more than one person per room'. It was worst in the inner cities where houses were usually small (many only had one room upstairs and one downstairs) and family size was large. Where slum housing was cleared, the terraced houses were often replaced with equally high-density high-rise flats.

**Employment** Many workers became unemployed as traditional inner-city industries declined and local factories closed. Those in employment were usually unskilled manual workers earning low wages in return for long hours.

**Figure 9.29** Inner-city Manchester in the late 1980s

**Home ownership** Few of the low-income families could afford to buy their own homes. Many rented houses were often left in a poor state of repair. Ethnic minorities, even when they could afford to buy a property, found many obstacles put in their way.

**Environment** Traffic and the remaining factories caused high levels of noise and air pollution, and rivers and canals were often polluted. Factories and slum housing were either left derelict or pulled down, leaving waste land (Figure 9.29). Litter was rarely collected.

**Health** Inner-city residents had higher death and infant mortality rates, a lower life expectancy and a greater incidence of illness than people living in other parts of the city.

## The 1991 Census

Despite many improvement schemes and, at times, large amounts of money allocated to the inner cities, the 1991 Census showed that many problems still remained (e.g. over 1 million dwellings were still without either a bathroom, WC or hot water). An interpretation of the 1991 Census data showed that the three main indicators of poverty were: no car, no owned home, and no job (compare Figure 9.30). The census also showed that there were still 5–6 million 'deprived' people, and that the vast majority of these lived in inner-city areas (Figure 9.31).

The question remains, however: Will the results of this census reduce the level of deprivation and lead to improvements in racial equality and people's quality of life?

**Figure 9.30** An index of poverty based on the 1991 Census

| | Indicator | Category |
|---|---|---|
| 1 | Percentage of households with no car | A Car ownership |
| 2 | Unemployment rate | B Unemployment |
| 3 | Percentage of households in rented accommodation | C Housing |
| 4 | Inactivity rate – 20–59 year olds | D Inactivity |
| 5 | Percentage of working-age males inactive | |
| 6 | Percentage of working-age females inactive | |
| 7 | Semi-skilled and labourers as percentage of economically active | E Social class |
| 8 | Percentage of economically active with no occupation | |

**Figure 9.31** Deprivation index by wards, Newcastle upon Tyne 1991

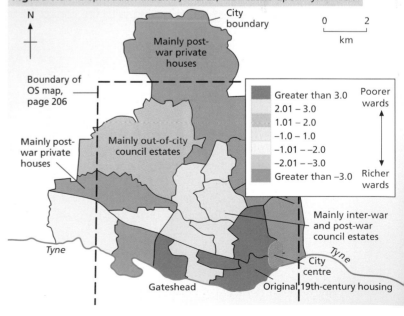

**1** *(Pages 104 and 105)*
Look at the urban land use model.
 **a** i) What do the letters CBD stand for?
   ii) What does *residential* mean?
 **b** i) Where in the city are most shops found?
   ii) Why is this a good place to have shops?
 **c** i) Which of the zones is likely to have the most large houses with gardens?
   ii) Suggest a reason for this location.

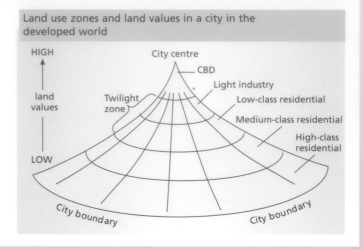
Land use zones and land values in a city in the developed world

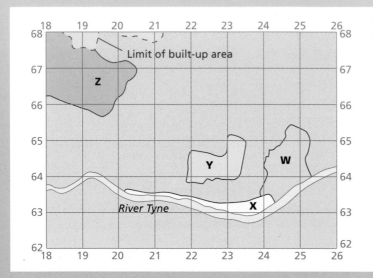

**2** *(Pages 104 to 109)*
Study the OS map extract on page 206. The map here shows part of the OS map at a smaller scale.
 **a** Area W is the CBD. Name two kinds of land use found here.
 **b** Using evidence from the OS map:
   i) suggest why **this** CBD might have more traffic than most
   ii) give the likely advantages of area X for the location of industry.
 **c** i) Describe the housing in area Y.
   ii) Describe the housing in area Z.
   iii) Suggest why the types of housing in these areas are so different.

**3** *(Pages 104 to 109)*
 **a** Match each of the following with the correct letter on the map.
   i) Area of low-cost housing.
   ii) Area of expensive, high-quality housing.
   iii) Area of shops and offices.
   iv) Site of older traditional industries.
   v) Urban–rural fringe.
 **b** Explain why the CBD is a good location for businesses.
 **c** Suggest reasons for the development of new industry at places 1 and 2.
 **d** Many growing cities such as Liverpool have a green belt. What is the purpose of a green belt?

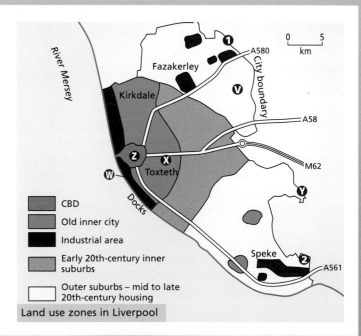
Land use zones in Liverpool

**4** *(Pages 110 and 111)*

  **a** Answer the following the questions from the map.
  i) Which region has the largest number of non-white residents?
  ii) In the West Midlands, which is the largest non-white group of people?
  iii) Which two regions have the lowest non-white population?

  **b** When migrants move to another country they often move into certain parts of large cities.
  i) Why are migrants attracted to large cities?
  ii) Which part of a city do immigrants concentrate in? Choose from:
      * Suburbs    * Inner city    * CBD
  iii) Explain why immigrants choose to live in this part of the city.

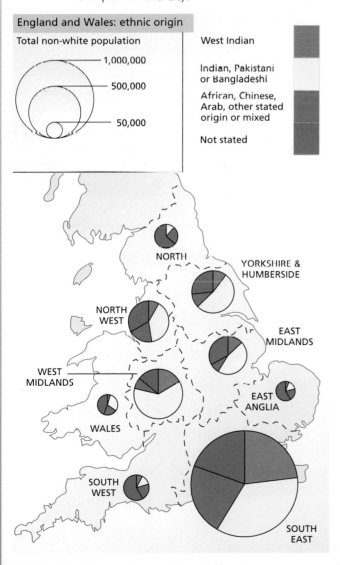

England and Wales: ethnic origin

Total non-white population
— 1,000,000
— 500,000
— 50,000

West Indian

Indian, Pakistani or Bangladeshi

African, Chinese, Arab, other stated origin or mixed

Not stated

NORTH
YORKSHIRE & HUMBERSIDE
NORTH WEST
EAST MIDLANDS
WEST MIDLANDS
EAST ANGLIA
WALES
SOUTH WEST
SOUTH EAST

**5** *(Pages 112 and 113)*

  **a** Look at the graph, which shows traffic flows in a large British city.
  i) At what time was the lowest traffic flow?
  ii) How many vehicles were on the road at that time?
  iii) At what time was the main peak flow?
  iv) Why are there two peak flows in the day?

  **b** i) What is meant by *the rush hour*?
  ii) What is a commuter?

  **c** i) What is meant by *traffic congestion*?
  ii) Describe the problems caused by traffic congestion in urban areas.

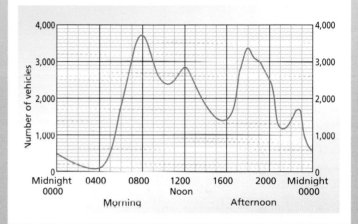

**6** *(Pages 112 to 115)*

  Rapid growth in cities in rich countries causes problems and can lead to urban deprivation. Some of these problems are shown in the diagram.

  **a** i) What is meant by *urban deprivation*?
  ii) Give four ways of measuring urban deprivation.

  **b** Choose any four of the problems shown on the diagram. For each one, describe the problem, its causes and effects.

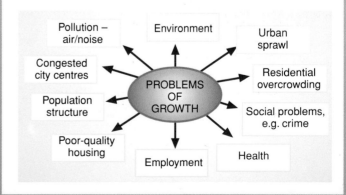

Pollution – air/noise
Environment
Urban sprawl
Congested city centres
PROBLEMS OF GROWTH
Residential overcrowding
Population structure
Social problems, e.g. crime
Poor-quality housing
Employment
Health

## Urban regeneration – Cardiff Bay

**Figure 10.1** Cardiff Docks in 1913

### 1913

Cardiff Docks were originally built to import the ore needed by the ironworks of Merthyr Tydfil (Figure 10.1). More docks were built between 1839 (Bute Dock) and 1907 (Queen Alexandra Dock), mainly for the export of coal mined in the South Wales coalfield. In 1913, when over 10 million tons were exported, coal exports reached their peak. Cardiff, which was a small of town of about 10,000 people in 1850, had grown into a city with a population of nearly 250,000.

### 1987 – the problem

By 1987 the iron and, later, steelworks at Merthyr Tydfil had closed, and the number of working collieries in the South Wales coalfield was rapidly decreasing. Consequently, with no iron ore being imported and virtually no coal being exported, Cardiff Docks were becoming increasingly idle. The area had a high level of unemployment, included areas of derelict land and substandard housing, and lacked modern amenities. It was because there was an urgent need to *regenerate* the area that the Cardiff Bay Development Corporation was set up.

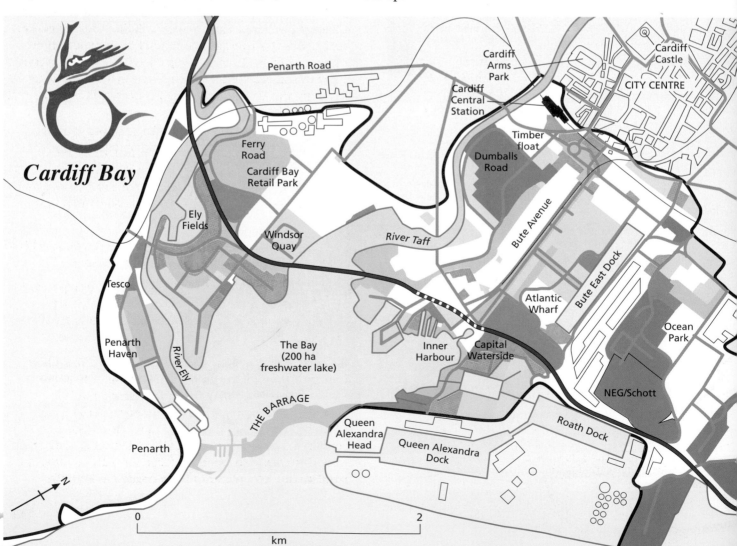

## The proposed solution – the Cardiff Bay Development Plan

Cardiff Bay forms the estuary for the rivers Taff and Ely. It has a large tidal range of 14 metres. At low tide the bay is inaccessible, with mudflats exposed for up to 14 hours a day. These mudflats formed the habitat for thousands of sea and migratory birds but hindered economic development.

The Barrage, environmentally the most controversial part of the whole regeneration plan, was begun in 1993 and is expected to be completed by 1998. The 1.1 km long barrage crosses the bay in a curving 'S' shape (Figures 10.2 and 10.3). The landward-facing slope and the 100 metre wide crest will be landscaped to create 7 hectares of public open space. The completed barrage will hold back the waters of the Taff and Ely to create a 200 hectare freshwater bay and a new permanent waterfront extending 12.8 km. Five sluice gates, which normally will allow river water to escape, can be closed to prevent the flooding which now sometimes occurs at times of highest tides. Three 40 metre long locks will allow entry for yachts and fishing boats. The entrance to these locks will be protected by breakwaters. A fish by-pass will provide a passage for migratory salmon and other fish.

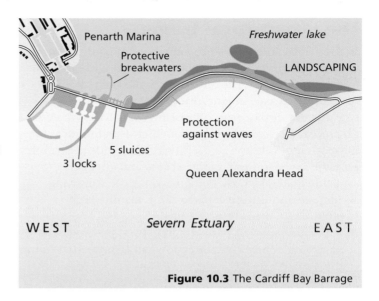

**Figure 10.3** The Cardiff Bay Barrage

**Figure 10.2** The Cardiff Bay Development Plan

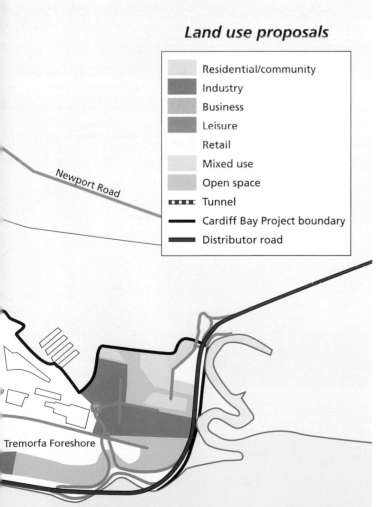

### Land use proposals

- Residential/community
- Industry
- Business
- Leisure
- Retail
- Mixed use
- Open space
- ▪▪▪▪ Tunnel
- — Cardiff Bay Project boundary
- ━ Distributor road

Newport Road

Tremorfa Foreshore

**Transport** The Peripheral Distributor Road (PDR), passing through a tunnel in its central part, cuts across the development area. This new dual-carriageway provides access to the heart of the Bay and a direct link with the M4 to both the east and the west of Cardiff. Construction of Bute Avenue began in 1966. This is to be a 1.5 km elegant tree-lined boulevard, similar to the Champs Elysées in Paris, which will link the city centre with the waterfront. By the time of its completion in 2000, as well as a dual-carriageway there will be a light rapid transit rail system linking the Bay with the regional rail network. Cardiff's rail station and a new heliport will also be in the Project Area.

**Industry and business** The project will create almost 500,000 square metres of industrial space, 375,000 square metres of office space and up to 30,000 new jobs. Mount Stuart Square, site of the historic Exchange Building, is to provide a prestigious office location.

**Residential** Eventually up to 6,000 new houses will be built of which 25 per cent will be 'social housing'.

**Retail** Apart from extending the CBD shopping area along Bute Avenue and improving local shopping centres, the showpiece will be the 14 hectare Cardiff Bay Retail Park.

**Leisure and tourism** It is hoped to attract 2 million visitors to Cardiff Bay by the millennium. The major tourist centre is around the Inner Harbour with its Welsh Industrial and Maritime Museum, Norwegian Church, Techniquest, Visitor Centre, new hotels, restaurants and access to the Embankment (Figure 10.2). Bute Dock East has been enclosed for water sports. A large marina complex has been created at Penarth.

# The urban–rural fringe

In the 1950s and 1960s the main type of land use on the urban–rural fringe was usually residential with areas of open space (pages 108 and 109). Since then, mainly as a result of increases in land prices and congestion towards the city centre, other land-users have viewed *greenfield* sites on the edges of cities as being ideal for development (Figure 10.4). These sites, with their more pleasant environment, easier access and cheaper, available land, are now being used for the following:

- Science and business parks with, mainly, high-technology firms (pages 154–155).
- Superstores, retail parks (Figure 10.3) and regional shopping centres, e.g. Meadowhall (Figure 10.5) and the MetroCentre (Newcastle). Figure 10.5 presents several location factors which explain why large shopping centres are attracted to these sites.
- Office development, now that modern technology and easier access to information allows a freer choice of location (pages 122–123).
- Hotels and conference centres, many of which stand in several hectares of ground and which may include woodland, lakes and a golf course.
- Parking for park-and-ride traffic schemes (page 124).
- Road-widening schemes and urban by-passes.
- Housing developments, including those in adjacent *suburbanised villages*.
- Recreation by urban residents, e.g. footpaths, bridleways, sports grounds.
- Tipping ground for city waste (landfill sites) and sewage works.

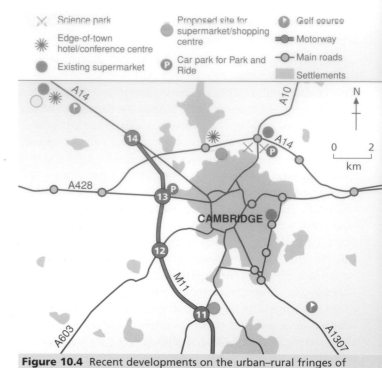

**Figure 10.4** Recent developments on the urban–rural fringes of Cambridge

**Figure 10.5** Location factors for the regional shopping centre at Meadowhall, Sheffield

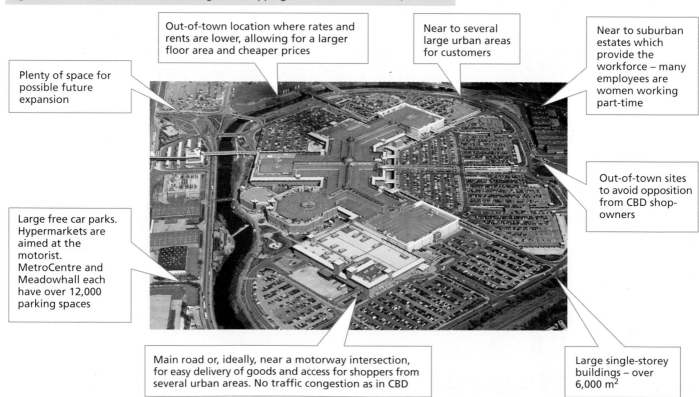

Out-of-town location where rates and rents are lower, allowing for a larger floor area and cheaper prices

Near to several large urban areas for customers

Near to suburban estates which provide the workforce – many employees are women working part-time

Plenty of space for possible future expansion

Large free car parks. Hypermarkets are aimed at the motorist. MetroCentre and Meadowhall each have over 12,000 parking spaces

Out-of-town sites to avoid opposition from CBD shop-owners

Main road or, ideally, near a motorway intersection, for easy delivery of goods and access for shoppers from several urban areas. No traffic congestion as in CBD

Large single-storey buildings – over 6,000 m$^2$

## Meadowhall – a regional shopping centre

A survey in the mid-1980s showed that Yorkshire and Humberside had the least retail space of all the industrial regions, the number of people per shop being well above the national average. It also showed that Sheffield and seven other towns within 45 minutes' drive had the lowest shopping provision in the UK. At the same time, the Sheffield Development Corporation was planning to regenerate the Don Valley (page 122). At the northern end of this valley, near to the M1, was the recently cleared 56 hectare site of the former Hadfield's steelworks (it had closed in 1983).

Construction of the new Meadowhall Centre began in mid-1988 and it was opened in September 1990 (Figures 10.5 and 10.6). The centre has direct access from junctions 34 North and 34 South on the M1, and from Sheffield and the surrounding area by road, rail and Supertram (page 125). Nine million people (1 in 6 of the UK's population) are within one hour's driving time (Figure 10.7). For those arriving by car, there are 12,000 free parking spaces. The newly built bus station can handle 120 buses an hour, while the Supertram link with the city centre was opened in 1994 (Figure 10.15) and there is parking for 300 coaches. Two new rail stations have been opened and 220 trains a day call at one or the other. Apart from being a shopping centre, Meadowhall is also a leisure centre. It is the main employer in the region, and, hopefully, will prove a catalyst for further development in the Don Valley.

**Figure 10.6** The Meadowhall shopping centre

**Figure 10.7** Meadowhall: towns and number of people within selected driving times

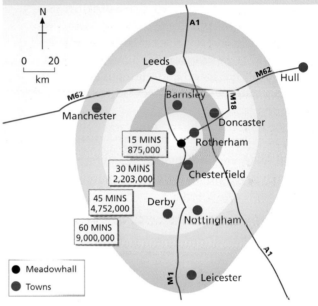

**Figure 10.8** Results of a survey on Meadowhall

# Meadowhall FACTFILE
## cares

- The number of visitors has increased annually from 2 million in the first year (1990/91) to 31 million in its fifth year (1994/95).
- 49% travelled over 16 km; 30% travelled less than 8 km.
- 72% travelled by car, 19% by bus or coach.
- 43% were aged 35 and under.
- The average party size was 2.3. Of the parties, 32% contained at least one person under the age of 16.
- The further people travelled, the longer they stayed (an average of 1.5 hours if less than 24 km, almost 3 hours if over 24 km).
- The further they travelled, the more money they spent (an average of £18.40 per person travelling less than 1.5 km, up to £76.80 per person travelling over 24 km).
- 49% claimed they did all their shopping in Meadowhall.
- 23% did their shopping after 6 p.m.

## Urban planning

### The regeneration of the Don Valley, Sheffield

The Lower Don Valley was once the steel forge of Europe, providing employment for over 40,000 workers at its peak. But over 23,000 jobs were lost in just five years in the 1980s and by June 1988, when the Sheffield Development Corporation was set up, employment in the Valley was down to 17,960 with some 364 hectares of derelict or under-used land. Similarly, of the 3,500 cramped workers' houses, only a few remained in 1988.

### The Sheffield Development Corporation (SDC)

The SDC's main aim is to regenerate 800 hectares of the Lower Don Valley and to create jobs by providing suitable sites in attractive surroundings with good access. The SDC has listed its four main tasks:

- reclaiming and securing the development of derelict and unused land
- providing land for industry, commerce, housing and leisure
- building roads and improving the environment
- encouraging private investment to protect existing jobs and create new ones.

The SDC was able to obtain grants from the EU as well as from sources within the UK. By the end of 1994, over 900 firms had located on development sites within the Valley and the number of employees had risen to 25,000. The current showpiece is Victoria Quays, which was completed in 1995. Here the refurbishment and conversion of warehouse buildings has been carefully integrated with new developments (bottom left, Figure 10.9). Land uses include offices, housing, shopping, leisure, tourism, the arts and a hotel.

Office space has been provided in several areas. Already many firms have moved into new premises, including the Abbey National which has located its Share Registry headquarters here (Figure 10.10). Apart from the Meadowhall Centre (page 121), there is also the Meadowhall Retail Park.

**Figure 10.10** Abbey National's Share Registry headquarters building

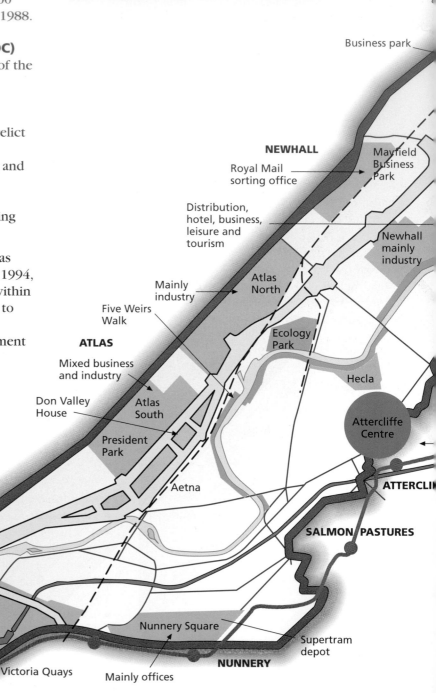

**Figure 10.9** The Lower Don Valley

Junction 34
North

CARBROOK
Business
try

Meadowhall
Shopping and
Leisure Centre

Junction
34 South

Carbook
East

Jessops
Riverside

Carbrook
Hall

TINSLEY
LOCKS

Arena
Square

Meadowhall
Retail Park

byssinia

Broughton
Lane

Mainly
industry

Sheffield
Arena

Greenland
Road

n Valley
dium

Business, leisure,
tourism and
housing

TINSLEY PARK

Terminal

Industrial
Park

Airport

Sheffield
Technology
Park

Green belt

M1 motorway

Marshalling
yard

The traditional industries of the Valley still exist,
especially in Tinsley where advanced technology is
used to produce high-quality steel. Both offices and
industry are benefiting from improved
communications. These include turning the Don
Valley Link Road into a dual-carriageway, the
introduction of the Supertram (page 125) and the
creation of a small airport to link with national
airports and for short-haul journeys to EU countries.
Leisure amenities have been provided at both the
Meadowhall Centre and Victoria Quays. The
25,000-seat Don Valley International Athletics
Stadium was originally built for the World
Student Games (Figure 10.11).
Environmental clean-up schemes
have improved the water quality of
both the river and the canal. The
Five Weirs Walk provides a
footpath and cycleway from
the city centre to the city
boundary. All of the
development sites
have been
landscaped.

| | |
|---|---|
| ⌄⌄⌄ | SDC boundary |
| ▓▓ | Development sites |
| - - - | Railway |
| 〰 | River Don |
| ▬ | Canal |
| ═ | Don Valley Link Road |
| ●━● | Supertram |
| ▓▓ | Environmental improvements |

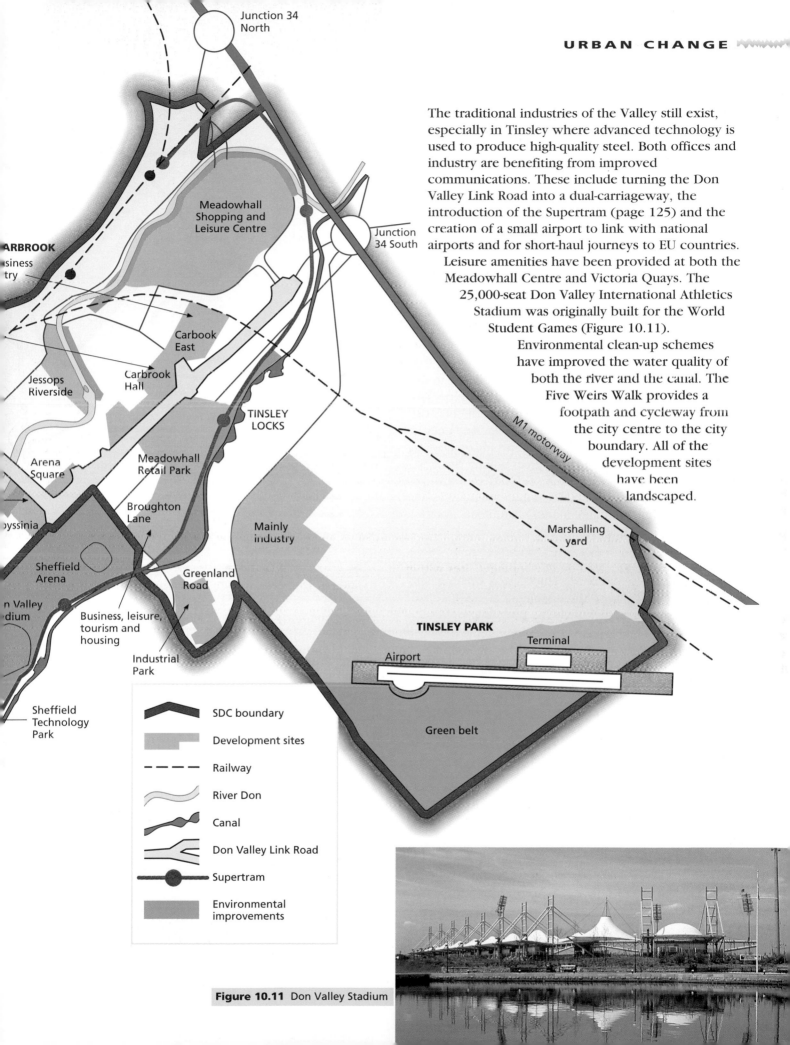

**Figure 10.11** Don Valley Stadium

# Urban traffic solutions

We have already seen some of the adverse effects of traffic upon cities and their inhabitants (page 112). Increased congestion wastes people's time and money, while increased pollution harms their health. Most people accept that urgent solutions must be found – so long as the solutions do not affect their own mobility and independence.

A Royal Commission on Transport published its report in late 1994. The report set out a range of targets and made recommendations as to how these might be achieved. Several of the main points which make reference to traffic in cities are given in Figure 10.12.

In recent years there have been many wide-ranging attempts to solve, or at least reduce, urban traffic problems. Twenty of these schemes are shown in Figure 10.13. The schemes vary from the relatively cheap disc parking to the construction of an extremely expensive underground system. One role of town-planners is to determine the most *cost-effective* scheme. Any decision is likely to be a compromise – a compromise between how much it will cost and how great will be the benefits, and a compromise between different groups of interested people.

When seeking solutions to traffic problems in city centres, planners may decide to:

- *exclude traffic* completely by creating traffic-free zones – but then exceptions have to be made for delivery vehicles, service vehicles (e.g. fire-engines and ambulances) and the disabled
- *limit traffic*, especially cars, by providing public transport and encouraging people to use it – this may be achieved by park-and-ride schemes, e.g. as at Cambridge (Figure 10.4), Nottingham and Exeter, or

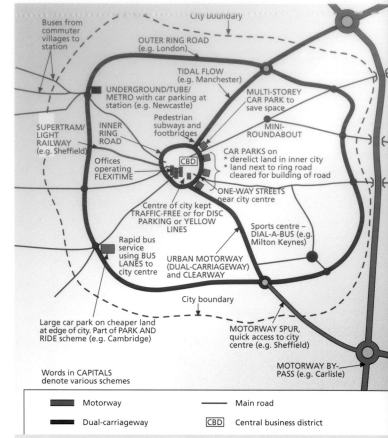

**Figure 10.13** Some possible solutions to traffic problems in a large city

by urban light railways, e.g. Tyne and Wear Metro, London Docklands, Manchester and Sheffield (Figure 10.14)

- *accommodate* as many vehicles as possible by building urban motorways and providing numerous multi-storey car parks.

## Targets

- Increase the proportion of journeys by public transport (measured in total passenger km) from 12% in 1993 to 20% in 2002 and 30% in 2020.
- Increase the fuel efficiency of new cars sold in Britain by 40% by 2005.
- Cut the proportion of journeys in London made by cars from 50% in 1993 to 35% in 2020; corresponding reductions elsewhere.
- Raise urban bicycle use fourfold by 2000, from 2.5% of all journeys to 10%.
- Achieve full compliance by 2002 with World Health Organisation air-quality guidelines for pollution produced mainly by vehicles. Freeze emissions of carbon dioxide, the principal global warming pollutant, from road and rail at their 1990 level by 2000, and reduce them by 20% by 2020.
- Reduce road and rail noise.

**Figure 10.12** The Royal Commission Report on Transport, October 1994

## Recommendations

- Increase fuel duty annually in order to double the real price of fuel by 2005, and base the annual car vehicle excise duty (road tax) on a car's efficiency.
- Introduce tougher emissions checks during the annual MOT test, which should be compulsory when the vehicle is 1 year old.
- Reduce road tax for vehicles already meeting the more stringent pollution standards.
- Stop sales of unleaded super-premium petrol because of its high content of cancer-causing benzene.
- Introduce stronger protection from road building for cherished landscapes and wildlife sites.
- Enforce speed limits more strictly.
- Give bigger subsidies to the railways and more government support to modern tram schemes.
- Consider giving incentives to bus companies switching to less-polluting natural gas, and give government support to the development of electric vehicles.

## Sheffield's Supertram

The Supertram is an example of a *surface light railway*, which means that its route runs along existing roads. Priority is given to the tram at traffic lights and road crossings. Its advantages include being:

- cheaper and quicker to build than a conventional railway
- a fast, safe and (being electric) environmentally friendly form of transport (Figure 10.14)
- able to carry up to 250 people – a large saving on the number of cars needed to move the same number
- flexible – it can negotiate relatively steep bends and gradients, which is important in a hilly city such as Sheffield.

The first phase to be opened was along the Lower Don Valley (Figure 10.9). By 1995 the total network of 29 km had been completed (Figure 10.15). Initially, as with many new traffic schemes, the Supertrams lost money as most motorists still preferred to use their cars. However, by the end of 1996 an increasing number had begun to accept this alternative new *rapid transit system*, and the future of the Supertram system seemed more assured.

## Traffic within housing estates

Of perhaps even greater concern is the growing problem of traffic in residential areas. Many housing estates, both in the inner city and on the edges of cities, are introducing traffic-calming schemes. Traffic calming is designed to slow down the traffic and to make the area safer for pedestrians, especially for children and the elderly. Such schemes include one-way streets, speed ramps, rumble strips, narrowing of roads, and limiting parking to residents only (Figure 10.16).

Partly as a response to a lack of nearby open space and partly because of the dangers of traffic, several housing areas within the UK have held 'Reclaim the Streets' parties. The first week in June 1996 was designated 'Green Transport Week'. Residents were encouraged to take over local streets and turn them into 'public living and breathing spaces'. In places as far afield as London, Birmingham and Manchester, people organised such festivities as street markets and carnivals. In one street in Leeds, grass was actually laid along its entire length.

**Figure 10.14** A Sheffield Supertram

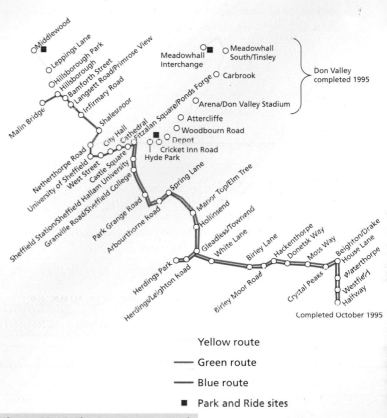

**Figure 10.15** The Supertram network

**Figure 10.16** A traffic-calming scheme

# Urban planning – new towns

New towns have been built in several parts of western Europe for a variety of reasons. These include:

- to take overspill from expanding conurbations or from inner-city clearances
- to attract new industries to areas of high unemployment
- to create a more pleasant environment and a higher quality of life.

The main aim when planning a new town is to make it self-contained. New towns create housing and jobs (to reduce the time, distance and cost of journeys between home and work) and provide services such as schools, hospitals, good communications and leisure amenities – all in an attractive environment (Figure 10.19).

One of the fastest-growing new towns in western Europe is Marne-la-Vallée, which lies to the east of Paris (Figure 10.17).

## Marne-la-Vallée

Marne-la-Vallée was designated a new town in the 1960s. Before that the area consisted of 26 small villages, the nearest being 20 km east of Paris. The new town's development was based on the extension of the 'A' line of the RER (Regional Express Train). By 2020, when Marne-la-Vallée should be completed, the new town will cover 15,000 hectares (Paris only covers 10,000 hectares). This eventual size, which would cause environmental concerns in the UK, is seen as one of Marne-la-Vallée's greatest assets.

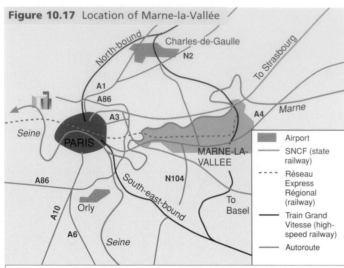

**Figure 10.17** Location of Marne-la-Vallée

**Figure 10.18** Land use plan for Marne-la-Vallée

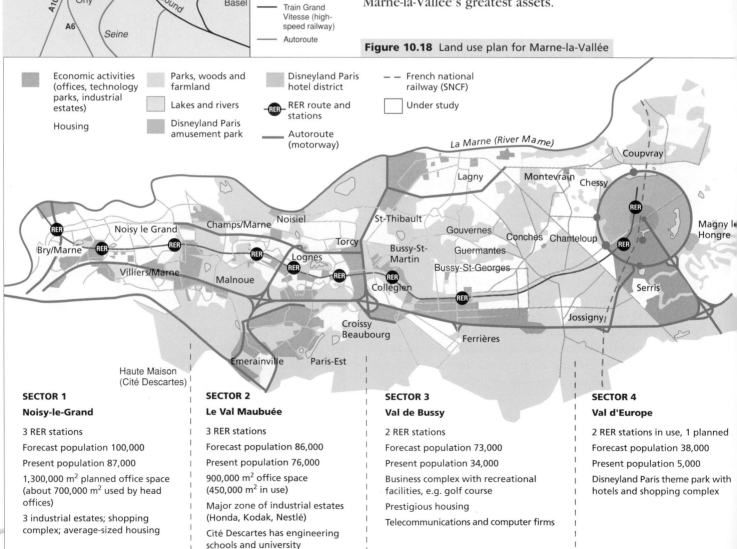

| SECTOR 1 | SECTOR 2 | SECTOR 3 | SECTOR 4 |
|---|---|---|---|
| **Noisy-le-Grand** | **Le Val Maubuée** | **Val de Bussy** | **Val d'Europe** |
| 3 RER stations | 3 RER stations | 2 RER stations | 2 RER stations in use, 1 planned |
| Forecast population 100,000 | Forecast population 86,000 | Forecast population 73,000 | Forecast population 38,000 |
| Present population 87,000 | Present population 76,000 | Present population 34,000 | Present population 5,000 |
| 1,300,000 m² planned office space (about 700,000 m² used by head offices) | 900,000 m² office space (450,000 m² in use) | Business complex with recreational facilities, e.g. golf course | Disneyland Paris theme park with hotels and shopping complex |
| 3 industrial estates; shopping complex; average-sized housing | Major zone of industrial estates (Honda, Kodak, Nestlé) | Prestigious housing | |
| | Cité Descartes has engineering schools and university | Telecommunications and computer firms | |

**Figure 10.19** Aerial view of the A4 at Noisy-le-Grand

The plan for the new town was based on a modern *transport network* (Figure 10.18). The RER, with ten stations now open and large car parking areas, gets passengers to central Paris in under 20 minutes. The A4 (Figure 10.19) acts as a central spine and links with four other autoroutes (motorways). The TGV (high-speed train) has its own station at Disneyland Paris. There are two SNCF lines nearby and Noisy-le-Grand is less than 20 minutes' travel time from Paris's two international airports.

Marne-la-Vallée is divided into four sectors (Figure 10.18). Noisy-le-Grand and Le Val Maubuée were the first two to be developed. Each consists of numerous office blocks, residential areas and open space, together with shopping and leisure complexes (Figure 10.19). At present, most development is taking place in Sector 3 – Val de Bussy.

## Economic activities

Many of the new *office* properties have been built within 5 minutes' walking time of an RER station, with the headquarters of a number of large firms locating in Noisy-le-Grand (Figure 10.19). Each sector has its own *industrial estates*, although the majority are located in the two western sectors. Firms are offered sites of varying sizes but all are close to access roads, especially the A4. Most of the 5,000 firms are multinationals. *Technological parks*, which are between industrial estates and business centres, offer companies involved in high-tech the chance to work in a landscaped setting and within easy reach of large research and training centres. The leading parks are Cité Descartes and Croix-Blanche. *Business complexes*, such as the Rentilly centre in Bussy-Saint-Georges, offer a wide range of leisure facilities for business people.

*Housing* was always a top priority, with a proposed 65,000 units in the two western sectors (58,000 are at present occupied). Moving eastwards, housing in the Val de Bussy is more diversified and expensive.

Open space includes 4,000 hectares of woods and forest, 35 lakes covering 94 hectares, 30 km of embankments along the River Marne landscaped for recreation and, in Val d'Europe, the huge Disneyland Paris amusement theme park.

**1** *(Pages 118, 119, 122, 124)*

Regeneration schemes in places like Cardiff and Sheffield have helped reduce the problems caused by old housing and industry. Choose **either** Cardiff **or** Sheffield and:

**a** describe the urban problems in the area

**b** describe the attempts being made to tackle the problems

**c** state how successful you think these attempts have been, giving reasons for your opinion.

**3** *(Pages 120 and 121)*

Look at the OS map on page 206. At grid reference 215625 there is a major out-of-town shopping and leisure complex called the MetroCentre.

**a** Using map evidence only, suggest why this place (location) may have been chosen for the site of the MetroCentre.

**b** Give three ways that a shopping centre like this is different from a town centre shopping area.

**c** i) How might the centre cause problems for:
  • local residents
  • the surrounding natural environment?

  ii) Suggest two ways to reduce these problems.

**2** *(Pages 120 and 121)*

**a** Look at Figure 10.7 on page 121.
  i) Name five towns within 30 minutes' driving time of Meadowhall.
  ii) How many people are within an hour's driving time of the Centre?

**b** Look at the graphs below.
  i) Why is the provision of car parking so important at Meadowhall?
  ii) Describe the pattern of journeys to Meadowhall shown by the graphs.

**c** Explain why Meadowhall is a good location for an out-of-town shopping centre.

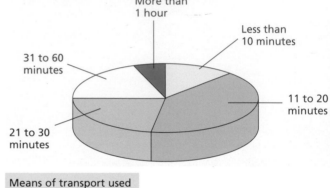

Time taken by users to reach Meadowhall

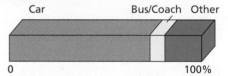

Means of transport used

0                                                   100%

**4** *(Pages 124 and 125)*

In an attempt to reduce traffic congestion in Newcastle, a new main road has been built around the western side of the city.

**a** Look at the OS map on page 206.
  i) What is the length of the new road from Scotswood Bridge (195640) to North Brunton (238712)?
  ii) How many interchanges are there on this stretch of road?

**b** For each of the people shown here, suggest whether they would be for or against the road. Give reasons for your answers.

**Mrs Elliot** – advisor to the city transport department

**Mr Billings** – long-distance lorry driver

**Mr Begum** – resident of Denton Burn (194657)

**Mrs Charlton** – manager of DIY store at Kingston Park (213684)

**5** *(Pages 124 and 125)*

Many schemes have been introduced to reduce traffic congestion in towns and cities. Some of these are shown here.

**a** Name three other schemes for reducing traffic congestion in cities.

**b** Describe in detail any scheme to reduce traffic congestion in a named town or city that you have studied.

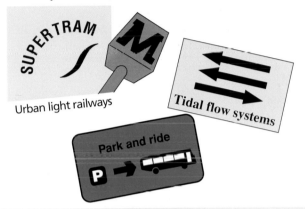

Urban light railways

Tidal flow systems

Park and ride

**6** *(Pages 126 and 127)*

Marne-la-Vallée is a new town near Paris.

**a** Give three reasons for building new towns.

**b** Describe the main features of Marne-la-Vallée using the following headings:

| Location | Transport | Economic activities |
|---|---|---|

| Leisure facilities | Housing |
|---|---|

**7** *(Pages 126 and 127)*

Look at the information about a proposed new town in the south of England.

**a** Using the map, describe the location of the proposed new town.

**b** Explain how the plan for the new town will meet the needs of the people who live there.

**c** Plans such as these may cause problems and upset people. Choose any three of the problems and explain why people would be upset.

## Locals concerned over new town proposals

### 1. The location

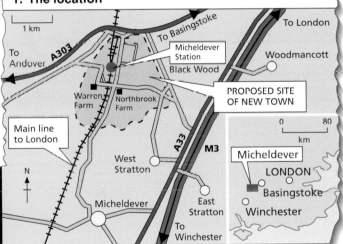

### 2. The plan

Hampshire has set a target of 65,000 new homes by the year 2001. A new town has been proposed at Micheldever.

- Total area of 350 hectares
- Built in traditional style
- 5,000 homes for sale and rent
- 40 hectares of parkland
- 18 hectares of light industry

### 3. The problems

If the plan goes ahead, the following problems may arise:

- Loss of greenbelt land
- Destruction of traditional village life
- Loss of valuable farmland
- Loss of income in shops
- High housing costs that local people cannot afford
- Increased traffic, noise and pollution

# Farming systems and farming types

## Farming systems

Farming is an industry and operates like other industries with *inputs* into the farm, *processes* which take place on the farm, and *outputs* from the farm. This system is shown at its simplest in Figure 11.1. In reality the system is much more complicated, as seen when applied to a typical British dairy farm (Figure 11.2).

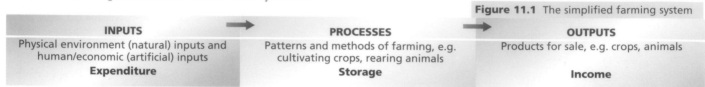

**Figure 11.1** The simplified farming system

| INPUTS | PROCESSES | OUTPUTS |
|---|---|---|
| Physical environment (natural) inputs and human/economic (artificial) inputs | Patterns and methods of farming, e.g. cultivating crops, rearing animals | Products for sale, e.g. crops, animals |
| **Expenditure** | **Storage** | **Income** |

**Figure 11.2** The farming system applied to a British dairy farm

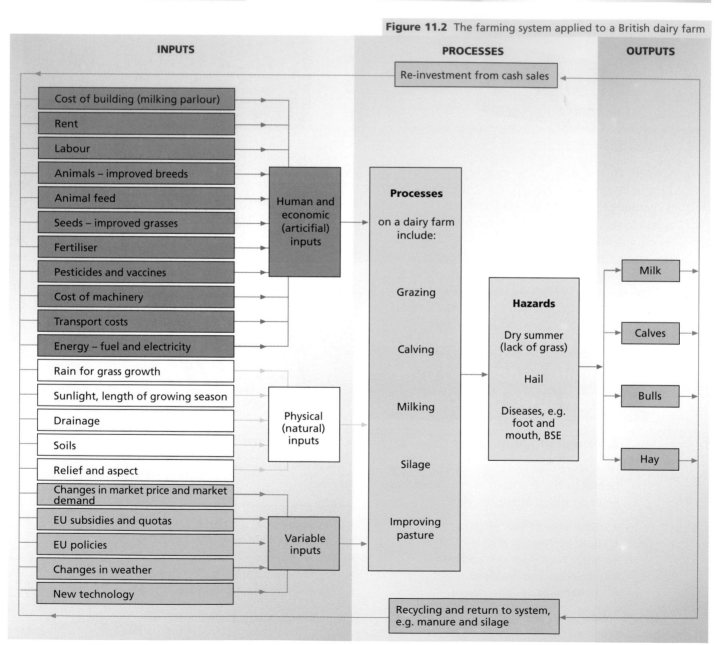

## The farmer as a decision maker

Each individual farmer's decision on what crops to grow or animals to rear, and which methods to use to produce the outputs, depends on an understanding of the most favourable physical and economic conditions for the farm (Figure 11.2). Sometimes the farmer may have several choices and so the decision may depend upon individual likes and expertise. On other occasions the farmer's choice may be limited by extreme physical conditions or political pressures.

## Classification of farming systems

It is possible to classify farming types and methods under three headings.

1 **Specialisation** This includes *arable* (the growing of crops), *pastoral* (the rearing of animals) and *mixed* (both crops and animals).

2 **Economic status** *Commercial* farming is the growing of crops or rearing of animals for sale. In this type of farming, outputs exceed inputs so that the farmer makes a profit. *Subsistence* farming is providing just sufficient food for the farmer's own family. Here the output may be less than the inputs, leaving the farmer and his family to struggle for survival.

3 **Nature of land use** This may either be intensive or extensive, depending upon the ratio between land, labour and capital (money). *Extensive* is where farm size is very large in comparison with either the numbers working on it (e.g. in the Paris Basin) or the amount of money spent (e.g. sheep farming in the English Lake District). *Intensive* is where farm size is small in comparison with either the numbers working on it (e.g. parts of southern Spain and Italy) or when considerable amounts of money are spent (e.g. the Dutch polders).

Figure 11.3 shows the main types of farming in the British Isles. Remember that a map at this scale has to be simplified and so it does not show local variations. The map shows how physical and human inputs for places in the north and west of Britain differ from those in the south and east, and how these differences affect the main types of farming.

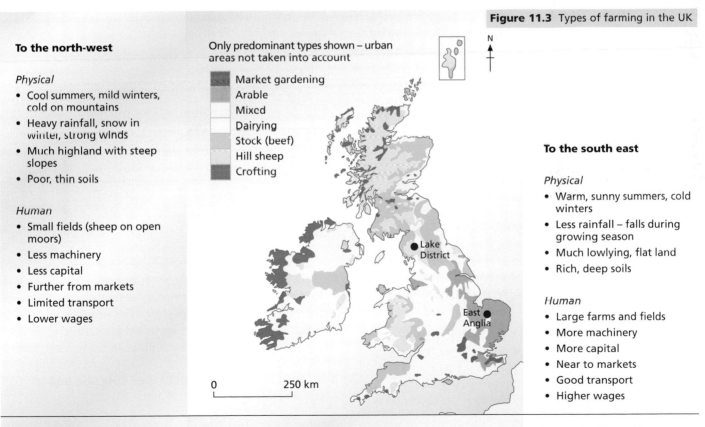

**Figure 11.3** Types of farming in the UK

**To the north-west**

*Physical*
- Cool summers, mild winters, cold on mountains
- Heavy rainfall, snow in winter, strong winds
- Much highland with steep slopes
- Poor, thin soils

*Human*
- Small fields (sheep on open moors)
- Less machinery
- Less capital
- Further from markets
- Limited transport
- Lower wages

Only predominant types shown – urban areas not taken into account

- Market gardening
- Arable
- Mixed
- Dairying
- Stock (beef)
- Hill sheep
- Crofting

Lake District

East Anglia

0    250 km

**To the south east**

*Physical*
- Warm, sunny summers, cold winters
- Less rainfall – falls during growing season
- Much lowlying, flat land
- Rich, deep soils

*Human*
- Large farms and fields
- More machinery
- More capital
- Near to markets
- Good transport
- Higher wages

More suited to pastoral farming with cattle on lower ground and sheep on higher land (pages 134–135)

Central areas are a transition zone and so many have mixed farming with both crops and animals

More suited to arable farming (pages 136–137)

# Farming in the European Union

## Factors affecting farming in the EU

Before Austria, Finland and Sweden became members of the European Union in 1995, farmland accounted for over half of the total land use in virtually every EU country (Figure 11.5). Although the number of farmers and the proportion of income earned by individual countries from agriculture have declined rapidly since 1945, farming and its associated industries still provide a livelihood for many EU citizens (Figure 11.5). As with the UK (Figure 11.3), the location and distribution of the various types of farming in the EU are largely dependent upon an understanding of the most favourable physical and economic conditions of an area (Figure 11.4).

**Figure 11.4** Factors affecting the location and distribution of farming in the EU

| Physical inputs | |
| --- | --- |
| Relief and altitude | Usually the flatter the land, the more efficient and commercial is the farm (Paris Basin, Dutch polders). Output tends to decrease as land gets steeper and higher, and farming becomes less commercial and more extensive and pastoral (Lake District, Massif Central). |
| Soils | The deeper and richer the soil, the more intensive and commercial the farming (*limon* of the Paris Basin, alluvium of the Po Valley). Ideally soils should be well drained. |
| Temperature and sunshine (pages 4–5) | In Scandinavia, summers are cool and the growing season is short for cereals. Towards the Mediterranean the higher temperatures and greater amount of sunshine encourage vines and fruit. Aspect is an important local factor. |
| Rainfall and water supply (pages 6–7) | Areas with adequate and reliable rainfall throughout the year tend to produce good grass for rearing animals. Drier areas to the east grow cereals and, to the south, fruit and vines. |
| **Human and economic inputs** | |
| Land ownership (tenure) | In many parts of north-west Europe, most farmers own their own farm. In southern and eastern parts, more farms are rented – self-owned farms are usually more commercial. |
| Size of farm | Apart from areas around the southern North Sea, most farms in Europe are small, especially in peripheral areas such as Greece and Portugal. Recently farm size has increased. |
| Competition for land (pages 109–109) | Many traditional areas are under threat from urbanisation and its new roads, industry, housing and recreational demand. Mediterranean coasts have competition from tourists. |
| Transport and marketing | Perishable goods need to be produced near to markets for freshness, and bulky goods near to markets because of their weight. Fruit and vegetables (market gardening) are grown near most large cities. |
| Capital | As most EU countries are relatively well off, they can find money to build up dairy farms (Denmark), market gardening (Holland) and cereals (East Anglia). Farmers can afford fertiliser, pesticide and good-quality seed and animals. |
| Mechanisation | The increased use of labour-saving machinery increases outputs but has led to a decrease in employment. Mediterranean farms tend to be less mechanised than those further north. |
| Government (EU) policies | Governments have provided grants for new stock and machinery and subsidies to guarantee a fixed price. This now comes under the EU. |

## 1962 – The Common Agricultural Policy (CAP)

Before 1962, each country in Europe had its own farming policy. This resulted in inefficient methods, high prices and trade barriers. The setting up in 1962 of the CAP created benefits to member states such as:

- a single market in which agricultural goods could move freely
- Community preference which made the European Community (EC, as it then was) more self-sufficient, as it allowed outputs from EC farms to be sold rather than produce being imported from elsewhere
- financial support which included guaranteed prices (*subsidies*), and therefore a guaranteed market, for unlimited production
- an increase in average field size, farm size and farmers' income.

**Figure 11.5** Land use and the percentage of people employed in agriculture in the EU

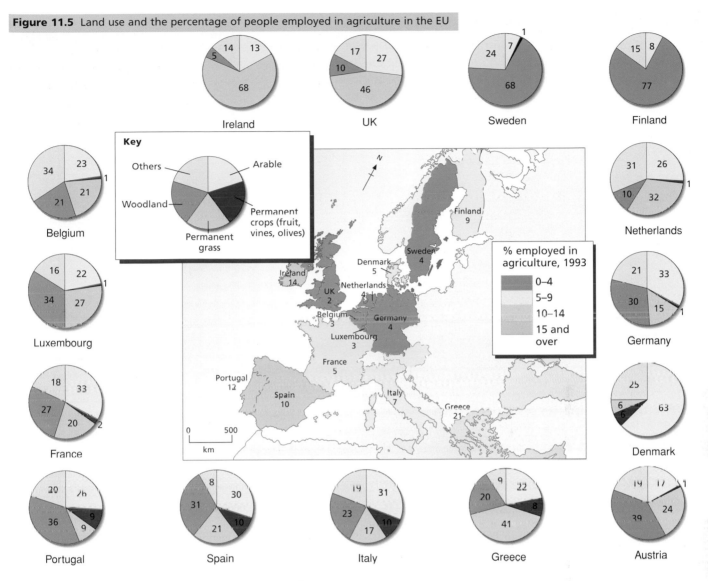

Ireland
UK
Sweden
Finland

**Key**
- Others
- Woodland
- Permanent grass
- Permanent crops (fruit, vines, olives)
- Arable

Belgium
Netherlands

Luxembourg
Germany

France
Denmark

Portugal
Spain
Italy
Greece
Austria

% employed in agriculture, 1993
- 0–4
- 5–9
- 10–14
- 15 and over

## 1970s and 1980s – concerns over the CAP

- 70 per cent of the EC's budget was spent supporting farming when farming only provided 5 per cent of the EC's total income.
- As farmers were encouraged to produce as much as possible and as improved technology increased output, then large surpluses were created – the so-called cereal, butter and beef 'mountains' and the wine and milk 'lakes'.
- Imports were subject to duties to make them less competitive with EC prices. This handicapped economically less developed countries.
- Although EC farms became larger and more efficient, only the most prosperous farmers benefited and often at the expense both of farmers on the periphery and of the environment (page 142).

## 1992 – agricultural reform

Five aims were defined. These were:

1 To increase the EC's agricultural competitiveness by concentrating on quality rather than quantity and in training young farmers.

2 To stabilise markets and match supply with demand by reducing subsidies and quotas on commodities which had a surplus.

3 To ensure a fair standard of living for farmers by providing income support and early retirement to those in less favourable and marginal areas (Figure 11.8).

4 To maintain jobs on the land and limit migration to the towns by introducing alternative forms of land use.

5 To protect and enhance the natural environment by paying farmers to 'set aside' (page 137) or change the use of their land (Figure 11.25).

# An upland farm in the Lake District

The amount of flat, lowlying land in the English Lake District is limited to valley floors. The valley sides, which are usually steep and rocky, often rise to over 500 metres (Figure 5.32). Rainfall in the central parts exceeds 2,500 mm a year. This, together with the cool, cloudy summers, is ideal for the growth of grass and the practice of *pastoral* farming on an *extensive* scale. Over half a million cattle thrive on the lush pastures of the valley floors, while over one and a half million sheep graze on the poorer upland pastures.

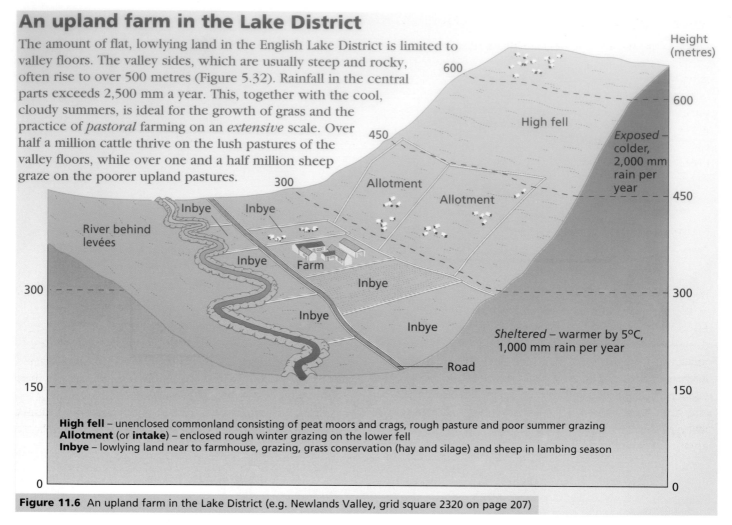

**High fell** – unenclosed commonland consisting of peat moors and crags, rough pasture and poor summer grazing
**Allotment** (or **intake**) – enclosed rough winter grazing on the lower fell
**Inbye** – lowlying land near to farmhouse, grazing, grass conservation (hay and silage) and sheep in lambing season

**Figure 11.6** An upland farm in the Lake District (e.g. Newlands Valley, grid square 2320 on page 207)

Figure 11.6 is a plan of a typical upland farm. Figure 11.7 shows the three types of land referred to on the plan.

## Recent problems

In the last decade, hill farmers in the Lake District, and in other upland areas of Britain, have been adversely affected by the following.

- Radioactive fall-out from the Chernobyl accident (1986) affected grazing land and led to a restriction on the movement of sheep. This restriction is still in force in some parts of the Lake District.
- The EC (1993) set limits on the number of sheep which could receive premium payments. This, and a fall in the price for sheep and sheep products, has meant a drop in income for upland farmers.
- The sale and movement of young beef cattle, fattened on lower land, have been restricted following the BSE scare (1996).
- There has been a general increase in the cost of fuel and fodder.

**Figure 11.7** A Lake District farm

## Recent changes

Since 1988, the EU has been using some of its money to promote rural development. One way has been to give special allowances to farmers in mountainous regions and less favoured areas where soil and climate are a disadvantage to farming. Mountainous and less favoured areas include over 50 per cent of the area farmed within the EU (Figure 11.8). The objective of the scheme is to ensure the continuation of livestock farming in upland areas.

The EU is also encouraging farmers to diversify into other types of land use and activities such as tourism, arts and crafts and small-scale food processing. Farmers are also given grants to protect and to improve their farm environment. Improvement schemes include the restoration of wetlands (pages 84 and 85) and replanting small areas with trees.

Most of the Lake District has been declared an Environmentally Sensitive Area (ESA). ESAs were first designated in the UK in 1987. They were set up as a result of a growing concern over the considerable influence which agriculture can have on the conservation and enhancement of landscape, wildlife and historical features. Farmers working within the Lake District, or any of the UK's 19 ESAs, are now encouraged to maintain or adopt farming practices that

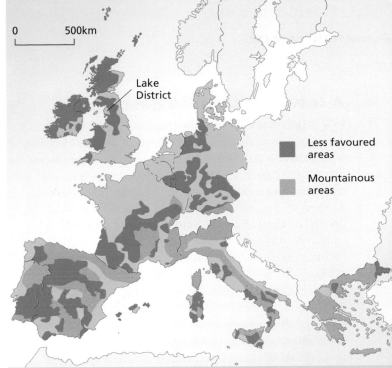

**Figure 11.8** Mountainous and less favoured areas in the EU 1993

will conserve the environment. For example, they are paid £10 per hectare if they agree to reduce the use of fertiliser on arable land (remember, there is very little arable land in the Lake District), £40 per hectare if they 'conserve and restore heather moorland and hill landscapes', and £60 per hectare for restoring wetlands. Money is also available for rebuilding drystone walls and replanting hedgerows.

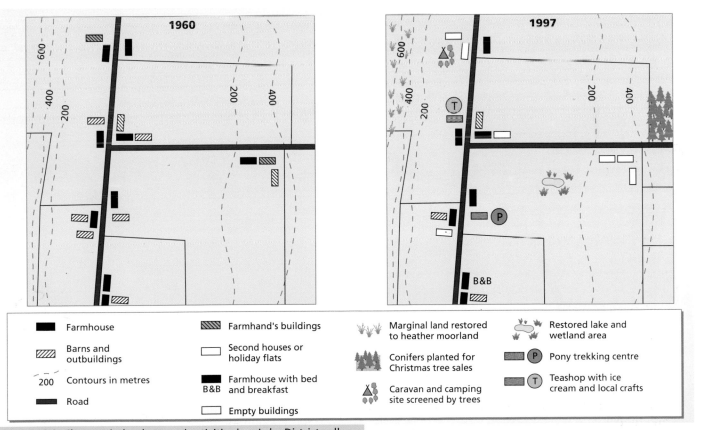

**Figure 11.9** Changes in land use and activities in a Lake District valley

# A lowland farm in East Anglia

East Anglia has the most mechanised and profitable farming system in Britain. The land, which is lowlying and relatively flat, is ideal for the use of labour-saving machines (Figure 11.10). Soils are deep, rich in nutrients and moderately well drained. They were formed when glaciers deposited material (boulder clay) on top of chalk. Rainfall is under 650 mm a year. Although this is the driest part of Britain (Figure 1.15), fortunately most rain falls during the summer growing season. The warm, sunny summers are ideal for ripening cereals, while the cold winters help to break up the soil. The physical inputs allow arable farming on an *extensive, commercial* scale. Wheat and barley are the main crops (Figure 11.11), although root crops (potatoes and sugar beet) and vegetables (peas and beans) are also important.

Human inputs have ensured that farms in East Anglia have high yields. Drainage has been improved and soils made lighter by adding lime – a process known as 'marling'. The application of fertiliser, the use of pesticides and the development of disease-resistant

**Figure 11.10** Extensive cereal growing in East Anglia

seeds have enabled crop yields to double. Transport has improved so that the outputs from the farm, especially those that are perishable and bulky, reach their markets as soon and as easily as possible. Each farm is mechanised with combine harvesters (Figure 11.10), potato pickers (Figure 11.12) and pea-mobiles.

**Figure 11.11** Farm management on an East Anglian farm

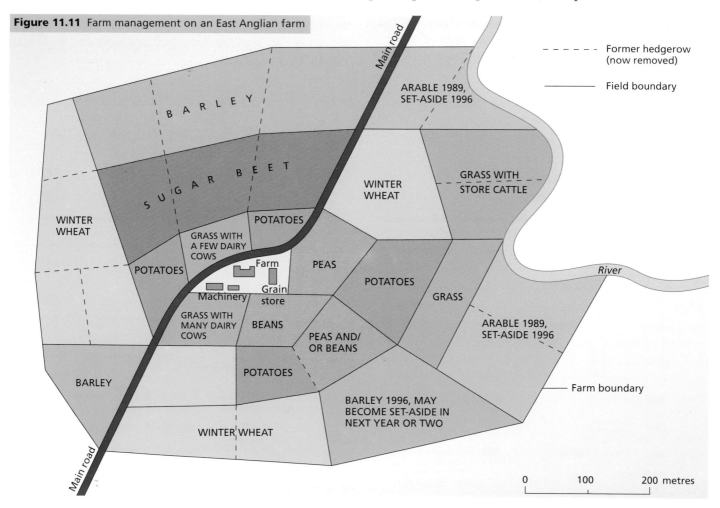

## Recent problems

- After 1945, first the British government and later the EC paid subsidies to farmers to encourage them to grow more cereals. This was so successful that by 1985 the EU had become 121 per cent self-sufficient in cereals – a figure which, by 1990, had risen to 127 per cent. In other words, there was a surplus of cereals in the EU which built up, year after year, to form the 'grain mountain'.
- The increase in production was often at the expense of the environment (pages 142–143). Hedgerows were removed (Figure 11.11) creating a prairie-type landscape (Figure 11.10), large amounts of fertiliser and pesticides were used, wetlands were drained and heathlands ploughed.
- The loss of hedgerows, while an advantage for heavy machinery, meant an increase in soil erosion, especially by the wind in winter before crops had grown, or in summer when there is a risk of convectional storms.

## Recent changes

In 1988 the EU brought in a voluntary *set-aside* scheme. This scheme paid farmers who took out of production 20 per cent or more of their 'supported arable crops'

**Figure 11.12** Farm mechanisation

for five years – although the farmer could opt out after three years. 'Support arable crops' included all cereals, peas and beans, sugar beet, hops, oilseed rape and fresh vegetables. The set-aside land had either to remain as fallow (with a green cover crop to reduce erosion), be converted to woodland (under the woodland management scheme), or put to non-agricultural use (e.g. tourism, restored wetlands).

Relatively few farmers in the UK and the EU opted for the set-aside scheme. As a result the EU, in 1992, decided to:

**a** reduce cereal prices by 29 per cent by 1996

**b** enforce the set-aside scheme on all farmers whose land exceeded 20 hectares. Initially 15 per cent of the total farmland had to be set aside. Within two years, set-aside land in East Anglia increased sevenfold to over 10 per cent (Figure 11.13).

Farmers are paid, at present (1996), £142 per hectare for not growing crops, and £253 per hectare for planting broad-leaved trees.

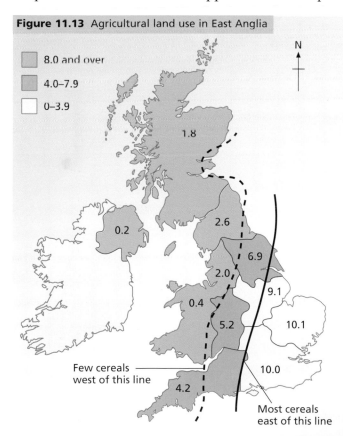

**Figure 11.13** Agricultural land use in East Anglia

Legend:
- 8.0 and over
- 4.0–7.9
- 0–3.9

N

1.8

2.6

0.2

6.9

2.0

9.1

0.4

5.2

10.1

Few cereals west of this line

10.0

4.2

Most cereals east of this line

(a) East Anglian agriculture (percentage figures)

|  | 1991 | 1994 |
|---|---|---|
| Arable | 82.9 | 73.3 |
| Rough grazing | 10.3 | 10.8 |
| Woodland | 5.3 | 5.8 |
| Set-aside | 1.5 | 10.1 |

(b) Percentage of agricultural land left as set-aside, 1994

# Extensive farming in Spain – La Mancha

About three-quarters of Spain consists of a high, dry plateau, or tableland, known as the Meseta. At its centre is Madrid. In the south is La Mancha which, translated into English, means 'The droughty land' (Figure 11.14). La Mancha has always been one of the least productive parts of Spain.

## Relief and soils

Most of La Mancha is over 600 metres high. The soil is dry, thin and red in colour. The hard, resistant underlying rocks frequently appear on the surface (Figure 11.16). The natural vegetation used to be drought-resistant trees but these have long since been cleared to leave a poor-quality grass. This grass cover is uneven and places where the soil is exposed are subject to wind erosion.

## Climate

La Mancha is surrounded by mountains which block out maritime influences to give a continental climate. Without any moderating effect of the sea, summers are very hot, with daytime temperatures reaching 40°C, and winters often extremely cold, frequently below freezing (Figure 11.15). Indeed winters, with their persistent cold and penetrating frost, are a contrast to the Mediterranean coastlands (page 140) located just to the south-east. The mountains also act as a barrier to rain-bearing winds so that La Mancha lies in a rainshadow area. Most places receive less than 400 mm of rain a year. Very little of this falls during the summer months, while winters are cold enough for much of the precipitation to fall as snow. Amounts of rain and the length of the summer drought increase towards the south-east.

## Traditional farming

The extreme climate, high elevation and infertile soil meant that La Mancha was of little agricultural use other than the rearing of sheep (Figure 11.16). Much of the land was divided into large estates and *pastoral* farming was practised on an *extensive*, almost *subsistence* level. For centuries sheep-herding was a way of life. The shepherds and their sheep used to migrate between the winter pastures on the plateau and the highland summer pastures in the mountains surrounding the region – a process known as *transhumance*. By the 1930s many sheep were moved by rail, taking advantage of special seasonal rates.

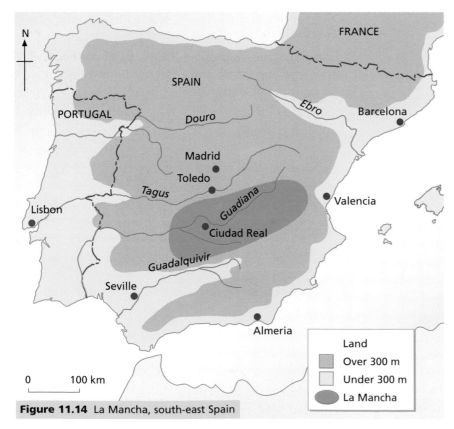

Figure 11.14 La Mancha, south-east Spain

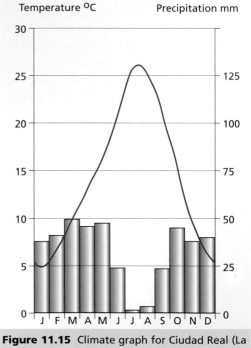

**Figure 11.15** Climate graph for Ciudad Real (La Mancha)

**Figure 11.16** La Mancha, south-east Spain

## Modern farming

Today, very few farmers hold to the traditional way of life. Those who do tend to live in more isolated and less favoured areas. The upper Tagus and Guadiana rivers (Figure 11.14) have been dammed and the water used for irrigation. Much of La Mancha has now been ploughed and turned into *arable* land with wheat grown on an *extensive* scale (Figure 11.17). The use of chemical fertiliser and mechanical harvesters has enabled the wheat to be grown on a *commercial* scale. Saffron, collected from crocuses and introduced by the Moors (page 141), and vines are also grown.

Farming accounts for most of La Mancha's wealth, but the region remains one of the poorest in the EU.

**Figure 11.17** Extensive wheat growing in La Mancha

# Intensive farming in Spain – the Mediterranean coastal lands

The Mediterranean coastal area is a long narrow strip of land lying between the Meseta and the mountains to the north and west, and the sea to the south and east (Figure 11.18). This coastal region has always been one of the most productive areas in Spain.

## Relief and soils

The coastal area consists of a series of narrow plains separated by mountains which in places extend down to the sea. Within these plains are alluvial deltas formed by rivers bringing material down from the mountains. These lowlying areas provide some of the most fertile land in the country. The largest plain surrounds the city of Valencia.

## Climate

The coastal lands have a Mediterranean climate (Figure 1.23). Summers are very hot and sunny with winds often blowing from the Sahara Desert to the south. Winters are generally mild, due mainly to the low altitude and the moderating influence of the sea. There is a continuous growing season.

The coastal strip lies in a rainshadow area of the Spanish Meseta. Most rain falls either during the winter or in individual autumn storms which can cause severe damage at the end of the summer drought. The summer drought increases in length and intensity towards the south and many rivers dry up seasonally (Figure 2.8).

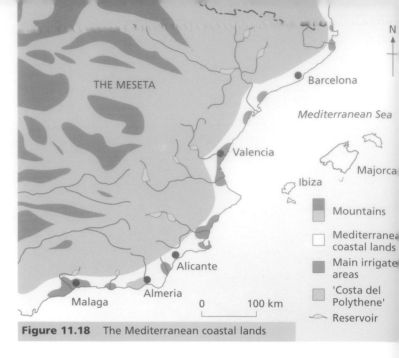

**Figure 11.18**   The Mediterranean coastal lands

Although Barcelona receives over 800 mm of rain a year, amounts decrease rapidly southwards (Valencia 425 mm, Almeria 230 mm). The area behind Almeria is so dry that it was used in the 1960 and 1970s to film 'spaghetti westerns'.

## Traditional farming

The area around Valencia was first irrigated by the Romans. They built a complex network of canals and conduits, using water from springs, winter rains and spring snowmelt (Figure 11.19), to create *huertas* (meaning 'cultivated plains'). Even today the daily running of these waterways is governed by a committee of eight men – one for each of the original Roman canals. The huertas, many with farms no larger than a garden, can produce up to four crops a year.

**Figure 11.19**   A traditional field irrigation system on a Valencian huerta

**Figure 11.20**   Cultivation on terraced hillsides near Valencia

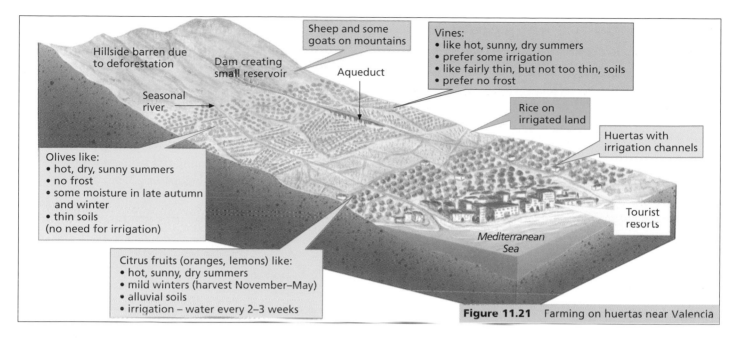

Hillside barren due to deforestation

Seasonal river

Dam creating small reservoir

Sheep and some goats on mountains

Aqueduct

**Vines:**
• like hot, sunny, dry summers
• prefer some irrigation
• like fairly thin, but not too thin, soils
• prefer no frost

Rice on irrigated land

Huertas with irrigation channels

**Olives like:**
• hot, dry, sunny summers
• no frost
• some moisture in late autumn and winter
• thin soils (no need for irrigation)

Tourist resorts

Mediterranean Sea

**Citrus fruits (oranges, lemons) like:**
• hot, sunny, dry summers
• mild winters (harvest November–May)
• alluvial soils
• irrigation – water every 2–3 weeks

**Figure 11.21** Farming on huertas near Valencia

The irrigation system was later extended by the Moors (between 711 and 1482). The Moors also began the terracing of hillsides (Figure 11.20) and introduced orange and almond trees, mulberry and cotton bushes and rice. Their farming methods, like those today, were both *intensive* and *commercial* (Figure 11.21). Olives were planted on the drier upper slopes, vines on the lower slopes, and citrus fruits (oranges, tangerines and clementines), vegetables and some wheat and maize on the flatter areas next to the sea. Before the growth of tourism, oranges were Spain's most important foreign money earner.

## Modern farming

Farmland is facing competition from tourism (page 170). However, although tourist resorts have taken over large areas that were once farmed, tourists themselves have often increased the demand for local produce. Mild winters and improved transport links mean that fruit and early vegetables (*primeurs*) can be grown here and sold in northern Europe before they are available there.

The huertas in the Valencia and Alicante regions still specialise in oranges, vegetables, mulberries and rice. However, it is the area around Almeria which has seen the greatest transformation (Figure 11.18). In the early 1970s this was semi-desert. By the mid-1990s it had become known as the 'Costa del Polythene', with huge areas of land growing crops under irrigation and the world's largest concentration of plastic (Figure 11.22). The plastic, which is stretched across 3 metre high poles, creates a hothouse environment suitable for the growth of tomatoes and other vegetables including green beans, peppers, cucumbers, courgettes, aubergines, melons and water melons. The crops are harvested twice-yearly when they are out of season in northern Europe. Although the plastic is an eyesore, the region, with 15,000 smallholdings, now has the lowest unemployment in Spain.

**Figure 11.22** The 'Costa del Polythene'

FARMING

# Farming and the environment

The EU, in its booklet *Environmental Policy in the European Community* (1990), stated:

> Farmers have traditionally lived and worked in harmony with nature, shaping, maintaining and protecting their land from damaging ecological consequences. To a large extent that remains true today.
>
> In the past 40 years, however, agriculture has undergone a technological revolution which has led to widespread mechanisation, the growing use of agrochemicals, and vastly improved cultivation techniques. Such intensification of farming has produced higher yields and greater wealth but also fuelled the growth of Community food surpluses and left its mark on a bruised countryside.

Some of the ways that farming has bruised the environment are given in Figure 11.23.

| Environmental problems listed by the EU | Causes/effects of these problems |
|---|---|
| A Deterioration of animal habitats and the extinction of some species | ● Hedgerow clearances<br>● Wetland drainage<br>● Heathland conversion<br>● Heather moorland loss<br>● Use of pesticides and herbicides – also kill bees and other useful insects |
| B Low water quality | ● Misuse and overuse of chemical fertiliser, especially nitrogen, leading to eutrophication<br>● Misuse of animal manures (slurry) |
| C Soil degradation and erosion (Figure 11.24) | ● Abandonment of farming in upland areas<br>● Removal of protective vegetation cover<br>● Salinisation caused by poor irrigation techniques |
| D Declining air quality | ● Ammonia evaporated from fertiliser and manure<br>● Burning of straw |

**Figure 11.23**  Damage to the environment by farming

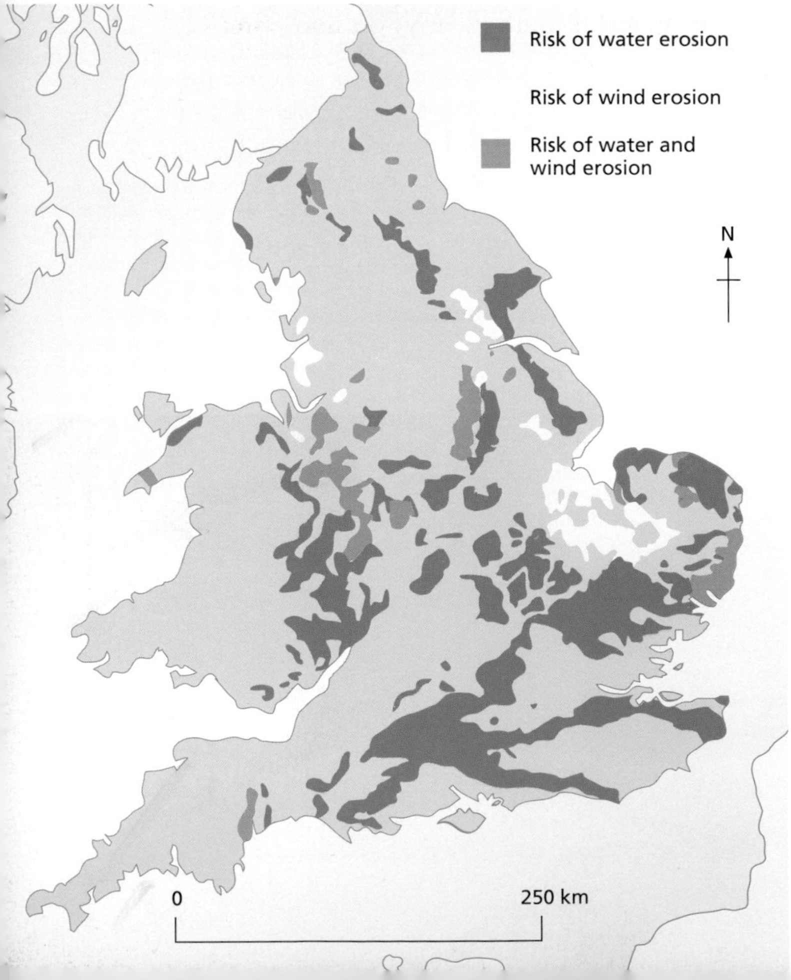

## CAP and the environment

The CAP reforms of 1992 listed, as one of their five aims, the need to protect and enhance the environment (page 133). It was stated that the CAP must:

> enable productive farmers to live and work where their presence is necessary for the maintenance of life and the upkeep of the soil. The CAP can no longer ignore the ecological constraints. For this reason one of the tasks of the Community's environmental policy must be to provide incentives for better farming without damage to the countryside or natural resources. This will apply to all farms large or small.

Some of the ways by which this aim is being pursued by both the EU and the British government are given in Figure 11.25.

Risk of water erosion
Risk of wind erosion
Risk of water and wind erosion

0   250 km

**Figure 11.24**  Land in England and Wales at most risk from erosion

**Figure 11.25** Improving the farming environment

| Environmental improvement schemes | What each scheme involves |
|---|---|
| *Set-aside* (page 137) | Taking arable land out of production, leaving it fallow with a protective vegetation cover to improve humus content and reduce soil erosion. |
| *Woodland Management (Grants) Scheme* | Grants given for planting trees, especially broad-leaved species. |
| *Environmentally Sensitive Areas* (ESAs) (page 135) | There are 19 ESAs. Voluntary scheme. Farmers taking part are given payments to protect the existing environment, and larger payments if they improve the environment, e.g. replanting hedges or rebuilding stone walls, restoring wetlands, heathland and moorland. |
| *National Nature Reserves* (NNRs) and *Sites of Special Scientific Interest* (SSSIs) | 286 NNRs and 5,671 SSSIs, to safeguard wildlife habitats and natural features in the environment. |

## Organic farming

Organic farming is a method of farming that relies on renewable resources and which does not harm the environment. It is sustainable, and the opposite to the modern, intensive, high technology 'agribusiness' associated with many western European countries.

An organic farmer *does not*:
- use chemical (artificial) fertiliser, which is expensive to buy and which – especially nitrates – can pollute water supplies
- use pesticides, which can kill useful as well as harmful insects (e.g. bees), or herbicides – although this means a greater risk of weeds
- use battery cages, sow stalls and other intensive methods of rearing animals
- use livestock feed (growth) additives.

An organic farmer *does*:
- use animal manure, green manures (compost) and mineral fertiliser (rock salt, fish and bone)

- use crop rotation which includes:
  - fallow, as this allows humus to build up in the soil, conserves moisture and protects the soil from erosion
  - legumes (peas and beans), as these put nitrogen back into the soil
  - mixed farming, as this is less likely to cause soil exhaustion
- encourage ladybirds, as these live on harmful blackfly and aphids
- protect wildlife habitats.

However, organic farming has its problems. Crop yields initially fall due to a lack of chemical fertiliser; more hand labour is needed (e.g. weeding); care is needed not to let animal manures (slurry) get into water supplies; and shop prices for produce are higher.

In 1994, when organic food only accounted for 1 per cent of total household food in the UK, the MAFF (Ministry of Agriculture, Fisheries and Food) announced higher grants for farmers wishing to become 'organic'.

**Figure 11.26** An organic farm in Somerset

## 1
(Pages 130 and 134)

**a** i)  Match each of the following with the letters A, B, C, D, E and F on the systems diagram.
   * wool   * shearing   * labour   * lamb
   * EU subsidies   * soil

ii)  Name two other inputs.

iii)  Name two hazards that might affect this farm.

**b** i)  Why is it important that the value of outputs is greater than the cost of inputs?

ii)  Explain why the farmer should re-invest surplus money.

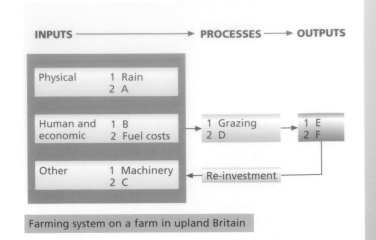

Farming system on a farm in upland Britain

## 2
(Pages 131 and 132)

**a**  Look at the map.

i)  What is the main type of farming in eastern England?

ii)  Match four of the types of farming on the map with these meanings.
   A – rearing animals
   B – growing crops
   C – growing crops and rearing animals
   D – rearing cattle for milk

**b**  The pattern of farming is the result of farmers acting as decision makers. Give two *physical* factors and two *human* factors which may influence a farmer's decisions.

**c**  Choose **either** the Lake District **or** East Anglia.

i)  Describe the main features of farming there.

ii)  Explain why the type of farming is suitable to the area. Consider both physical and human factors.

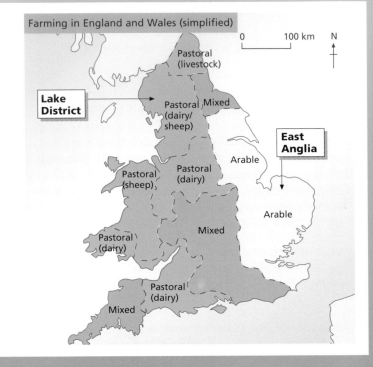

Farming in England and Wales (simplified)

## 3
(Pages 132, 133, 142)

**a**  What were the aims of the Common Agricultural Policy (CAP) when it was set up in 1962?

**b**  Describe how the CAP has tried to reduce the output of products of which there were surpluses.

**c**  State two ways in which the CAP might affect a farm like the one shown in question 5.

**d**  How has the CAP contributed to changes in the environment shown in question 6?

## 4
(Pages 132 and 138–142)

La Mancha and the Mediterranean coastal lands are two very different farming areas in Spain.

**a**  For each place in turn:

i)  briefly describe the main features of farming

ii)  give two *physical* inputs and two *human* inputs that affect modern farming there.

**b**  Explain why farming in the La Mancha area is described as *extensive* and in the Mediterranean coastal lands as *intensive*.

**c**  How can farming in both areas now be

**5** *(Pages 132, 136, 137)*

**a**  i)  Name the land use at places 1, 2 and 3 on the cross-section.

   ii)  Using information from the map and cross-section, suggest why:
   * crops are grown in field A
   * field B is left as rough grass
   * field C is given to pasture for dairy cows.

   iii)  One of the farmer's fields is given to set-aside. What is set-aside, and what are the benefits of this scheme?

**b**  Lowland farms like this have been affected by many changes in recent years. Describe how these changes have brought about:
   i)  improvements in farming and
   ii)  problems for farming.

described as *commercial*?

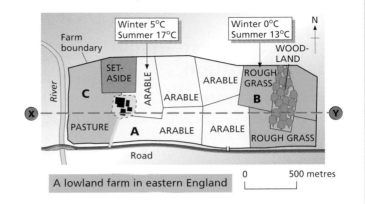

A lowland farm in eastern England

0          500 metres

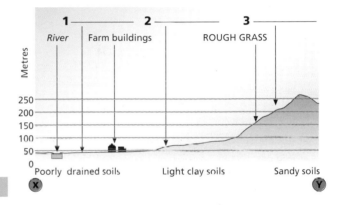

Cross-section from X to Y

---

**6**  *(Pages 142 and 143)*

**a**  From the information below:
   i)  state two ways in which modern farming may pollute or damage the environment
   ii)  describe three ways that the landscape may be changed by modern farming methods
   iii)  give three problems for wildlife.

**b**  People have different opinions about farming changes like the ones shown below. Describe the contrasting views of the following people:
   * an organic farmer
   * an agribusiness farmer
   * a member of a countryside protection group
   * the government's Minister of Agriculture.

**c**  Describe two schemes that may help protect the farming environment.

Changes in agriculture – modern farming in East Anglia

## The industrial system and industrial location

### The industrial system

Industry as a whole, or a factory as an individual unit, can be regarded, like farming (page 130), as a *system*. At its simplest, there are *inputs* into a factory (or industry), *processes* which take place in that factory, and *outputs* from the factory (Figure 12.1). For a firm to be profitable and to remain in business, the value of its outputs must be greater than the cost of its inputs. Some of the profit should then be re-invested, for example in modernising the factory and introducing new technology.

**Figure 12.1** The industrial system

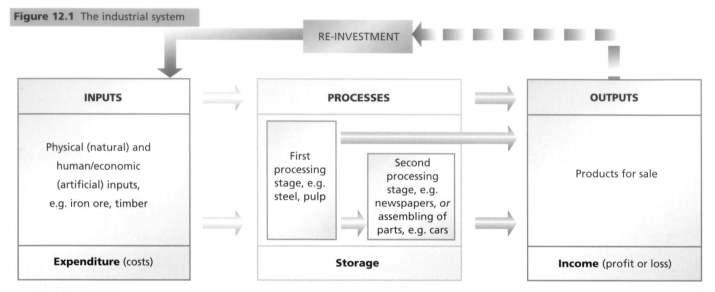

### Factors affecting the location of industry

Factories may be built by an individual entrepreneur, a private firm, a nationalised company or a multinational corporation. Before the factory is built, however, decisions have to be made as to which will be the best site for its location. It is unlikely that any site will possess all the factors listed as advantages in Figure 12.2. Where several sites are available, the individual or the company must decide which is likely to provide the best location. In many cases this decision is determined by predicting which site will give the greatest profit. This will be where the costs of raw materials, land, energy, labour and transport are minimised and where there is a large market for the product. The decision may also be influenced by government intervention.

The main factors that influence the location of a factory, and which led to the growth of the major industrial regions in the EU, are explained in Figure 12.3. Notice that:

- In the nineteenth century it was mainly physical factors such as the nearness of raw materials (e.g. iron ore) and sources of energy (e.g. coal) that affected the location of industry.

**Figure 12.2** Factors affecting the location of industry

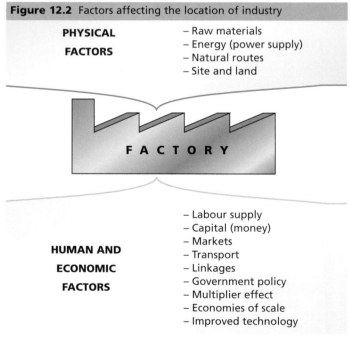

**PHYSICAL FACTORS**
- Raw materials
- Energy (power supply)
- Natural routes
- Site and land

**FACTORY**

**HUMAN AND ECONOMIC FACTORS**
- Labour supply
- Capital (money)
- Markets
- Transport
- Linkages
- Government policy
- Multiplier effect
- Economies of scale
- Improved technology

- By the late twentieth century it was often the three human/economic factors of nearness to a large market, the availability of skilled labour and government policy that determined the location of industry.

### Physical factors

| | |
|---|---|
| *Raw materials* | The bulkier and heavier these are to transport, the nearer the factory should be located to the raw materials (e.g. the Ruhr, Sambre-Meuse Valley). This was even more important in times when transport was less developed. |
| *Energy (power supply)* | This is needed to work the machines in the factory. Early industry needed to be sited near to fast-flowing rivers (Sheffield) or coal reserves (north-east England, the Ruhr). Today electricity can be transported long distances. |
| *Natural routes* | River valleys (Sambre-Meuse, the Ruhr) and flat areas (North Italy) were essential in the days before the railway, car or lorry. Natural harbours (Marseille, Genoa). |
| *Site and land* | Although early industry did not at first take up much space, it did need flat land (flood plains next to rivers, e.g. Sheffield). As the size of factory increased, more land was needed (steelworks at Port Talbot and Newport). Ideally such sites should be on low-quality farmland where the cost of purchase is lower (the Ruhr). During the last century many sites were in today's 'inner-city areas' (Yorkshire and Lancashire textile mills) whereas now they tend to be in edge-of-city 'greenfield' locations (car factories). |

### Human and economic factors

| | |
|---|---|
| *Labour supply* | This includes both quantity (large numbers in nineteenth-century factories) and quality (special skills) as technology develops. |
| *Capital (money)* | Early industry depended on wealthy entrepreneurs. Now banks and governments may provide the money. |
| *Markets* | The size (the EU) and the location (proximity) of markets is increasingly important (Paris). |
| *Transport* | Costs increase when items moved are bulky, fragile, heavy or perishable. |
| *Linkages* | Various firms making parts for the same industry tend to group together (car assembly plants in North Italy and Germany). |
| *Government policy* | As governments tend to control most wealth, they can influence industrial location (South Italy). |
| *Multiplier effect* | If one industry or firm is successful in an area, others will be attracted to that area (potteries in Stoke-on-Trent, Nissan in north-east England). |
| *Economies of scale* | Small units may become unprofitable and so merge with, or are taken over by, other firms (cars). |
| *Improved technology* | Modern communications such as fax machines and e-mail give factories freedom to locate in a variety of places (M4 corridor). |
| *Recreation facilities/environment* | People want to work in more pleasant areas (the 'banana belt' of the western Mediterranean), with access to recreational facilities (Marne la-Vallée, page 126). |

**Figure 12.3** Factors affecting the location of industry in the EU

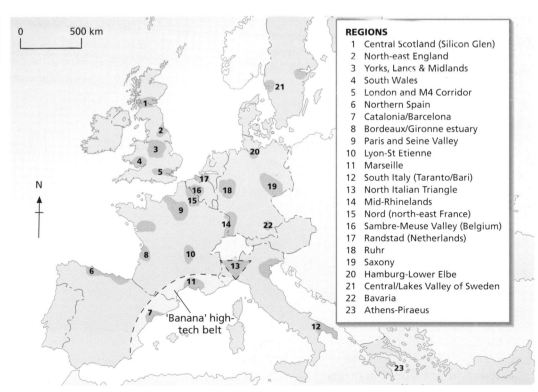

REGIONS
1 Central Scotland (Silicon Glen)
2 North-east England
3 Yorks, Lancs & Midlands
4 South Wales
5 London and M4 Corridor
6 Northern Spain
7 Catalonia/Barcelona
8 Bordeaux/Gironne estuary
9 Paris and Seine Valley
10 Lyon-St Etienne
11 Marseille
12 South Italy (Taranto/Bari)
13 North Italian Triangle
14 Mid-Rhinelands
15 Nord (north-east France)
16 Sambre-Meuse Valley (Belgium)
17 Randstad (Netherlands)
18 Ruhr
19 Saxony
20 Hamburg-Lower Elbe
21 Central/Lakes Valley of Sweden
22 Bavaria
23 Athens-Piraeus

0    500 km

'Banana' high-tech belt

**Figure 12.4** Main industrial regions of the EU

## Industrial decline and changing locations

Industrial decline is not new in the UK. The large-scale closures of coalmines began in parts of north-east England, South Wales and Central Scotland in the 1930s; textile mills in Yorkshire and Lancashire in the 1960s; shipyards on the Clyde and in north-east England in the 1970s; and steelworks in the 1980s. The numbers employed in the textile industry, for example, declined by two-thirds between 1970 and 1986. Just a few of the many reasons for these job losses are given in Figure 12.5.

| Reasons for closure | Examples |
|---|---|
| Exhaustion of local resources | Coal, iron ore |
| Introduction of new machinery/methods (computers/robots) | Newspapers |
| Out-dated machinery/premises | Textile mills |
| Congested site/no room for expansion | Inner-city areas |
| Fall in demand for product/introduction of a rival product | Steel replaced by aluminium |
| Site needed for redevelopment/alternative land use | Motorway |
| High costs of production/low productivity | High salaries/jobs done manually |
| Overseas competition | Textiles, ships, cars |
| Lack of money for investment (times of recession) | |
| Political/EU decisions denying assistance (peripheral regions may be ignored) | |
| Rationalisation/take-over by larger company | Multinationals with overseas HQ |
| Unpleasant/polluted environment | Inner cities, old chemical works |

Figure 12.5 Reasons for factory closures and job losses

### Consequences of factory closures and job losses

Factory closures can have far-reaching effects on the economic and social life of a place and its inhabitants. For example:

- When a large steelworks (Consett, Sheffield) or shipyard (Tyneside) closes, thousands of jobs are lost. There is always considerable difficulty in finding replacement jobs for such large numbers.
- When a large employer closes, it leads to job losses in associated firms.
- If a place relies upon one firm/industry, then its closure affects everyone in that place (less money for shopping and entertainment).
- Many replacement jobs are in service industries which often prefer part-time workers, in high-tech industries which require fewer but highly skilled workers, or in different parts of a country which forces people to move.

### Changing industrial locations in the EU

The initial growth, subsequent decline and possible later re-emergence of industrial regions has been uneven in location, time and scale (Figure 12.6).

Figure 12.6 Decline and growth of industry at different scales

| Scale | Decline | Growth |
|---|---|---|
| International | A grouping of several countries (the EU) | Pacific Rim countries (including Japan, Singapore, Hong Kong, Taiwan) |
| National/Regional | One country or a place within that country. Nineteenth-century traditional, heavy industrial areas (northern England, north-east France, the Ruhr). Conurbations/large cities (London) | Modern high-tech industries in a pleasant environment (south of France). Smaller towns (East Anglia) and new towns (Marne-la-Vallée) |
| Local/small areas | Inner cities (Yorkshire and Lancashire textile towns) | Edge of cities (car factories, science parks) |

## Shipbuilding – a declining European industry

Shipbuilding, first practised by the Greeks and Romans, is one of the oldest industries in Europe. The modern industry became established in places (Figure 12.7) which had the following advantages:

- river estuaries which were sufficiently deep, wide and sheltered for the launching of ships
- rivers with a clay or gravel bed which could easily be excavated for the construction of docks and dredged to enable ships of increasing size, such as oil-tankers, to be built
- relatively steep banks to allow ships to slide into the river under gravity on launching
- large areas of cheap, available land
- near to steelworks and other factories making subsidiary parts, e.g. ships' engines and boilers
- a large labour force, both skilled and unskilled
- places with large amounts of overseas trade.

The UK was the world's leading shipbuilding nation during the inter-war years (1919–39). Since then it has slumped to fourteenth (Figure 12.8) and many firms have been forced to close (Figure 12.9). Shipbuilding has also declined in most other western European countries. This is mainly due to:

- a decline in orders caused by increased overseas competition, especially from the Pacific Rim countries of Japan, South Korea and Taiwan, which have newer shipyards and lower salaries (this is now less true of Japan)
- several global economic recessions which have led to a decline in world trade and, therefore, less need for ships
- a decline in the need for warships, oil-tankers and specialised cargo ships
- poor labour relations in several western European countries, which led to strikes and failures to complete orders on time
- a lack of investment, and high production costs.

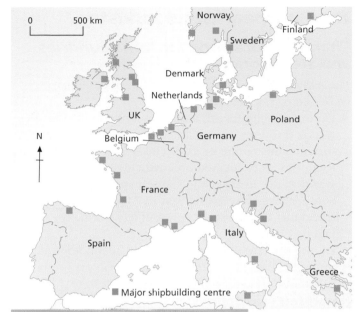

**Figure 12.7** Major shipyards in Europe, 1980

| | 1970 | 1980 | 1994 | World rank |
|---|---|---|---|---|
| | (thousand gross registered tonnes) | | | |
| Germany | 2,021 | 802 | 876 | 4 |
| Denmark | 514 | 227 | 397 | 6 |
| Spain | 926 | 509 | 241 | 7 |
| France | 960 | 328 | 172 | 9 |
| Netherlands | 461 | 125 | 170 | 10 |
| Italy | 598 | 168 | 144 | 12 |
| UK | 1,237 | 244 | 60 | 14 |
| Belgium | 155 | 99 | 45 | 16 |
| Sweden | 1,711 | 338 | 1 | – |
| Finland | 222 | 198 | 0 | – |
| Greece | 73 | 22 | 0 | – |

**Figure 12.8** Merchant vessels launched by EU countries

**Figure 12.9** Shipbuilding on the Tyne (a) In the 1920s (b) Today

# The European steel industry

## Changing locations for iron foundries and steelworks

The early iron industry and, later, the steel industry were tied to raw materials.

- During the eighteenth and early nineteenth centuries it took 8 tonnes of coal and 4 tonnes of iron ore to produce one tonne of iron. This meant that most iron foundries were located on coalfields and where there was iron ore nearby, e.g. Consett (page 158), the South Wales Valleys, the Sambre-Meuse Valley (Belgium) and the Ruhr (present-day Germany) – Figure 12.10.
- During the late nineteenth century, technological improvements allowed lower-grade iron ores to be smelted more economically. As a result new steelworks were opened near to iron ore deposits, e.g. at Scunthorpe and Corby in England and in Lorraine in France.
- By the mid-twentieth century many of the longer worked coal and iron ore fields were becoming exhausted and so the UK and other western European countries had to import these raw materials. This meant that the ideal location for any new integrated steelworks was a coastal, tidal site, e.g. Port Talbot and Redcar in the UK, IJmuiden in the Netherlands and Dunkirk in France. It also meant that many older steelworks with an inland location were forced to close, e.g. Consett and Ebbw Vale.
- As the construction of new steelworks is extremely expensive, steel companies had to ask individual

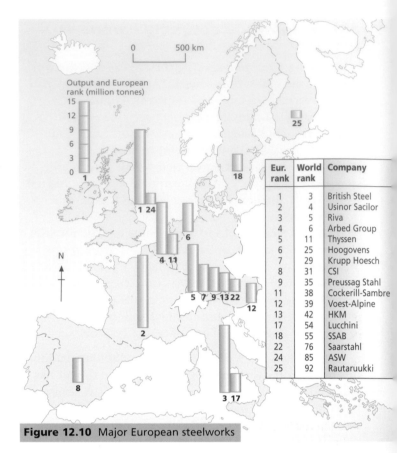

| Eur. rank | World rank | Company |
|---|---|---|
| 1 | 3 | British Steel |
| 2 | 4 | Usinor Sacilor |
| 3 | 5 | Riva |
| 4 | 6 | Arbed Group |
| 5 | 11 | Thyssen |
| 6 | 25 | Hoogovens |
| 7 | 29 | Krupp Hoesch |
| 8 | 31 | CSI |
| 9 | 35 | Preussag Stahl |
| 11 | 38 | Cockerill-Sambre |
| 12 | 39 | Voest-Alpine |
| 13 | 42 | HKM |
| 17 | 54 | Lucchini |
| 18 | 55 | SSAB |
| 22 | 76 | Saarstahl |
| 24 | 85 | ASW |
| 25 | 92 | Rautaruukki |

**Figure 12.10** Major European steelworks

governments and the EU for the required capital. This money was often only granted if the steel company located at a site chosen by the government. In other words, the most recent locations have often resulted from political decisions, e.g. Taranto in the economically less well off south of Italy (Figure 12.11).

**Figure 12.11** Taranto steelworks in southern Italy

## The decline of the European steel industry

As late as 1960, two out of every three tonnes of steel came from, in rank order, the USA, the USSR (as it was then), Germany, the UK and Japan. Europe, including the USSR, still produced 57 per cent of the world's total (Figure 12.12). By 1993, when two out of every three tonnes came from the former USSR, Japan, the USA, China and Germany, Europe's share had fallen to 37 per cent.

Figure 12.13 shows that the world production of crude steel rose steadily to a 1987 peak, since when it has fallen slightly due to a world economic recession. However, Figure 12.13 also shows that the decline in Europe's production has been much greater than elsewhere in the world and that this decline has been most marked in the UK. There are several reasons for this decline, mainly at the expense of such Pacific Rim countries as Japan, China, South Korea and Taiwan.

- **Increased competition**   In 1950 there were 32 steel producing countries. In the late 1990s there were 54.

- **Raw materials**   Europe now produces relatively little of the world's coal and iron ore. In the mid-1990s the major coal producers were, in order, China, the USA, India, Russia and Australia, while the leading iron ore producers were China, Brazil, Australia, the Ukraine and India. None of these producers is close to western Europe.

- **Improved technology**   The need for higher-quality steel requires increased automation and computer control. This can be achieved more easily and more cheaply by building new factories than in trying to modernise older sites.

- **Economies of scale and efficiency**   Pacific Rim countries have constructed large-scale, fully modernised factories which are cheaper to operate than those in Europe. A modern steelworks requires a large area of land ideally on a coastal site, and needs to operate 24 hours a day. The Asian countries also have highly skilled and cheaper labour, which reduces costs and raises efficiency (production per worker is one-third higher in South Korea than in the UK).

- **Structural changes**   Many western European countries, including the UK, are becoming more 'deindustrialised', with increasingly larger numbers employed in the tertiary and quaternary sectors rather than in the secondary sector (page 194).

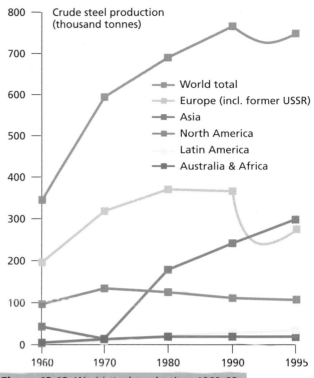

Figure 12.12 shows:
- World total
- Europe (incl. former USSR)
- Asia
- North America
- Latin America
- Australia & Africa

**Figure 12.12** World steel production, 1960–93

| % world/ share 1995 | World rank 1995 | | 1960 | 1970 | 1980 | 1990 | 1995 |
|---|---|---|---|---|---|---|---|
| | | | | | (million tonnes) | | |
| 5.6 | 5 | Germany | 34.0 | 48.0 | 51.1 | 38.0 | 41.8 |
| 3.7 | 7 | Italy | 8.4 | 17.3 | 26.5 | 25.4 | 27.7 |
| 2.4 | 11 | France | 17.3 | 23.8 | 25.2 | 19.0 | 18.1 |
| 2.4 | 12 | UK | 24.7 | 28.3 | 11.3 | 17.8 | 17.9 |
| 1.9 | 14 | Spain | 2.0 | 7.4 | 12.6 | 13.0 | 13.9 |
| 1.6 | 19 | Belgium | 9.0 | 12.6 | 12.3 | 11.4 | 11.6 |
| | 24 | Netherlands | 2.0 | 5.0 | 5.0 | 5.4 | 6.4 |
| | 26 | Austria | 3.1 | 4.1 | 4.6 | 4.3 | 5.0 |
| | 27 | Sweden | 3.2 | 5.5 | 4.2 | 4.4 | 4.9 |
| | 33 | Finland | 0.3 | 1.2 | 2.5 | 2.9 | 3.3 |
| | 37 | Luxembourg | 4.1 | 5.5 | 4.6 | 3.6 | 2.6 |
| | | Greece | 0.1 | 0.4 | 0.9 | 1.0 | 1.0 |
| | | Denmark | 0.3 | 0.5 | 0.7 | 0.6 | 0.6 |
| | | Portugal | 0.0 | 0.4 | 0.7 | 0.7 | 0.5 |
| | | Ireland | 0.0 | 0.0 | 0.0 | 0.3 | 0.3 |

**Figure 12.13** EU steel production

- **Government policies**   Governments in many Asian countries appear to be more prepared to put money into creating industrial wealth than are their counterparts in Europe.

## Government intervention – South Wales

Since 1945 a range of methods have been tried by successive British governments to encourage industry to move to areas of high unemployment. Some of these are presented in Figure 12.14, with examples from South Wales.

- The construction of new towns (Cwmbran).
- Financial aid in the form of removal grants, rent-free periods, tax relief on new machinery, and reduced interest rates.
- Decentralising government offices – the Royal Mint to Llantrisant, DVLC (car licences) to Swansea.
- Improving communications (M4 and the Heads of the Valleys road).
- Setting up Development Areas (Figure 12.14), Enterprise Zones (Swansea, Milford Haven) and Urban Development Corporations (Cardiff).
- Grants and loans from the EU Regional Development Fund Britain's own attempt to develop Assisted Areas (the Welsh Development Agency), and encouraging inward investment from overseas (North America, Japan and the EU).

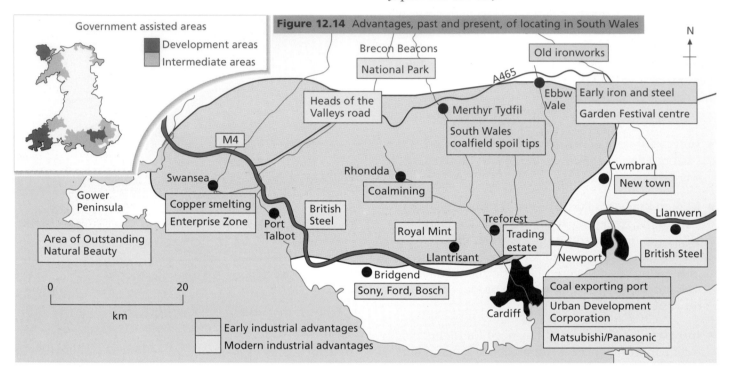

Figure 12.14 Advantages, past and present, of locating in South Wales

### The Welsh Development Agency (WDA)

#### The position in 1976

The WDA was set up in 1976 'to attract high-quality investment in Wales, to help the growth of Welsh businesses and to improve the environment'. In 1976 Wales, and South Wales in particular, still depended on the traditional industries which had created its economic wealth a century earlier. However, these industries were now declining, causing considerable job losses (only Northern Ireland had higher unemployment) and leaving a derelict and scarred environment (Figure 12.15a).

#### 1976 to 1996

During this period 100,000 jobs were lost in the coal and steel industries. The WDA used public money and obtained private investment to try to regenerate the Welsh economy. It actively sought inward (overseas) investment by setting up offices in several Asian, North American and European cities. These offices, together with high-power delegations, set out to 'sell' the advantages of investing and locating in Wales. The advantages included the Welsh workforce, the transport infrastructure, financial inducements, available advanced factory sites, the attractive Welsh countryside and the Welsh culture. The result has been the arrival of over 380 overseas firms, many of which are connected to the car industry or to the new high-tech electronics industries (page 154). Most of the new jobs created by the multinational firms (page 156) were for women and are, hopefully, permanent.

Land reclamation also had a high priority. In addition to the Cardiff Bay Project (page 118), many schemes involved removing and landscaping old coal and slag spoil heaps and converting former coalmines and ironworks into industrial and housing estates, schools and hospitals, shopping centres and recreational areas, e.g. the Swansea Valley Project (Figure 12.15b).

### Position in 1997

South Wales, no longer dependent upon traditional industries, now has a more varied and broader economic base. Manufacturing and inward investment continue to grow at the fastest rate in the UK. Apart from British firms, over 380 international companies have located here. Of these, 140 are North American (Ford, General Electric), 50 are German (Bosch) and 40 are Japanese (Sony, Aiwa). Other companies have come from Italy, France, Taiwan, Singapore and Korea. According to the WDA Chairman (1996):

> 'Unemployment is still too high in some pockets of our country. We still need more high-skilled jobs to close the "prosperity gap" with other parts of the UK. Some of our urban areas are in need of further substantial investment. But Wales has, undeniably, achieved a great deal over the past twenty years in improving its prosperity and the quality of life of its people.'

### *The Swansea Valley Project*

In the late eighteenth century, the Lower Swansea Valley was the major world area for copper smelting. Long before 1976 all that remained were derelict buildings, waste heaps and a concentration of copper and zinc, which prevented vegetation growing, and

polluted water supplies (Figure 12.15a).

Since then 180 hectares of the valley have been reclaimed at a cost of £6 million. Apart from a small area where some of the old industrial remains have been left as a reminder, five 'parks' with a variety of land uses have been created (Figure 12.15c).

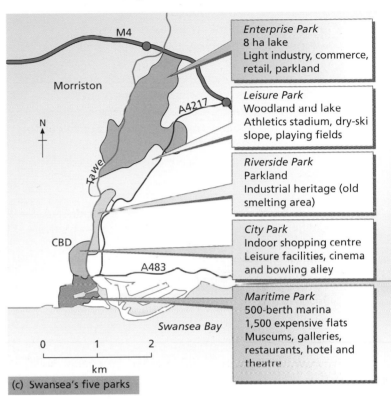

Enterprise Park
8 ha lake
Light industry, commerce, retail, parkland

Leisure Park
Woodland and lake
Athletics stadium, dry-ski slope, playing fields

Riverside Park
Parkland
Industrial heritage (old smelting area)

City Park
Indoor shopping centre
Leisure facilities, cinema and bowling alley

Maritime Park
500-berth marina
1,500 expensive flats
Museums, galleries, restaurants, hotel and theatre

(c) Swansea's five parks

**Figure 12.15** The Swansea Valley Project

(a) The Valley as it was in 1976

(b) As it is now

# High-technology industries

The term *high-technology*, or *high-tech*, refers to those industries whose processing techniques usually involve micro-electronics and demand a high level of information and expertise. Collectively they are referred to as *quaternary industries* (page 194).

High-tech industries include:

- information technology industries involving computers, telecommunications and office equipment
- electronic components which include silicon wafers, semiconductors and printed circuit boards
- consumer electronics such as televisions, video-cassette and audio-tape recorders, pocket calculators and electronic games
- biotechnology, pharmaceuticals and medical equipment
- aerospace and defence industries
- research and development (R & D) – because to remain successful and competitive, high-tech firms rely on the development of new products and technologies.

As traditional industrial location factors such as raw materials, energy supplies and transport costs have little influence on the choice of location, high-tech industries are said to be 'footloose'. However, in reality, high-tech industries often group together in selected locations. These include 'Silicon Glen' in central Scotland (Figure 12.16), along the M4 corridor, and around Cambridge (Figure 12.17) in England; and in Grenoble and in the Côte d'Azur in southern France. By locating close together, high-tech firms cans exchange ideas and information and share basic amenities such as attractively laid out *science parks* and *business parks*.

Most science parks have grown up on edge-of-city greenfield sites where the cost of land is relatively low and there is a pleasant working environment. Science parks have a low density of buildings. Usually over 70 per cent of the land is left under grass and trees or converted into ornamental gardens and lakes (Figure 12.17 ). Firms have close links with universities (for research) and rely upon a highly skilled, inventive workforce – a high proportion of which is female. Science parks are often located near to motorways and, ideally, an international airport.

The Cambridge Science Park, now covering 52 hectares, was established in 1970 by Trinity College. It has close links with the scientific excellence of Cambridge University, is a low-density development in a park-like setting, with high-quality, flexible buildings suited to office, laboratory or manufacturing use. It is close to residential areas for its workforce yet well separated from them, and has excellent communications via the A14 Cambridge northern by-pass (which links with the M11, M25 and Stansted airport). Only selected firms, using buildings for specific purposes, are allowed to locate on the park.

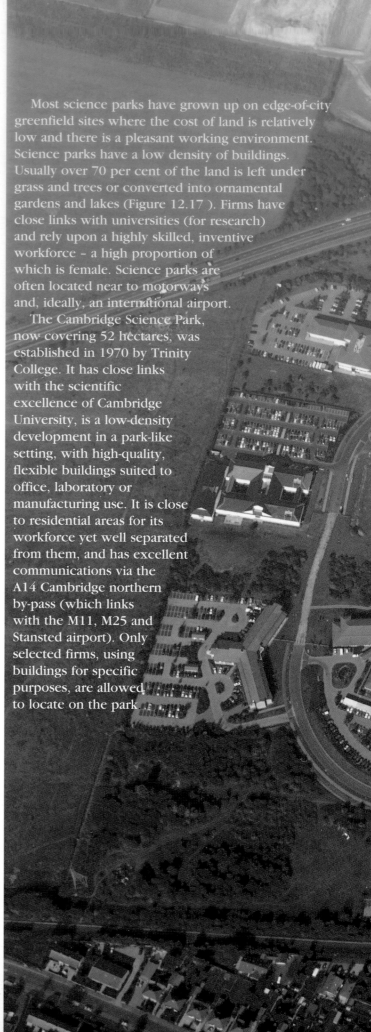

**Figure 12.16** The IBM factory in 'Silicon Glen'

Companies by types

Others

Drugs and pharma- ceuticals

Scientific instruments

Electronics

A14

A10

**Figure 12.17** Cambridge Science Park

# Transnational (or multinational) corporations

A transnational, or multinational, corporation is one that has factories in several countries and which operates regardless of national boundaries. Transnationals are believed to employ nearly 40 million people around the world, and indirectly influence an even greater number. The largest are oil companies such as Shell and Exxon and car manufacturers such as Ford, Toyota and Nissan. The largest of all, General Motors, has an annual turnover which exceeds the GNP of all but 20 countries in the world. The major advantage of transnational corporations is their economy of scale (Figure 12.3) – that is, their large size allows companies to reduce costs, to finance re-investment and to compete in world markets.

## *The car industry*

Car firms were amongst the first to opt for transnational operations. They found that by locating in different parts of the world they could:

- get around local trade barriers which may have been erected to protect home markets
- reduce costs by gaining access to cheaper labour and/or raw materials
- be near to large markets (centres of population).

### The car industry in western Europe

In 1950 almost 85 per cent of cars were produced in the USA and 11 per cent in Europe (Figure 12.18). By 1970 Europe produced half the world's cars, with nearly all the remainder coming from either Japan or North America. Today, Japan is the world leader and Germany the European leader (Figure 12.19).

Japanese cars began to flood the European market in the late 1970s. This led to negotiated agreements between individual countries and Japan, aimed at restricting the number of imported cars, e.g. Japanese cars into the UK could not exceed 11 per cent of Britain's total car sales. To try to overcome this barrier, Japanese car manufacturers either:

- produced cars at assembly plants (*transplants*) within Europe (Nissan and Toyota in the UK) or
- amalgamated with European car manufacturers (Rover-Honda).

Meanwhile European and North American companies became more transnational by assembling cars in one country using components manufactured in several countries (e.g. the Ford Sierra uses components from Belgium, Germany, France, the USA and the UK), and by amalgamating with other Western firms (Volvo-Renault; General Motors-Saab).

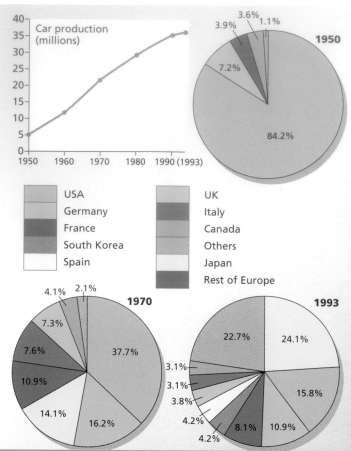

**Figure 12.18** World car production and the leading producers, 1950–93

**Figure 12.19** Vehicle plants and production in the EU, 1993

| EU motor vehicle production, 1993 (thousand vehicles) | |
|---|---|
| *EU total* | *12,392* |
| Germany | 3,990 |
| France | 3,156 |
| Spain | 1,766 |
| UK | 1,339 |
| Italy | 1,267 |
| Belgium | 406 |
| Sweden | 337 |
| Netherlands | 86 |
| Austria | 45 |

Major vehicle assembly plants in the EU, 1995

- 'Old' assembly plants
- New flexible assembly plants

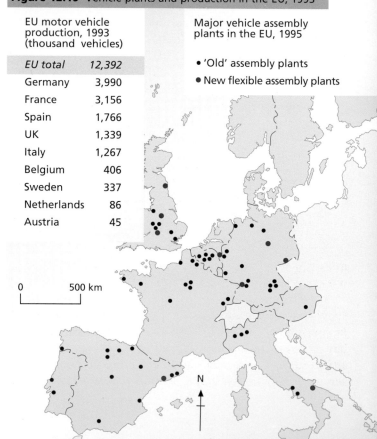

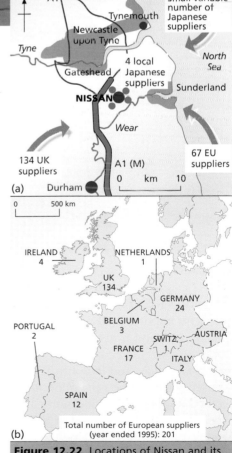

Figure 12.21 Automation within the plant

Figure 12.20 The Nissan car plant at Washington

## Nissan in the UK

Nissan was the first Japanese company to locate in Europe. Having first signed an agreement with the British government, Nissan then had to select a site. It chose one at Sunderland for several reasons.

* It was on flat land that was once Sunderland Airfield, with a greenfield location and room for future expansion (Figure 12.20).
* It was near to deepwater ports for the import of components and the export of assembled cars, and close to the A1(M) (Figure 12.22a).
* There was a large supply of local skilled and unskilled labour, it was near to Washington new town, the region was known for its engineering, and there were training colleges nearby.
* Being in an Assisted Area, government grants were available.

Part of the agreement to allow Nissan to locate in the UK was that most components, as part of the '80 per cent local content deal', should be made either within Britain itself or in the EU. At the end of 1995 there were 201 European suppliers, 134 of which were UK based (Figure 12.22b). Local suppliers are essential as Nissan, like other Japanese firms, operates a 'just-in-time' (JIT) policy. JIT is using the minimum amount of resources in the most efficient way, e.g. component parts are delivered as they are needed, which eliminates expensive storage.

The growth of Nissan also created a *multiplier effect*. This is when the success of one industry leads to the growth of other industries. Four other Japanese firms, making car exhausts, car seats, tyres and body pressings, have located within minutes of the Nissan factory. They in turn have attracted other industries and have increased demand for local jobs in the service sector (more shops, schools and places of entertainment).

Figure 12.22 Locations of Nissan and its main suppliers

# A cycle of industrial change – Consett

## The growth of the steel town

The first iron makers in the Consett region were the Romans and, by the late seventeenth century, the area was well known for its swords and cutlery. The modern iron and steel industry began in 1840 when the Derwent Iron Company began operations with two blast furnaces. At that time Consett was an ideal location for the iron industry (page 150). It was on a coalfield, it had local supplies of iron ore and it was close to limestone areas in the Pennines. Although the iron ore was soon exhausted, it was relatively easy to transport the ore initially from the Cleveland Hills (south of Middlesbrough) and later from Spain (via the River Tyne). By the end of the nineteenth century, the Consett Iron Company (as it had been called since 1864) employed 7,500 people, provided houses, an infirmary and a library for its employees, and operated ten blast furnaces. It is estimated that at its peak 23,000 people found employment in coalmining, in the steelworks and in associated industries (Figure 12.24).

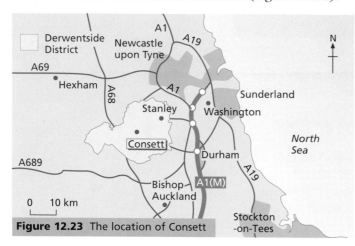

Figure 12.23 The location of Consett

## The decline of the steel town

The late 1970s saw a dramatic fall in the demand for steel. Despite Consett's claim to high productivity, the steelworks found itself geographically isolated. Britain was now importing all of its iron ore and most of its coking coal, and Consett's inland location could not compete with the coastal sites of the new integrated works at Redcar and in South Wales. Added to this, Consett had neither a mainline railway nor easy access to the motorway system (Figure 12.23). The steelworks closed in 1980, as did the last local deep coalmine. During 1981 local firms dependent upon the steel industry were also forced to close – the multiplier effect in reverse (page 157). Unemployment reached 27 per cent.

Figure 12.24 The Consett steelworks in the late 1970s

The closure of the steelworks was dramatic because:
- Consett had become too dependent on one main industry and had virtually no alternative forms of employment
- it led to mass unemployment at one time rather than being spread over a period of years.
- it left a huge area (280 hectares) of derelict and, in places, contaminated land (Figure 12.25).

Despite financial aid from the British government and the European Regional Development Fund (ERDF), the industries that were needed to replace the thousands of lost jobs, the retraining of people for those new types of industry and the conversion of land for the new industries, could not be achieved overnight.

Figure 12.25 The derelict steelworks site in the early 1980s

## The regeneration of the former steel town

Much of the early work and money was spent improving the site of the former steelworks.

**Phase 1 (1981)** Several spoil heaps were regraded to create woodland, agricultural and public amenity areas.

**Phase 2 (1982)** Slag and waste from the most contaminated areas were removed, the land drained and topsoil added. By 1984 the area was being grazed by cows and sheep.

**Phase 3 (1984)** This included clearing 130 hectares of the old steel-making plant. 3.5 million cubic metres of slag was excavated and 65 hectares of trees planted.

**Phase 4 (1987)** The former Hownsgill Plate Mill and BR marshalling yards were cleared and seeded with grass.

### The Genesis Project

The Genesis Project is the plan to redevelop 240 hectares of the former steelworks site and 1.5 hectares within the town centre of Consett. When complete:

'. . . the Genesis Project will create an extensive area of parkland within which industrial premises, offices and leisure facilities will be attractively set in their own landscaped environments. The Genesis Project breaks new ground in a number of ways. It is the first major scheme of its kind in Europe to promote the concept of *sustainability*, in which industry, commerce and leisure are totally integrated within an energy-conscious and environmentally-sound framework. The project has won enthusiastic support from both the UK government and the LU, particularly the incorporation of innovative plans to generate energy from within the Consett site, using cost-efficient renewable resources.'

*Derwentside District Council, 1996*

The project aims to redevelop former industrial land within urban areas rather than, as often is the case, using greenfield sites.

**Figure 12.26** The Genesis Project

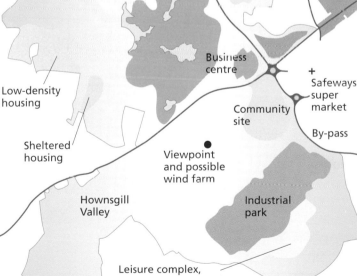

- Low-density housing
- Sheltered housing and starter homes
- Town centre
- Leisure and swimming-pool complex
- Low-density housing
- Business centre
- Safeways super market
- Community site
- By-pass
- Sheltered housing
- Viewpoint and possible wind farm
- Hownsgill Valley
- Industrial park
- Leisure complex, including sports pitches

N

0    300 metres

**Berry Edge Business Park**
240 hectares. Panoramic views over Derwent Valley, in a landscaped environment. High-quality premises now being developed (1997).

**Hownsgill Prestige Industrial Park**
19 hectares. Developed in early 1990s, partly funded by Department of the Environment and ERDF. Highest possible environmental design. Firms limited to 'clean' technology sector, e.g. recycling and environmental technology.

**Housing**
14 hectares. Emphasis on low-density housing and low-cost sheltered housing for the elderly, and starter homes. Over 150 units planned.

**Retail/commerce**
14 hectares, plus 1.5 hectares in town centre being redeveloped (including a new bus terminal).

**Open space**
194 hectares. Large areas of woodland. Also open space surrounding industrial, commercial and housing areas.

**Leisure/education**
14 hectares. Both indoor and outdoor facilities.

◯ Ornamental lakes      ── New roads

The Project area

**January 1997**
Many local firms relocated here – an advantage as national firms tend to move. Unemployment still high, but reduced to 15%. Some firms began by using redundancy money. For example, three people began the Derwent Valley Foods Ltd – this firm is now part of the larger Phineas Fogg, employing 250 people.

# Industrial and environmental change – the Ruhr

The planning region known as 'The Ruhr' is more an economic/environmental unit than a geographical one. In 1920 eleven independent cities and four administrative districts joined together to form an economic union (Figure 12.27) and, in 1979, the *Kommunalverband Ruhrgebiet* (the KVR or Community of Ruhr Districts). The tasks of the KVR include environmental protection, the development of leisure facilities, community services for its members, and public relations.

## *The industrial Ruhr*

Geographically the region consists of the drainage basins of three tributaries of the River Rhine – the Lippe, Emscher and Ruhr. For well over a century it has been the leading industrial region in Europe. The basis for its economic growth was coal, and its continued prosperity was due to steel and its related industries.

Large-scale coalmining began in the 1830s, with production reaching a peak in 1938. Since then output has declined and many pits, especially on the exposed coalfield (Figure 12.28), have closed, leaving social and environmental problems. Several towns had relied on mining as their main source of income. Bochum had 65,000 miners at its peak – now there are none. Former miners have had to seek alternative employment or move to newer collieries in the north.

The region was ideally suited to the manufacture of steel. There were large amounts of high-grade, easily obtainable coking coal, local deposits of iron ore, water transport either by river (Rhine) or canal (Dortmund-Ems), and a large local population which provided both a labour force and a domestic market.

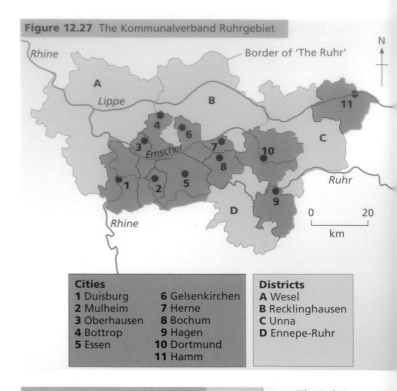

**Figure 12.27** The Kommunalverband Ruhrgebiet

| Cities | | Districts |
|---|---|---|
| 1 Duisburg | 6 Gelsenkirchen | A Wesel |
| 2 Mulheim | 7 Herne | B Recklinghausen |
| 3 Oberhausen | 8 Bochum | C Unna |
| 4 Bottrop | 9 Hagen | D Ennepe-Ruhr |
| 5 Essen | 10 Dortmund | |
| | 11 Hamm | |

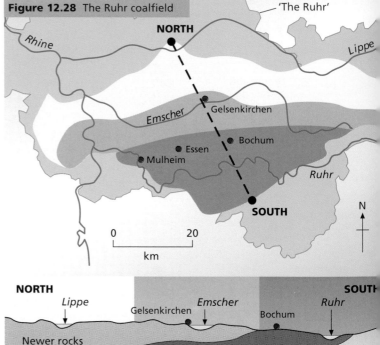

**Figure 12.28** The Ruhr coalfield

| CONCEALED COALFIELD | | EXPOSED COALFIELD |
|---|---|---|
| Coal at a depth of 100 m. Late 20th-century mines. High investment and productivity. Few towns – mainly a rural area. | Coal at a depth up to 150 m. Early 20th-century mines. Many closed since 1960. | Coal was at surface, now used up. 19th-century mines now closed, mining towns decayed. |

**Figure 12.29** The environment in 1920 and in 1979

'Pit-heads and foundries, miners black with coal and panting steelworkers, slag heaps and boggy industrial wastelands, smog and thunder, the sky full of smoke of chimneys in the daytime, and at night the glowing red reflections of 1,000 soot-belching fires. Part pride, part revulsion, Germany's industrial heartland, the nation's environmental blackspot. These were problems to be tackled when, in 1920, the forerunner of the Ruhr planning region was set up.'

Despite early attempts to improve the environment, the situation continued to worsen. By the time the RVT came into being in 1979 . . . .

'Parts of the region had 3,000 people to every kilometre of open space, many living in houses lacking basic amenities. The region had derelict mines and machines, disused transport routes, polluted rivers and air, lakes caused by mining subsidence, and slag and waste heaps.'

KVR Report

## The Ruhr today

### Industry

Although green areas now make up almost 70 per cent of the Ruhr, it is still perceived as an industrial area. Indeed it still is the most important economic centre in Europe, producing 28 per cent of Germany's coal and 15 per cent of its steel. However, there has been a considerable change in the employment structure (page 194), with fewer people in the primary and secondary sectors and more in the tertiary sector (Figure 12.30).

The losses in the secondary sector would have been even greater had it not been for the growth of high-tech industries. Unemployment has slowly fallen, with twice as many jobs created in the tertiary sector as have been lost in the other two sectors.

| % | 1960 | 1970 | 1980 | 1993 |
|---|---|---|---|---|
| Primary | 5 | 3 | 2 | 2 |
| Secondary | 62 | 58 | 53 | 44 |
| Tertiary (services) | 33 | 39 | 45 | 54 |

**Figure 12.30** Employment structure in the Ruhr, 1960–93

### Environment

The first attempt to improve the environment was in the 1920s with a series of riverside walks in the Ruhr Valley. However, it was not until the creation of the KVR that an overall plan was drawn up (remember that two functions of the KVR were to protect and improve the environment and to create leisure facilities).

- Five green areas, or belts, were created as 'lungs'. Running from north to south, they separate the main urban areas (Figure 12.31). Over 30,000 trees have been planted to try to re-establish an ecological balance.

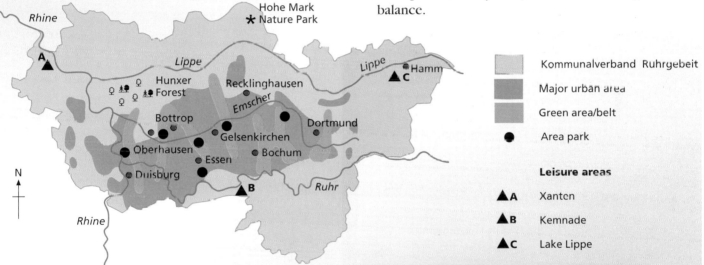

**Figure 12.31** Environmental improvements in the Ruhr

- Five area parks have been built as close to urban areas as possible (Figure 12.32). They include swimming pools, fitness centres and sports fields.
- Smaller leisure areas (under 300 hectares) were provided, with a strong emphasis on water sports.
- Air pollution has been reduced to one-seventh of its previous level.
- Rivers have had the quality of their water improved.
- Old coal heaps have been converted into new factories (Opel cars), golf courses (at Oberhausen), offices and shopping centres (between Mulheim and Essen).

**Figure 12.32** The Neinhausen Area Park, between Essen and Gelsenkirchen

**1** (Pages 146 and 147)

**a** List four factors *not* shown on the diagram that are important in locating industries.

**b** From the diagram, choose two *physical* factors and two *human* factors and explain how they affect where industry should be located.

**c** What were the main location factors for:
   i)   industries established in the nineteenth century
   ii)  late twentieth-century modern industry?

**d** Look at the OS map on page 206. **Using map evidence only**, list the advantages for industry at map references 205635, 703190 and 238710.

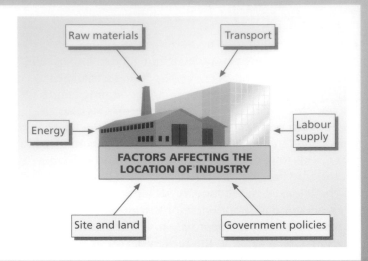

Raw materials

Transport

Energy

Labour supply

**FACTORS AFFECTING THE LOCATION OF INDUSTRY**

Site and land

Government policies

**2** (Pages 148 and 149)

**a** Look carefully at the map of Europe below.
   i)   Name one country that is completely within an area with the highest unemployment.
   ii)  Name one country that is completely within an area with the lowest unemployment.
   iii) Name one country that has both high and low unemployment.
   iv)  Describe what the map shows about unemployment in the UK.

**b** Unemployment occurs when industries decline or close down. Give five reasons why industries may decline or close down.

**c** Explain the reasons for growth and the reasons for the decline of the British shipbuilding industry.

**3** (Pages 150 and 151)

**a** Look at the map below.
   i)   Which site would be best for an ironworks in 1820? Give four reasons for your choice.
   ii)  Which site would be best for a steelworks in 1990? Give four reasons for your choice.
   iii) Suggest two other factors not on the map which could have influenced the decision on where to locate the steelworks in 1990.

**b** Europe's steel industry has undergone decline since the early 1990s. Choose any three of the following reasons and explain how they may have helped bring about that decline.
   * Increased competition    * Raw materials
   * Improved technology      * Economies of scale
   * Government policies       * Structural changes

**Unemployment in some countries of Europe**

Iceland
Norway
Sweden
Ireland
Denmark
UK
Germany
Portugal
France
Austria
Spain
Italy
Greece

Areas with highest unemployment

Areas with average unemployment

Areas with lowest unemployment

No data

N

0   500km

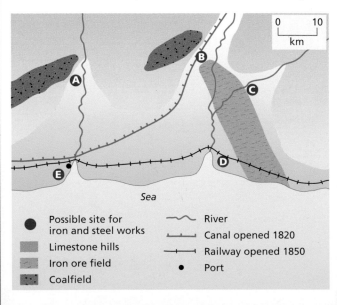

0   10
km

A
B
C
D
E

*Sea*

● Possible site for iron and steel works

Limestone hills

Iron ore field

Coalfield

〜 River

Canal opened 1820

Railway opened 1850

● Port

**4** *(Pages 154 and 155)*

**a** i) How many towns on the map show industry that is expanding?

ii) State three reasons from the map which would help to explain why modern industries have expanded in this area.

**b** Many of the industries in this area are described as *high-tech* and *footloose*. Give the meaning of these two terms.

**c** The Science Park at Cambridge is an example of modern industrial development.

i) Describe the main features of a science park.

ii) List the main location factors of a science park.

iii) Why is an attractive environment an important factor in the location of modern industry?

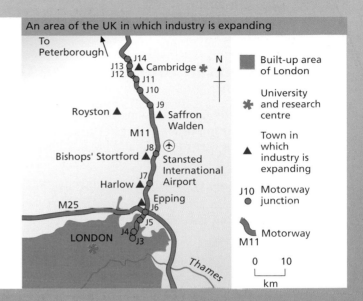

An area of the UK in which industry is expanding

**5** *(Pages 146, 147, 156, 157)*

**a** Look at the location factors below, which Nissan gives as important reasons why the company moved to the Sunderland area. Using the following headings, describe the advantages of Sunderland for a new Japanese car factory.

\* Labour  \* Transport  \* Site  \* Capital

**b** What benefits can a large company like Nissan bring to an area?

**c** Give two reasons why a Japanese company may wish to build a car factory in Britain.

**d** i) Nissan is a transnational (multinational) corporation. What is meant by this?

ii) Explain the advantages of large transnational companies.

**6** *(Pages 158 and 159)*

**a** Look at the diagram and explain the meaning of the term *cycle of industrial change*.

**b** Consett in north-east England is an example of this process. Explain what is happening there:

i) Describe Consett's location.

ii) Give the main reasons for early growth.

iii) Explain why industries there declined or closed down.

iv) Describe the new industries and explain why they have come to the area.

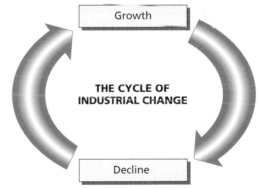

**7** *(Pages 160 and 161)*

Industrial development can bring many benefits but it can also cause problems. Careful management is needed to protect and conserve the environment.

**a** Describe how the Ruhr region of Germany has been affected by industrial development.

**b** Explain how planners and environmentalists in the Ruhr region have tried to reduce the

# Recent trends in tourism in the UK and Europe

Tourism is one of the fastest growing industries in the world today. It is an important factor in the economy of many countries as it earns income and creates jobs. According to the EU:

'Tourism involves many millions of people as both providers and consumers of a wide range of services. Tourists move outside their usual location and acquire benefits which are cultural, aesthetic and recreational, and which generate economic rewards to those offering them.' (Figure 13.2)

Some of the many reasons for the growth of tourism, and the changing demands made by tourists, are summarised in Figure 13.1.

| | |
|---|---|
| Greater affluence | People who have employment within Europe usually earn a high salary – certainly higher than several decades ago. People in full-time employment also receive holiday with pay. This means that they can take more than one holiday a year, and can travel further. |
| Greater mobility | The increase in car ownership has given people greater freedom to choose where and when they go for the day, or for a longer period. In 1951, only 1 UK family in 20 had a car; now, 2 in every 3 have one. Chartered aircraft reduce costs of overseas travel. |
| Improved accessibility and transport facilities | Improvements in roads, especially motorways (autobahns, autoroutes, etc.). Road by-passes. Improved and enlarged airports (e.g. Malaga) although many are still congested at peak periods. Reduced air fares. |
| More leisure time | – Shorter working week and longer paid holidays.<br>– Flexitime and more people working from home.<br>– An ageing population, many of whom are still active (page 95). |
| Changing lifestyles | – People are retiring early.<br>– People at work need longer/more frequent rest periods as pressure of work seems to increase.<br>– Changing fashions, e.g. health resorts, fitness holidays. |
| Changing recreational activities | Slight decline in the 'beach holiday' – partly due to the threat of skin cancer (page 25). Increase in active holidays (skiing, water sports). Most rapid growth in mid-1990s has been in 'cruise holidays'. Importance of theme parks, e.g. Alton Towers, Disneyland Paris. |
| Advertising and TV programmes | Holiday programmes and magazine brochures promote new and different places and activities. |
| 'Green' or sustainable tourism | Need to benefit local economy, environment and people without spoiling the attractiveness and amenities of the places visited (page 178). |

**Figure 13.1** Areas of growth in the tourist industry

**Figure 13.2** The range of tourism

Coastal tourism

Winter tourism

Cultural tourism

## Tourism and the EU economy

It is always difficult to assess how much money is earned through tourism. For example, does a hotel owner in Central London know whether a guest is on holiday or on business, or is food produced on a Greek island sold to hotels or to the local people? It has been estimated that tourism represents 2.1 per cent of GNP in the EU, with Austria achieving four times that level, and Portugal, Greece, Spain and Ireland being well above the average (Figures 13.3 and 13.4). About 60 per cent of the world's tourists visit, or stay, in Europe.

Tourism provides employment for about 9 million people in the EU – about 6 per cent of the total jobs. A high proportion of these jobs are taken by women. Many jobs, especially in hotels, holiday villages and at open-air facilities, are seasonal in nature. Jobs in restaurants and travel agencies are more permanent. Tourism has the ability to stimulate major investment in other parts of the economy too, for example new roads in southern Italy, the improved airport at Malaga, and improved local water supplies and health care in some areas. Tourism can also be a major contributor in the development of peripheral and less-developed regions such as the south of Italy, the Greek islands, the Algarve and south-west Ireland.

In 1995, tourism earned more for the UK than did North Sea oil or the country's financial institutions. Overseas visitors spent £11.7 billion – a record, and 18 per cent higher than in 1994.

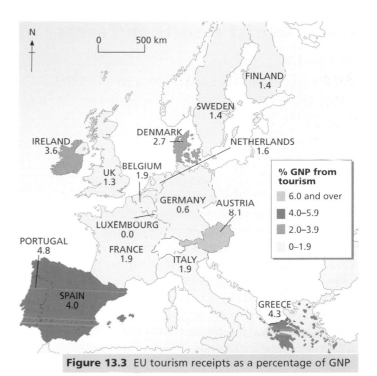

**Figure 13.3** EU tourism receipts as a percentage of GNP

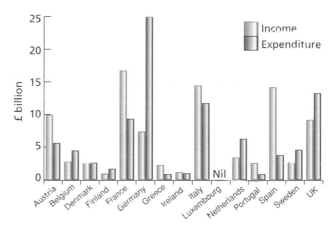

**Figure 13.4** Revenue from overseas tourists, and expenditure on visiting other countries, 1992

Benefits to the local economy

'Getting away from it all'

Cruise tourists

# Major tourist resorts and areas

## In the UK

As with farming and industry, several factors affect the location of tourist resorts and areas (Figure 13.5). Here too the importance of these factors may change over time, for example improvements in accessibility or changes in fashion.

Most 'day trip' resorts (Figure 13.6) are located on the coast and have good communications with nearby large urban areas (page 168). However, only 5 per cent of day visitors now go to the coast – 64 per cent go to towns and cities and 31 per cent to the countryside. The long-stay resorts are also on the coast, but these are too far from urban areas to make a day visit comfortable. Many have sandy beaches and are in areas with above average amounts of sunshine. Cultural and historic centres tend to be inland, usually in capital cities or places with castles and cathedrals. The Scottish Highlands, which have several months of snow cover, are suitable for winter sports (page 169).

Many parts of Britain which have attractive scenery, historic sites and important habitats for wildlife are now protected areas (Figure 13.7). The largest protected areas are the National Parks of England and Wales and the National Scenic Areas of Scotland. Also protected are places designated Areas of Outstanding Natural Beauty (AONBs), Sites of Special Scientific Interest (SSSIs), National Nature Reserves (NNRs), Heritage Coasts and Forest Parks.

| Factor | Specific example | Example (area/resort) |
|---|---|---|
| *Transport and accessibility* | • Early resorts: stage coach/spa towns<br>• Ferries<br>• Railways<br>• Car and coach<br><br>• Plane | Bath<br>Scottish islands<br>Blackpool, Brighton<br>Cornwall, Scottish Highlands<br>Channel Islands |
| *Scenery* | • Sandy coasts of outstanding beauty<br>• Coasts of outstanding beauty<br>• Mountains, lakes and rivers | Margate, Blackpool<br>Pembroke, Antrim<br>Lake District, Snowdonia |
| *Weather* | • Hot, dry, sunny summers<br>• Snow | Margate<br>Aviemore |
| *Accommodation* | • Hotels and boarding house resorts<br>• Holiday camps<br>• Caravan parks and campsites | Margate, Blackpool<br>Minehead, Pwllheli<br>National and Forest Parks |
| *Amenities* | • Cultural and historic centres (castles, cathedrals)<br>• Theme parks and famous buildings<br>• Active amenities (sailing, golf, water skiing)<br>• Passive amenities (shops, cinemas) | York, Edinburgh<br><br>Alton Towers, Tower of London<br>Kielder, St Andrews<br><br>Most resorts |

**Figure 13.5** Factors affecting the location of tourist regions and resorts in the UK

**Figure 13.6** Holiday regions and resorts in the UK

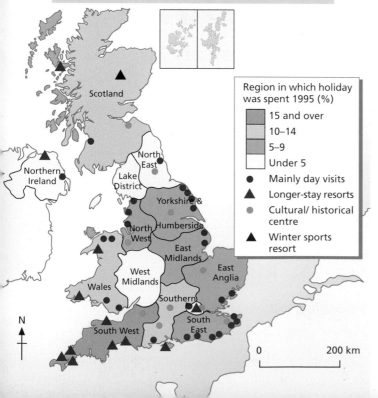

**Figure 13.7** Protected areas in the UK

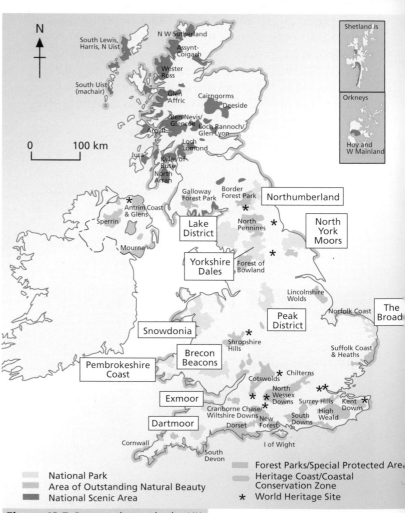

## In the EU

### Patterns of tourism (Figures 13.4 and 13.8)

- The Mediterranean countries of Spain, Italy and Greece attract many tourists during their hot, dry, sunny summers, and retired people during their mild winters (page 13).
- Portugal, Spain, Italy and Greece have large expanses of sandy beaches and warm seas backed by spectacular mountain scenery (page 170).
- Mountainous areas such as the Pyrenees and Alpine France, Italy and Austria attract skiers in winter and walkers and climbers in summer (page 172).
- Countries such as Italy, Greece, Spain and the UK offer cultural and historic holidays.
- People from the more affluent northern EU countries can afford to travel to places further south. In contrast, people in the less well off south of the EU either cannot afford to travel abroad, are too busy in their own tourist industry, or see little need to leave their own attractive climate and scenery.
- The long-established industrialised countries of Germany, Belgium and the UK are perceived to be less attractive.

## Policy on tourism

Even though tourism is likely to become the largest single employer in the EU by the year 2000, it was not until 1992–93 that the EC (as it then was) produced its first 'action programme' for tourism. The aims of this programme included:

- making it easier to cross the EC's internal frontiers
- improving information in the form of statistical knowledge for tourists
- improving protection for consumers, especially as many tourist products (tours, holidays, timeshare properties) are bought and paid for in advance and from a distance
- improving health and safety protection (clean beaches and seas, fire safety in hotels)
- restoring and protecting European monuments and sites of historic interest
- developing transnational forms of cultural tourism, and cultural routes
- vocational training in higher education for people seeking employment in the tourist industry
- financing small-scale tourist developments through the Regional Development Fund
- promoting Europe as a tourist destination, especially in the USA and Japan.

**Figure 13.8** Location of resorts and tourist areas in the EU

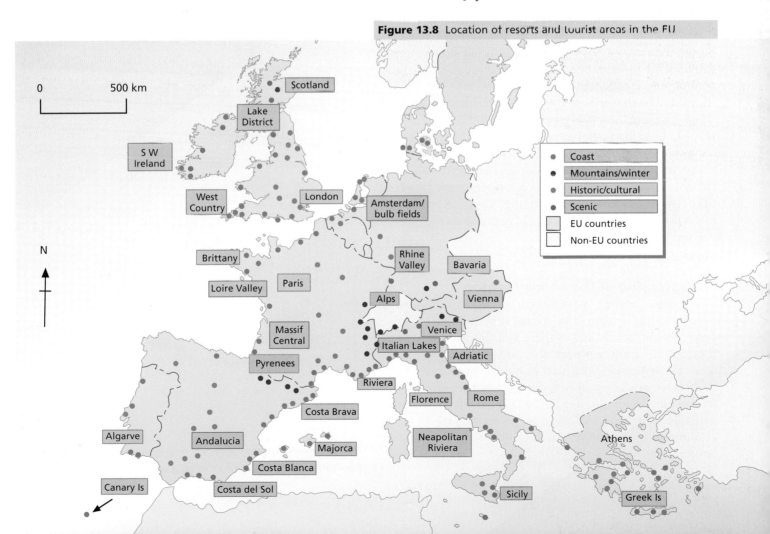

# Two contrasted tourist centres in the UK

## Blackpool – a coastal resort

During the nineteenth century, workers such as those in the Lancashire cotton towns were not given a holiday – and certainly not a paid holiday. To many of them, therefore, the highlight of the year was the annual works visit to the seaside. Blackpool with its 'Golden Sands' lay within an hour's train ride of these towns, so it grew rapidly as a tourist resort. The growth continued into the twentieth century with the introduction of cars and coaches.

Figure 13.9 shows Blackpool as it is today. The land use map (Figure 13.10) identifies and locates several of the main tourist attractions. It also shows how competition for land has produced a land use pattern which, although simplified here, is common to most British coastal resorts.

The large hotels have the best sites along the seafront. This is because they can afford the higher rates, as their guests are willing to pay more to be as close to, and even to overlook, the sea. Boarding houses, providing bed and breakfast, are found behind the hotels. They charge much less than hotels as their rates are lower. Still further away from the sea is self-catering accommodation and, often beyond the resort's boundary, camping and caravan sites.

At the centre of a holiday resort is the recreational business district (RBD) which, in Blackpool's case, includes the piers and the Tower. Behind the RBD is the central business district (CBD) which includes the main shops and banks for both tourists and residents. Most shops catering for tourists are found either near to the seafront or along main roads leading from the transport terminals (railway and coach). The transport terminals are also centrally situated to save tourists having to walk far either to their hotels (long-stay visitors) or to the beach (day visitors). Further away from the busy seafront are the residential districts, in areas where land values are cheapest, and, at the urban–rural fringe (page 120), areas of open space (zoo, golf courses).

### The extension of the holiday season

Due to the weather, most coastal resorts in Britain have a short tourist season. This means that much employment is seasonal as there is little need in winter for deck-chair and car park attendants, candy-floss and souvenir sellers or extra staff in hotels. Hotel owners try to attract guests by offering cheap out-of-season rates or by opening at lunchtimes for bar snacks. Blackpool also manages to extend its season by promoting its illuminations, the Tower Circus, and party political conferences.

**Figure 13.9** Blackpool

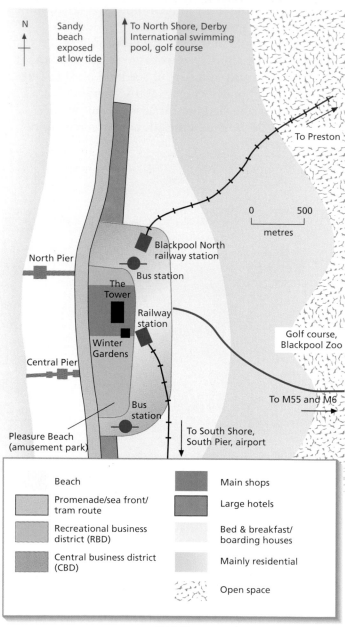

**Figure 13.10** Land use in Blackpool

## Aviemore and the Cairngorms – a ski resort

Before 1964 Aviemore was a small village situated in the narrow valley of the River Spey some 50 km south of Inverness (Figure 13.11). The only tourist attractions were trout and salmon fishing, long-distance walks and rock climbing. In 1966 the Aviemore Centre was opened. It provided a theatre, cinema, shops, indoor swimming pool, sauna and solarium, ice rink, skittle alley and an artificial ski-slope. The Centre was purpose-built to remain open all year.

Just 15 km south-east of Aviemore, but 1,200 metres higher in altitude, is the summit of Cairn Gorm. Even in May, Cairn Gorm and its neighbouring peaks can expect blizzards and a wind chill giving a temperature below zero (Figure 13.13). While the snow has helped to make this area the leading ski centre in Britain, the gales create problems. At present, to reach the top of the Cairngorms, tourists (including skiers) are hauled up the mountain by a chairlift – a 17-minute journey with no shelter from the weather. Once the wind speed reaches 40 knots, as it does for half the year, the lift is forced to close. To overcome this the Cairngorm Chairlift Company proposed a funicular railway. Figure 13.12 lists some of the many arguments put forward both for and against the scheme.

| FOR | AGAINST |
|---|---|
| • The railway would get tourists, including skiers, near to the summit in 3 minutes, regardless of the weather. (It could withstand gusts of 120 km/hr.) | • Conservation groups feared hordes of summer visitors tramping across the fragile arctic/alpine environment. |
| • The extra tourists would create jobs and generate income for local people. | • The Royal Society for the Protection of Birds feared the invasion would disturb the rare dotterels and also ptarmigan, golden eagles and ospreys. |
| • The railway would replace the ageing, existing chairlift equipment. | • The Ramblers Association saw their walks and climbs threatened by extra skiers and visitors. |
| • Skiers at present find it impossible to use the chairlifts on many days each winter. | • The National Trust for Scotland and Scottish Natural Heritage (a government body chaired by Magnus Magnusson) viewed the scheme as an eyesore and a threat to an important ecosystem. |
| LOCAL PEOPLE AND TOURISTS | NATIONAL AND INTERNATIONAL CONSERVATION GROUPS |

**Figure 13.12** The funicular railway debate

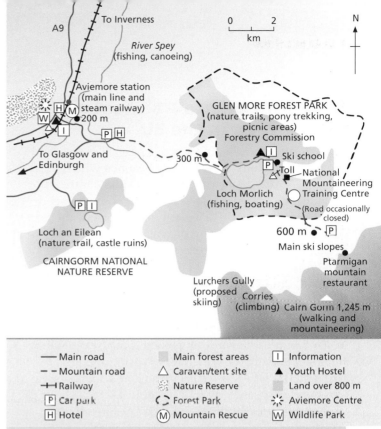

**Figure 13.11** Tourist attractions and amenities around Aviemore

**Figure 13.13** The Cairngorm arctic/alpine environment

In May 1966, the Highland Council decided to accept the proposal to build the railway after the Chairlift Company had agreed that summer visitors would only be allowed to take the funicular (to be completed by 1999) to the Ptarmigan Restaurant (a journey of three minutes), stroll around the new ecological interpretation centre (to be opened in the millennium year), admire the view and then return home without setting foot on the mountain itself.

# The Costa Blanca – a coastal tourist area in the EU

*Costa Blanca* means 'the White Coast'. It is so-called because of its long, white sandy beaches which extend along most of its 300 km coastline. At its centre, and untypical of the coastline as a whole, is the resort of Benidorm (Figure 13.14). Elsewhere much of the coast is undeveloped. Between Altea and Javea, to the north of Benidorm, there are towering cliffs. To the south are numerous small bays and inlets hidden behind rocky outcrops, and longer stretches of sand.

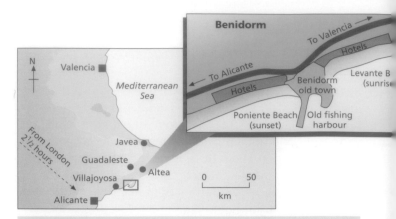

**Figure 13.14** Location of the Costa Blanca and Benidorm

## The growth of tourism in Benidorm

In 1960 Benidorm (meaning 'good sleep') was still a small white-walled fishing village surrounded by farmland. Its site was a small headland which separated two extensive sandy beaches (Figure 13.16). The two curving beaches are known as the Levante (to the north-east) as this is the one over which the sun rises (it gets the best of the morning sun), and the Poniente (to the south-west) which is where the sun eventually sets (and so gets the best of the late afternoon sun). Behind the resort rise steep, rounded hills covered in orange and lemon groves (pages 140–141).

Benidorm had several advantages which enabled it to become, within a decade, one of Europe's leading tourist resorts. These advantages included the following.

**Climate** Benidorm is reputed to enjoy the healthiest climate in Europe, with lots of sunshine (3,000 hours in an average year), warm temperatures, low humidity and clear air (Figure 13.15). Summers are hot, sunny and dry. As a result it attracts many tourists, especially those escaping for two or three weeks from Britain and Germany where the weather is cooler, wetter and cloudier. Winters, although quite wet, are still mild enough for people to sit out of doors. This is the time of year when retired people arrive, many of whom stay for several months.

**Coast** The long natural sandy beaches were a major attraction. In the last 30 years they have been enhanced by the addition of vast quantities of sand imported from Morocco. The sea is warm and clear and is usually calm (especially in summer).

**Transport** Alicante airport is just under 2½ hours' flying time from London, and an hour by road (40 km) from Benidorm.

**Package holidays** It was the introduction of the 'all paid in advance' cheap package holiday that really led to the resort's rapid transformation.

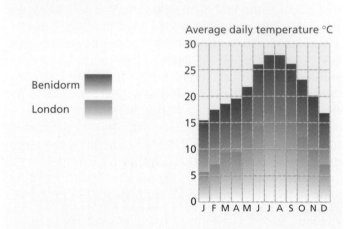

Average daily temperature °C

Benidorm

London

Average hours of sunshine

| | J | F | M | A | M | J | J | A | S | O | N | D |
|---|---|---|---|---|---|---|---|---|---|---|---|---|
| Benidorm | 6 | 7 | 7 | 9 | 10 | 11 | 12 | 11 | 9 | 7 | 6 | 6 |
| London | 2 | 3 | 4 | 5 | 6 | 7 | 6 | 6 | 5 | 3 | 2 | 2 |

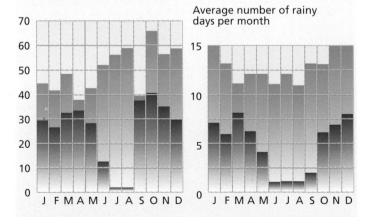

Precipitation mm

Average number of rainy days per month

**Figure 13.15** Comparison between the climates of Benidorm and London

**Accommodation** The beaches are fringed by modern, high-rise hotels (Figure 13.16). Most hotels have their own restaurants, bars, swimming pools and sun terraces. Behind are self-catering villas and an increasing number of time-share apartments.

**Amenities** Apart from the sun, most tourists are attracted to Benidorm by its nightlife. Numerous bars provide flamenco and disco music, cheap wine and beer, and Spanish and other European food. There are several nightclubs. Shops stay open late, selling everything from fine clothes and leather goods to ceramics, wickerwork and perfumes (Figure 13.17).

**The surrounding countryside** Inland are numerous small whitewashed villages still untouched by tourism (apart from providing seasonal workers for Benidorm). The 'Lemon Express' is a small railway which takes tourists inland through vineyards and olive, orange and lemon groves. Nearby are Altea, an old town which has survived by going upmarket, and Villajoyosa, which has tried to hide from tourism.

**Figure 13.16** Benidorm

## Recent changes in tourism

The Spanish government used to see tourism as one way to provide jobs and to raise the country's standard of living. It successfully encouraged places like Benidorm to cater for the mass tourist market. But fashions change. Fewer people now visit the Spanish 'costas' and the luxury hotels are often only half full. This trend has several causes.

- Spain has become more expensive. There has been successful competition from newer, cheaper resorts in the eastern Mediterranean and within the tropics (long-haul holidays).
- Many tourists to Spain now prefer self-catering and time-share accommodation as this is cheaper than staying in hotels and eating in restaurants.

- The Spanish government seems content to let coastal tourism decline and prefers to attract wealthier visitors inland (inland Spain is now more accessible as a result of road improvements in the 1980s, and can offer traditional culture, history, shops and food).
- The government has imposed stricter environmental controls (e.g. cleaner seas and beaches) which can often only be achieved by reducing numbers.
- Fears over skin cancer have brought a reduction in 'sun holidays', and active holidays are now more fashionable.

**Figure 13.17** Tourists in Benidorm

# The French Alps – a mountain tourist area in the EU

The Alps were formed by earth movements some 30 to 60 million years ago (Figure 3.21) and shaped by glaciation in the last 2 million years (page 62). The French Alps contain high mountain peaks (Mont Blanc 4,807 m), glacial lakes (Geneva) and glaciers (Mer de Glace – Figure 5.23). Their scenic attractions and opportunities for winter sports and mountaineering activities have made them into a major tourist region (Figure 13.18). Unlike most other tourist areas, however, the Alps have two distinct visitor seasons.

## Winter resorts

Many of the newer ski-resorts, such as Val d'Isère and Les Deux Alpes, have been purpose-built. While they are extremely crowded during winter (Figure 13.21), they are much quieter in summer. The more traditional ski resorts do attract a larger number of summer visitors.

## Summer resorts

Places beside the three main lakes of the region (Figure 13.18) are, in contrast, relatively quiet in winter but become congested in summer. Although lakeside towns such as Annecy (Figure 13.19) are popular in winter, most tourists prefer them in summer when they can take lake cruises and enjoy the scenery. At this time of the year Annecy becomes overcrowded. It has virtually everything that a tourist needs . . . except vacant accommodation and car parking space!

## All-year resorts

The spa towns of Evian and Aix-les-Bains are visited through-out the year by people 'taking the waters'. Chamonix, at the foot of the Mont Blanc range, is always busy (Figure 13.20). The period between Christmas and Easter belongs to the winter sports enthusiasts, and local sports shops remain open 12 hours a day hiring out ski equipment. The time between June and late September belongs to climbers, walkers, cable-car riders and paragliders. At this time of year sports shops, working equally long hours, sell walking and climbing gear.

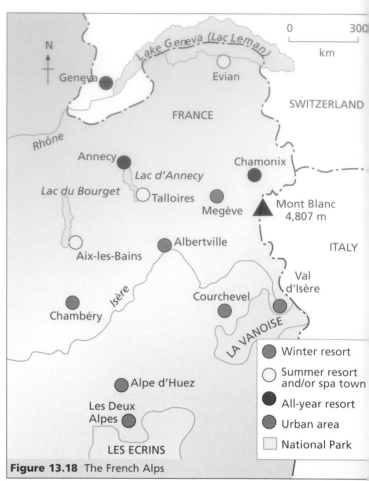

Figure 13.18 The French Alps

Figure 13.20 The Chamonix Valley

Figure 13.19 Annecy

## Val d'Isère – a ski resort

France, with its purpose-built resorts and their enormous lift systems and *après-ski* amenities, has become the most popular destination for British skiers. Of these resorts, Val d'Isère, at a height of 1,850 m, receives the greatest number (Figure 13.21). It is popular for several reasons.

- Although winter snowfall is heavy, many days are sunny and the air is clear.
- Chairlifts extend up to 3,600 metres, which means that:
  - the snow is as reliable as anywhere in Europe
  - the ski runs are extremely long and, if required, steep and challenging.
- There are 102 lifts, including two modern high-speed underground funiculars.
- There are 300 km of pistes, many equipped with snow-making machinery, as well as access to many vast off-piste ski-areas.
- The slopes are ideal for all levels of skiing. Experts can ski all day without getting bored, intermediates can find cruising terrain, and beginners can learn on top-quality snow.
- There is one luxury hotel, several bed-and-breakfasts, and a wide range of self-catering chalets.
- The *après-ski* scene is essentially young and vibrant.

**Figure 13.21** Val d'Isère

### Environmental impact

Deforestation of slopes for new and longer ski runs, for new and expanding resorts, and new access roads. This increases the risks of soil erosion and avalanches (page 63).

Skiing on this snow destroys vegetation and the arctic/alpine ecosystem.

Visual pollution from ski-lifts and resorts built on hillsides.

Less snow lower down makes skiers 'climb' higher onto fragile environments at higher altitudes.

Acid rain killing vegetation in Alpine areas has been blamed on the huge increase in traffic.

Congestion on local roads, and problems of parking cars and coaches.

### Community impact

House prices rise and they become too expensive for local people.

Seasonal unemployment – most jobs are limited to the winter skiing season.

Farmers and forestry workers have lost jobs as skiing takes over the area.

The traditional way of life has changed due to increase in traffic and people.

**Figure 13.22** Effects of tourism on a community and its environment

## The effects of ski resorts on the environment and local communities

Skiing has led to an increase in employment and improvements in transport and other services, raised the local standard of living, and reduced the number of young people having to leave the area. However, there have been costs to both the environment and the local community (Figure 13.22).

### Les Ecrins and La Vanoise

Both of these areas have been designated National Parks (Figure 13.18). It was considered that their mountainous landscape and their wildlife (including alpine flora, birds of prey and rare butterflies) were in need of protection against the advance of tourism. The main aim of the park planners is to study planning proposals and to conduct scientific studies.

Les Ecrins has been divided into two zones:

1 The outer park where controlled building and tourism is still allowed and cars are permitted. The park planners have improved footpaths, created information centres and established viewpoints. Camping is restricted to purpose-built caravan and camp sites.

2 The inner park where some tourism is allowed but with stricter controls, e.g. no hunting, no mountain bikes, no fires and no dogs. As the area lacks roads it is only accessible to high-level walkers and paragliders.

The role of the Ecrins Park planners is to try to balance the protection of the environment with local Alpine traditions and the economic potential of tourism.

# National Parks

The ten National Parks of England and Wales were defined by Act of Parliament (1949) as

'areas of great natural beauty giving opportunity for open air recreation, established so that natural beauty can be preserved and enhanced, and so that the enjoyment of the scenery by the public can be promoted'

(Figure 13.23). The Act also created National Park Authorities whose task it is to look after the parks. Two other notable areas with unique features also have special protection, although they are not formally designated as National Parks. These are the Norfolk Broads (page 84), given a status equivalent to a National Park in 1989, and the New Forest, which is managed by the Forestry Commission.

- The parks contain some of the most diverse upland scenery in England and Wales. The Pembrokeshire Coast is an exception, being mainly coastal.
- They provide a wide variety of scenery which in turn offers a range of recreational activities. All the parks provide basic opportunities for walking, riding and fishing, but some offer specialist attractions, e.g. caving and potholing in the limestone areas of the Brecon Beacons and the Peak District (Figure 13.23).
- Most of the land is owned privately, not by the nation (Figure 13.24). Although the parks are run by local committees known as Planning Boards, the government appoints one-third of the committee and funds three-quarters of the running costs. (This is in contrast to Europe where many National Parks are state-owned.)
- The Planning Boards control new building and have to ensure that new buildings use local materials and blend in with the environment. They also have the power to limit industry and to plan any new road very carefully.
- Public access to the parks is encouraged (except in military training areas and on grouse moors) but is restricted to footpaths, bridleways, open fells and mountains.
- People live and work in the National Parks. Most local people are dependent on primary (farming, forestry and quarrying – Figure 13.27) and tertiary (tourism) forms of employment.
- Most parks are within relatively easy access of the major conurbations where huge numbers of people live and work. Since the parks were designated, access has been improved through motorway construction and an increase in car ownership.

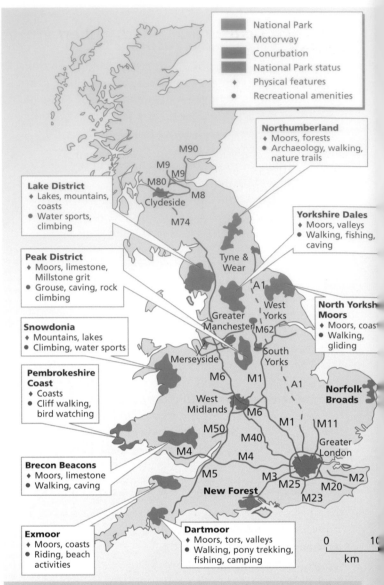

**Figure 13.23** National Parks, conurbations and motorways in the UK

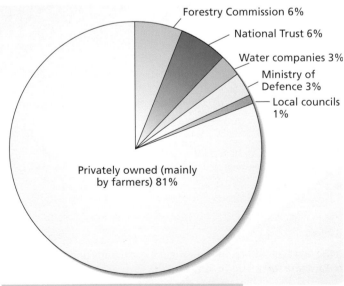

**Figure 13.24** Who owns the National Parks?

## The Lake District and Northumberland National Parks

The Countryside Commission, which 'works to conserve and enhance the beauty of the English countryside and to help people enjoy it' conducted a survey of visitors to all of the National Parks in England and Wales. Just over 50,000 people were interviewed and 15,000 completed a written questionnaire. Although the Lake District and Northumberland Parks came out at different ends of the spectrum (Figure 13.25), visitors to both places claimed that they were attracted there by the park's scenery, landscape, clean air, peace and quiet (Figure 13.26).

**Figure 13.26** Crummock Water, Lake District

| | LAKE DISTRICT | NORTHUMBERLAND |
|---|---|---|
| Visitors in survey year | 22 million | 1.4 million |
| Money spent by visitors | £284 million | £25 million |
| Places visited | Widely spaced | 45% day visitors to Roman Wall (page 179), 80% long-stay visitors |
| Travel to the park | 89% by car | 92% by car |
| % who walked in the park | 26% | 34% |
| Overcrowding and congestion | 24% said overcrowding spoilt their visit, 21% complained of traffic congestion on the way | Only a few complained of overcrowding at one or two sites along the Roman Wall |

**Figure 13.25** The Lake District and Northumberland National Parks: facts and figures

## Conflicts of use within National Parks

With people both living and working in National Parks and large numbers of tourists wishing to visit them, there are bound to be conflicts of interest. Competition for the use of land comes from a variety of sources.

- Farmers want to protect their land and animals, and reduce the number of visitors on their land.
- Urban dwellers wish to use the countryside for recreation and relaxation. These include walkers and climbers who want free access to all parts of the parks, caravanners and campers seeking more sites for overnight stops, and motorists wanting improved roads and car parking.
- The Forestry Commission has planted trees in large areas of the Northumberland (Figure 7.8), Snowdonia and North Yorkshire Moors Parks.
- Water authorities have created reservoirs in most parks (Figure 2.13).
- Quarrying companies obtain rocks from most of the parks. This includes slate from the Lake District and Snowdonia and limestone from the Peak District.
- The Ministry of Defence owns nearly one-quarter of the Northumberland Park.
- Despite planning controls, the demand for housing has led to an increase in the suburbanisation of villages and the use of property as 'second-homes'.
- Nature lovers and conservationists want to create nature reserves and Sites of Special Scientific Interest (SSSIs) to protect wildlife from tourist invasions.

Whether it is a quarry extension, a new caravan camp or a village by-pass planned, there are always several groups of people in favour of the proposal and several groups against it (Figure 13.27). The National Park Planning Boards have to consider all the views before any decision is made.

**Figure 13.27** Jobs or scenery? A quarry in the Peak District National Park

# National parks – traffic and honeypots

## *Traffic*

Any road improvement scheme seems guaranteed to cause controversy. In the case of a National Park, some groups of people want improvements so that they can reach the park more easily and so have more time to enjoy its scenery and amenities. In contrast, other groups want all traffic banned so that the environment will not be spoilt. Figure 13.28 gives some of the possible views of groups of people on a proposal to build a dual-carriageway through a National Park and which would also create a by-pass around a small town.

**FOR**

**The tourist**  With a dual-carriageway the tourist could reach the National Park more quickly, and travel to parks further afield. The tourist could also avoid congestion in the small town, avoid slow-moving heavy lorries and tractors, and could see more of the park in a short time without leaving the car.

**The lorry driver working at the quarry**  Wider roads, gentler gradients and crawler lanes would be created with the construction of a dual-carriageway, and perhaps also a special road which would separate heavy lorries from tourist traffic.

**The industrial firm beyond the National Park**  This firm would be able to get its raw materials faster, and move its manufactured goods out more quickly. It might also save money by reduced transport times. New customers would be attracted, and a bigger market created. This might lead to the growth of a subsidiary industry as executives would be attracted by the environment of the park.

**A retired couple living in the small town**  The by-pass would mean less noise, fewer traffic fumes, and less danger, due to a decrease in traffic.

**The farmer's wife**  There would be more potential bed-and-breakfast guests; surplus farm produce could also be sold.

**The local bus company**  Local services would find it easier to keep to their timetables, and tourist parties could be taken further afield.

**The young married couple**  Travelling to work would be easier.

**AGAINST**

**The shopkeeper in the small town**  Loss in trade would result from there being no through traffic. Local people could also travel more quickly to other towns. Shopkeepers would also find themselves paying rates to help build the new road.

**The farmer**  Increased traffic would mean more noise and more air pollution, and a loss of land because wider roads, car parks and picnic areas would be needed. More visitors would trample on his land, knock down walls and bring dogs which might worry the sheep.

**The conservationist**  Conservationists would object to the new road because they believe noise and fumes destroy wildlife, roads destroy the visual attractiveness of the area, and road verges would be eroded. There would also be an increase in litter.

**The local cycle club**  Greater danger would result from faster traffic, more noise, and traffic fumes.

**The local lorry driver**  There would be an increase in traffic, and lorries might be banned from certain roads.

**The young married couple**  There would be less chance of being able to buy a home, as more commuters could live in the area, and house prices would increase.

**Figure 13.28**  The pros and cons: dealing with traffic in a National Park

In the 1970s a similar scheme was proposed for Keswick in the Lake District. At that time, traffic congestion was a major problem within the town. It was caused not only by local people but also by visitors to the town and drivers of lorries and buses using the A66 between West Cumbria and the M6. Despite tremendous opposition the by-pass was built. It can be seen in Figure 13.29, and between grid squares 2524 and 2823 on the OS map on page 207.

It is now the late 1990s. Keswick is still congested with holiday traffic at peak periods even though long-distance lorries and buses now avoid the town and travel quickly along the by-pass. What do you think may now be the views of the various groups of people originally involved in the controversy? Indeed, what effects do you think the by-pass has had upon the residents of Keswick and their local environment?

**Figure 13.29**  Keswick by-pass

## Honeypots

The National Parks include many of the nation's honeypots. Honeypots can be:

- areas of attractive scenery, such as Malham Cove in the Yorkshire Dales (Figure 13.31)
- places of historic interest such as the Roman Wall in the Northumberland Park (Figure 13.35) and Beatrix Potter's house in the Lake District (Figure 13.32).

They are referred to a 'honeypots' because they are places to which tourists swarm in large numbers. The problem then is how to preserve the honeypots' natural beauty and natural surroundings while providing facilities for the hordes of people who arrive at peak summer periods. Figure 13.30 lists some of the problems created at honeypots and suggests some possible solutions to try to protect and conserve them.

| Problems | Possible solutions |
|---|---|
| Footpaths worn away | New routes planned; signposted routes; artificial surfaces laid |
| Destruction of vegetation | Areas fenced off; education of visitors |
| Litter, vandalism, trespassing | Provision of picnic areas with litter bins; park wardens |
| Cars parked on grass verges or in narrow lanes | Car parks; one-way systems; park-and-ride schemes |
| Congestion on narrow roads | Roads closed to traffic in tourist season/at weekends; park-and-ride; encouragement to use minibuses, to cycle or walk |
| Heavy lorries, local traffic and tourist traffic | Scenic routes separating local and tourist traffic |
| Honeypots (views, cafés) cause crowding | Develop alternative honeypots, direct visitors to other attractions |
| Conflict of users, e.g. local farmers and tourists, and between tourists | Restricting tourist access to footpaths and bridleways; separating activities, e.g. water skiing and angling |
| Unsightly new cafés, car parks and caravan parks | Screened behind trees; only 'natural' colours allowed in paint schemes |

**Figure 13.30** Managing honeypots

**Figure 13.31** Malham Cove

## Japanese honeypots in the Lake District

Although only 3 per cent of tourists visiting Britain are Japanese, in the Lake District they account for between 25 and 30 per cent of visitors. The Japanese have taken to Beatrix Potter, creator of Peter Rabbit, in a big way. They arrive at her former home, 'Hilltop' at Sawrey, by the busload. They are met by signs in English and Japanese advising them where to get afternoon tea and obtain souvenirs. They usually arrive, armed with cameras and camcorders, in groups exceeding thirty people. Because they spend so much money, they are made very welcome by hoteliers and shop owners. However, at Hilltop itself they cause problems by crowding (and sometimes eating) in the garden, blocking the small rooms and narrow hallways, and spending a long time taking photos and walking around the house – often to the irritation of other visitors.

Their numbers are causing concern to the National Trust. A spokesperson for the Trust claimed:

'We are facing a real dilemma. It has got to the stage where the number of visitors at Hilltop is so great that we have to think about the harm they are doing. The last thing we want to do is to put up "House Full" signs or restrict either the numbers or the time spent there. But we are going to have to explain to holiday companies in Japan that most properties in the Lake District are small and cannot cope with coachloads of visitors all arriving at once.'

**Figure 13.32** 'Hilltop', the home of Beatrix Potter

## Sustainable tourism

According to the Government Task Force report of 1991, 'sustainable tourism is about seeking a harmony between the needs of the visitor, the place and the host community. It is tourism which benefits the local economy and local people without diminishing the attractiveness of the place visited.' The concept is relevant to all places whether they are seaside resorts, urban areas or countryside. However, as rural and coastal areas often contain the more sensitive landscapes and smaller human communities, it is here that the impact of tourism is most obvious. Sustainable rural tourism, which will have an increasing influence in the future, involves the following.

1 **Reducing the impact of tourism on the environment** e.g. by adopting practices that save energy and reduce waste and pollution, which discourage the use of the car and which reduce the need to travel great distances.

2 **Maintaining the quality of the local environment** e.g. by restricting the number of visitors, improving footpaths and car parks, promoting tourist activities which provide new economic uses for traditional buildings and other landscape features, and raising visitor awareness of local environmental issues.

3 **Improving the quality of life for the host community** e.g. by providing forms of tourism which create jobs, involving local people in decisions about tourism, and solving problems such as overcrowding and traffic congestion.

4 **Increasing the enjoyment of visitors** e.g. by providing high-quality facilities and information, and encouraging direct contact between visitors and local people so that the former may appreciate rural life.

Figure 13.34 Visitors and wildlife

### The Norfolk Coast

The Norfolk Coast is one of the finest unspoilt natural areas in Britain (page 77). Its vast beaches, sand-dune systems, saltmarshes and wet grasslands attract over half a million visitors a year (Figure 13.33). This number of visitors results in pressures on wildlife and the habitats they live in. Balancing the needs of wildlife and people is a top priority for conservation groups and local authorities involved in the management of this coastline. An aim of the Norfolk Coast Project is to ensure that the quality and variety of habitats and wildlife are not adversely affected and that visitor support for their conservation is maximised. This, it is hoped, will be achieved by giving visitors more information on how special and vulnerable the coast is, for example telling people that the grazing marsh they cross on their way to the beach is home for lapwings and redshanks, the sand-dunes where children play are inhabited by insects and the rare natterjack toad, and along the high-tide mark there may be nests belonging to oystercatchers, ringed plovers and little terns (Figure 13.34).

Figure 13.33 On the North Norfolk coast

## The Roman Wall, Northumberland National Park

Hadrian's Wall, or the Roman Wall, was designated a World Heritage Site by UNESCO in 1987 (Figure 13.7). All such sites must have a comprehensive management plan to protect them – a task which in this case was given to English Heritage. However, English Heritage's proposals to develop the Roman Wall as a tourist attraction have caused much opposition from local landowners through whose land the wall passes. Figure 13.35 summarises some of the arguments put forward by the opposing groups in 1996.

**Figure 13.35** Conflict on the Roman Wall

### The landowners

Landowners are anxious to water down plans to further develop the wall as a tourist attraction. They are determined to prevent the imposition of stricter rules on the way they run their farms and rural businesses. Julian Acton, whose 200 hectare farm includes Housesteads, the most visited stretch of the wall, claims: 'Visitor centres are all very well, but you cannot have many more tourists on the wall itself without increasing erosion. Numbers will have to be controlled somehow. No one wants to see Hadrian's Wall go the same way as Stonehenge – fenced off and with public access forbidden. But nor does anyone want to see it suffer from trampling feet, as has happened in parts of the Lake District and along the Pennine Way.' Landowners also fear more car parks will be needed, more access points to the wall created and, worst of all, more people and their dogs walking on important sheep-grazing land.

### English Heritage

English Heritage sees the wall as an important part of Britain's history. As such it wants to encourage more people to visit the wall both to enjoy the landscape and to learn of our past. Dr Christopher Young, English Heritage's director for Hadrian's Wall, thinks the wall can cope. 'If we get the access of tourists right and can balance that with conservation, we can generate wealth for the region.' Certainly people in favour of the scheme see more jobs being created in visitor and information centres, car parks and souvenir shops as well as an increase in demand for accommodation and eating places. The present volume of traffic could be reduced by using minibuses to ferry visitors from places such as Carlisle and Newcastle upon Tyne.

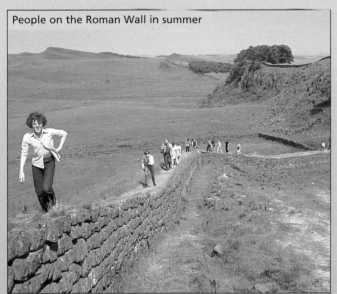
People on the Roman Wall in summer

Along the Wall in spring

### The Roman Wall and sustainable tourism

Having read the conflicting opinions of the landowners and National Heritage (Figure 13.35), go back to the text on page 178 and consider again the four points which suggest how sustainable tourism might be achieved in rural areas. Bearing these in mind, how would you try to develop sustainable tourism along the Roman Wall? Can you produce a plan that will benefit the local economy and people without diminishing the attractiveness and the historical importance of the area?

**1** *(Page 164)*

Look at the information about tourism in the UK.

**a** i) How many tourists were there in 1971?
  ii) How many tourists were there in 1991?
  iii) Describe the trend shown by the first graph.

**b** Use the information in the graphs to explain the growth of tourism.

**c** Describe three other reasons for this growth.

Tourist visits

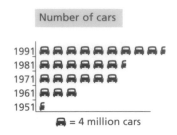

Number of cars

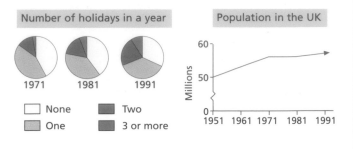

Number of holidays in a year | Population in the UK

**2** *(Pages 166 and 167)*

**a** Look carefully at the map.
  i) Which of the following statements are correct?
   - The UK and Ireland have most departures.
   - Spain and Greece have the most arrivals.
   - Germany and France have most departures.
   - Spain has more departures than Italy.
  ii) Make a list of countries that have:
   - more arrivals than departures
   - more departures than arrivals.
  iii) For each list, make **one** statement about which part of Europe the countries are in.

**b** Suggest why visitors from the north might be attracted to southern Europe for their holidays.

**c** Explain how tourism can affect the economy and employment opportunities of a country.

**3** *(Page 168)*

**a** Study the diagram. In which month of the year was the percentage of accommodation occupied:
  i) at its highest
  ii) at its lowest?
  iii) What was the occupation percentage in July?

**b** Explain why the summer occupation rates may vary from year to year.

**c** i) *Seasonal unemployment* is common in holiday resorts. What is meant by seasonal unemployment, and why does it happen?
  ii) What can resorts do to help reduce the problem of seasonal unemployment?

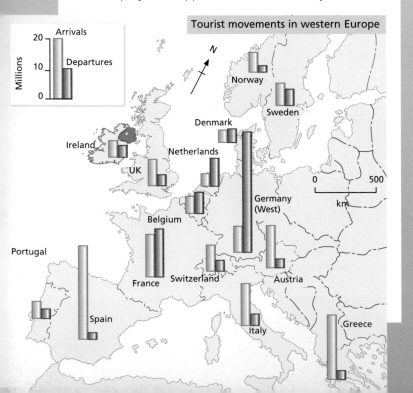

Tourist movements in western Europe

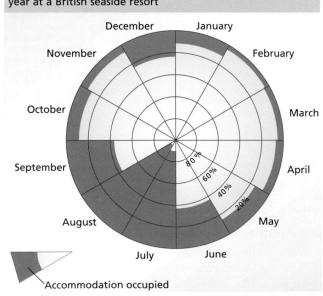

Percentage of the total accommodation occupied during one year at a British seaside resort

**4** *(Pages 167, 170, 171)*

**a** Look carefully at the map.
   i)   Name the non-European country with most visitors to Spain.
   ii)  Name the European country from which most visitors go to Spain.
   iii) Suggest why more visitors come from Portugal than Italy.

**b** Describe the physical and human attractions of Benidorm as a holiday resort.

**c** Benidorm has recently suffered a decline in popularity. Suggest reasons for this.

**d** Describe the action taken by the EU to help support tourism in Europe.

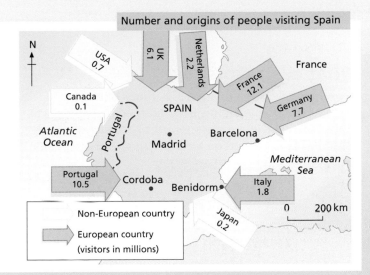

Number and origins of people visiting Spain

Non-European country

European country
(visitors in millions)

0    200 km

---

**5** *(Page 174)*

**a** Look at Figure 13.24 on page 174. Name a National Park for each of the following:
   i)   The park nearest to London.
   ii)  A coastal park in South Wales.
   iii) A park surrounded by motorways and conurbations.
   iv)  The most northerly park.

**b** Suggest why more people visit the Peak District Park than the Pembroke Coast Park.

**6** *(Pages 174 to 179)*

Look at the OS map on page 207 which shows part of the Lake District National Park. Under the headings **a** Physical and **b** Human, list the attractions shown in grid squares 2523, 2623, 2522 and 2622.

**7** *(Page 176)*

Look at the photo on page 176, the OS map on page 207 and the information below.

**a** Suggest how the environment may have been damaged by the building of the by-pass.

**b** For any **four** of the people shown, say if they would be for or against the by-pass. Give reasons for your answer.

**c** Do you think the by-pass should have been built? Give reasons for your answer.

**8** *(Pages 174 to 177)*

National Parks attract many tourists. This may lead to the growth of 'tourist honeypots'.

**a** Explain the meaning of *tourist honeypot*.

**b** Using an example that you have studied, describe a place that has become a honeypot.

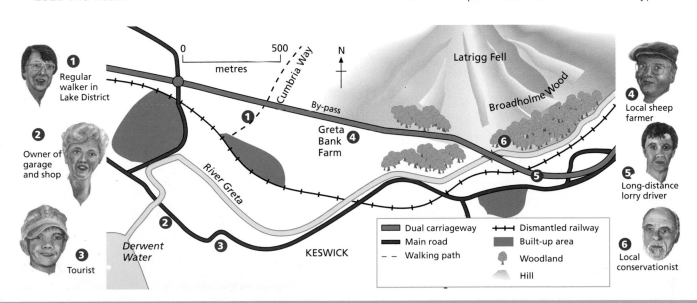

① Regular walker in Lake District
② Owner of garage and shop
③ Tourist
④ Local sheep farmer
⑤ Long-distance lorry driver
⑥ Local conservationist

Latrigg Fell
Broadholme Wood
Cumbria Way
By-pass
Greta Bank Farm
River Greta
Derwent Water
KESWICK

Dual carriageway
Main road
Walking path
Dismantled railway
Built-up area
Woodland
Hill

## What are resources?

Resources have been defined as features of the environment which are needed and used by people. The term is usually taken to mean *natural resources* which occur in air, water and on land. These resources include raw materials (minerals and fuels), climate, vegetation and soils. Sometimes the use of the term is widened (though not in this chapter) to include *human resources* such as labour, skills, machinery and capital (Figure 14.1).

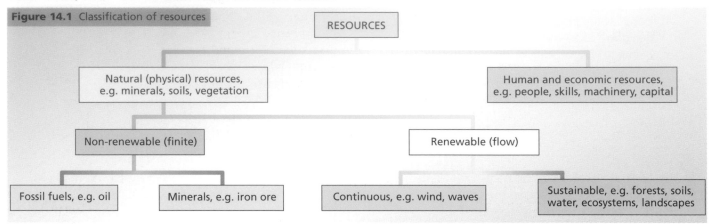

**Figure 14.1** Classification of resources

RESOURCES
- Natural (physical) resources, e.g. minerals, soils, vegetation
  - Non-renewable (finite)
    - Fossil fuels, e.g. oil
    - Minerals, e.g. iron ore
  - Renewable (flow)
    - Continuous, e.g. wind, waves
    - Sustainable, e.g. forests, soils, water, ecosystems, landscapes
- Human and economic resources, e.g. people, skills, machinery, capital

Natural resources are commonly sub-divided into two groups – *non-renewable* and *renewable*. Non-renewable resources are said to be *finite* as their exploitation and use will eventually lead to their exhaustion, e.g. fossil fuels and minerals (Figure 14.2). Renewable resources are a *flow* of nature and so can be used over and over again, e.g. solar energy. However, while some types of renewable resources are continuous, such as the wind and waves, others are said to be *sustainable*. Sustainable resources, which include trees, fish, soils, ecosystems and landscapes, are renewable if left to nature. But if they are used carelessly or are over-used by people then either:

- their value may be reduced, as when soils lose fertility and are eroded (Figure 14.3) or water supplies are polluted
- their existence is threatened, as with over-fishing and deforestation.

## Managing resources

The demand for, and use of, the world's resources continues to grow at an increasingly rapid rate. This is due mainly to:

**Economic development** – the demand for resources increases as more countries try to develop industrially and economically.

**Population growth** – more resources are either used (renewable) or consumed (non-renewable) as the world's population continues to increase.

The combined effects of economic development and population growth means that there is a growing need to manage the earth's resources. Management might be achieved through a range of approaches. These include conservation, recycling, greater efficiency in existing resource use, developing renewable resources, creating alternative resources, controlling pollution and adopting sustainable development (page 200).

**Figure 14.2** A disused slate quarry in Snowdonia

**Figure 14.3** Soil erosion in south-east England

Total for the EU15
countries (%)
Renewable 4.0

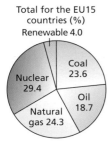

Individual countries
1993 (%)

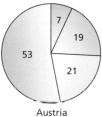

Austria

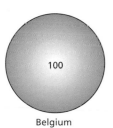

Belgium

Denmark

Finland

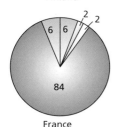

France

## Energy resources

The sun is the primary source of the earth's energy. Without energy, nothing can live and no work can be done. Green plants convert the sun's energy into a form that can be used by people.

### Non-renewable resources

Coal, oil and natural gas account for two-thirds of the sources of energy produced in the fifteen EU countries (Figure 14.4). They are forms of stored solar energy produced by photosynthesis in plants over thousands of years. As these three sources of energy, which are referred to as *fossil fuels*, take such long periods of time to form and to be replaced, they are regarded as non-renewable. In other words, they can only be used once and so, in time, their supply will run out. Fossil fuels have been relatively easy to obtain and cheap to use, but they have become major polluters of the environment. This is mainly because, when they are used, carbon from the former plants is released into the atmosphere. As carbon dioxide it is a major contributor to global warming.

Nuclear energy is a fourth non-renewable source of energy but it uses uranium and so is not a fossil fuel.

### Renewable (alternative) resources

Renewable sources of energy are mainly forces of nature which can be used over and over again. As they can be used continually and will not run out, they are said to be sustainable. Renewable energy resources include the sun (solar), running water (hydro-electricity), wind, waves, tides, heat from the earth (geothermal) and vegetation (biomass). At present, renewable energy accounts for only 4 per cent of the sources of energy produced by the EU15 (Figure 14.4). Apart from hydro-electricity, there are economic and technical problems in converting these potential energy sources into forms which can be used on a large scale. However, in time the world will have to look more to these resources as the supply of fossil fuels runs out.

UK

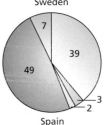

Sweden

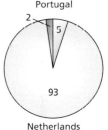

Spain

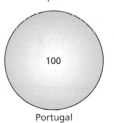

Portugal

Netherlands

Luxembourg

Germany

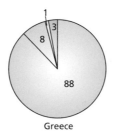

Greece

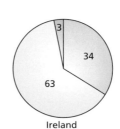

Ireland

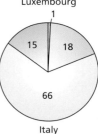

Italy

**Figure 14.4** Production of energy in the EU15, 1993

# Mining and quarrying

The extraction of rocks and minerals has been important since the earliest of human civilisations. In western Europe the Stone Age, when flint was excavated from chalk pits, was followed by the Bronze Age and the Iron Age. The modern world depends upon 80 major minerals extracted from the earth. Minerals are a finite, non-renewable resource. Although none is likely to run out in the near future, those easiest to mine or quarry have often already been used up.

Minerals can be obtained by:

- **Open-cast mining** where the vegetation and topsoil are removed to expose the mineral. Sand and gravel, for example, are extracted from shallow hollows, and coal by giant excavators from deeper depressions (Figure 14.9).
- **Quarrying** into hillsides to obtain harder rocks such as limestone (Figure 13.28) and slate (Figure 14.2).
- **Mining** where workers have to operate underground.

Extractive industries provide local jobs and create national wealth but, as shown in Figure 14.5, often at considerable cost to the local environment and to local communities.

**Figure 14.5** Effects of mining and quarrying on the environment and on local communities

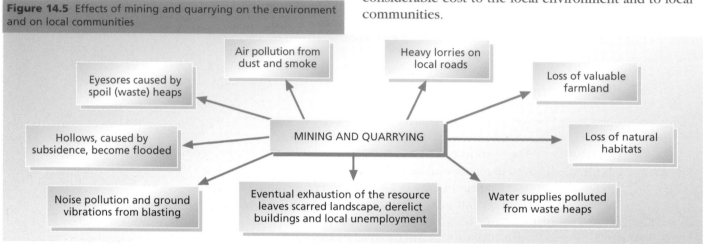

Air pollution from dust and smoke

Heavy lorries on local roads

Eyesores caused by spoil (waste) heaps

Loss of valuable farmland

Hollows, caused by subsidence, become flooded

MINING AND QUARRYING

Loss of natural habitats

Noise pollution and ground vibrations from blasting

Eventual exhaustion of the resource leaves scarred landscape, derelict buildings and local unemployment

Water supplies polluted from waste heaps

**Figure 14.6** Location of Kiruna

**Figure 14.7** Kiruna

## Iron ore from northern Sweden

For over a century iron ore has been mined north of the Arctic Circle at Kiruna and Malmberget-Gallivare in northern Sweden (Figure 14.6). It used to be mined by open-cast methods which created a series of large terraces in the side of an iron ore 'mountain' (Figure 14.7). Today the ore is mined underground. The high-quality ore occurs as a deposit 100 metres wide and 4 km long. However, in the Arctic there is a period each winter when the sun does not rise for six weeks and when temperatures can fall to –40°C. The nearby Swedish port of Lulea is frozen for five months each year (Figure 1.26) and so at that time the ore has to be exported via the ice-free Norwegian port of Narvik. Workers demand high wages for operating in such a difficult, isolated environment.

## Lignite mining in North Greece

The Ptolomaida Valley lies in the north of Greece (Figure 14.8). It is a rich farming area due largely to soil washed down from the surrounding mountains. The main crops are vines, cereals and sugar beet. Underneath the topsoil is sand and gravel, and below that is lignite. Lignite is a low-quality coal and is therefore a fossil fuel. The lignite here was formed under lakes, and the rock contains fossils of freshwater shellfish. Estimates suggest that there is enough lignite here to last for another 50 years.

Greece lacks sources of energy and therefore the mining of lignite is a valuable national resource. There are six large open-cast mines in the valley. Once the topsoil, sand and gravel (collectively called the *overburden*) is removed, huge excavators can start removing the lignite. Each excavator, which is longer than a football pitch and dwarfs humans, can move 1,500 tonnes per hour (Figure 14.9). The lignite, once excavated, is transferred to a conveyer belt which takes it to one of four power stations in the valley. The power stations were built nearby as lignite is both bulky and expensive to move.

### Effects on local communities and the environment

#### Disadvantages

- Large areas of good-quality farmland are lost each year as more topsoil is removed. Mining has also lowered the water table (page 41), reducing the amount of water available for irrigation.
- Farmers have been forced to leave their homes, two villages have become 'ghost towns', and several others have lost population and services.

**Figure 14.9** A giant excavator in the Ptolomaida Valley

---

- Huge, unsightly spoil heaps of overburden are created.
- Lignite, when burnt in the power stations, produces large quantities of ash. This has to be sprayed with water to prevent it blowing around. The smoke and dust is a health hazard and many local people have eye, throat and breathing problems.
- Although a new town has been built, it is further away from the mine, so people have further to travel to work. The town lacks the community spirit of the villages it has replaced.

**Figure 14.8** Location of the Ptolomaida Valley

#### Advantages

- The four power stations provide 70 per cent of Greece's electricity – important in a country which lacks alternative sources.
- The income creates wealth in a poor region of both Greece and the EU.
- Displaced farmers are offered jobs with the mining/electricity company. These jobs provide a more secure income and are better paid than farming.
- People forced to move to the new town receive compensation which allows them to live in larger houses with modern amenities.
- The electricity company is beginning to plant trees to reduce the amount of ash and dust blown about and to improve the environment visually.

# Energy resources

## Production and consumption in western Europe

Energy production varies from region to region, and energy consumption is different from country to country. Figure 14.10 shows the main locations in western Europe of the different types of energy, and Figure 14.11 the consumption per person of energy in each country. When you look at indicators of economic development in Chapter 15, you will see that one suggested link with economic development is energy consumption – that is, the more wealthy a country is, the more energy its inhabitants consume. Figure 14.11 shows that economic development tends to decrease from north to south, and confirms that Luxembourg is the most wealthy country in the EU, and that Greece and Portugal are the least wealthy.

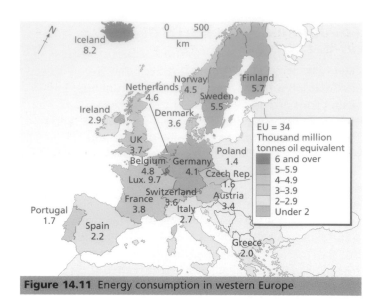

**Figure 14.11** Energy consumption in western Europe

**Figure 14.10** Energy production in western Europe

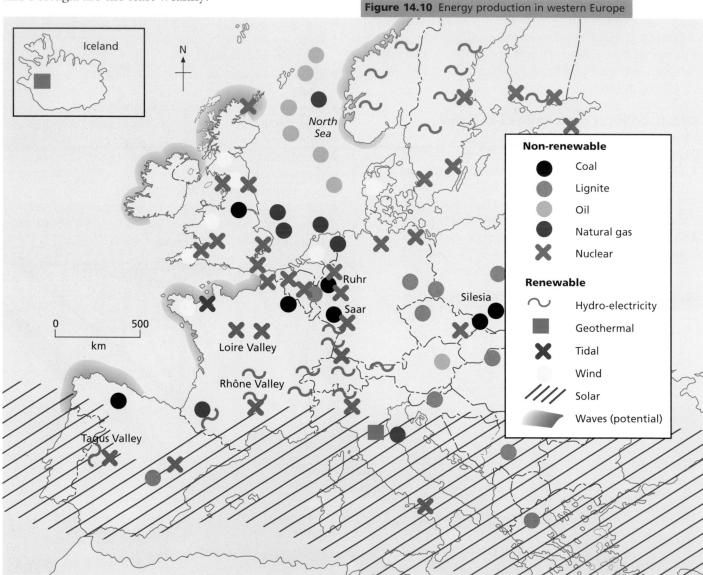

## Advantages and disadvantages of different types of energy

Each type of energy has its advantages and disadvantages. Figure 14.12 summarises the effects on people and on the environment of using each type of energy. It also shows whether each type of energy is relatively cheap or too expensive to produce, and if there is the technology available to develop and use it.

Remember that:
- non-renewable energy resources have a limited life span and often cause pollution, but are relatively cheap and have the technology for use on a large scale
- renewable energy resources have an infinite life span and rarely cause severe pollution, but are usually expensive and lack the technology for use on a large scale.

**Figure 14.12** Advantages and disadvantages of different types of energy

| | Resource | Advantages | Disadvantages |
|---|---|---|---|
| NON-RENEWABLE | Coal (and lignite) | Large reserves likely to last for two or three centuries. Relatively cheap to obtain, with increasingly new technology. Bulky to move. | Dangers of working underground. Most easily obtainable deposits have been used up. Causes air pollution, and a major contributor to global warming. |
| | Oil | More efficient to burn than coal and safer than nuclear. Relatively easy to handle and can be distributed by pipeline or oil tanker. | Limited reserves. Expensive to discover and exploit new fields. Terminals and refineries take up space. Danger of spillage, causing severe environmental pollution, and explosions. |
| | Natural gas | More efficient and cleaner to burn than coal or oil. Relatively easy to transport. Cheapest of the non-renewable resources. | Fairly limited reserves. Expensive to discover and exploit new fields. Terminals take up space. Danger of explosions. |
| | Nuclear | Little raw material (uranium) needed. Reserves far greater than coal, gas or oil. Less waste and less pollution than fossil fuels. | Danger of serious accident. Leaks can contaminate land and seas. Cannot be used for heating or transport. Problem of storing waste. |
| RENEWABLE | Hydro-electricity | Clean source of energy giving off no pollution. Renewable. Cheapest form of energy at present. | Needs a constant supply of fast-flowing water. Needs reservoirs to store water. These can flood large areas of land, forcing people to move. Danger of dams collapsing. |
| | Geothermal | Available in areas of crustal instability. Does not pollute environment. Relatively cheap to obtain. | Stations at risk as in possible earthquake/volcanic areas. Limited to a few areas. Costly to produce. |
| | Tidal | Most costal places experience two tides a day. Does not pollute environment. Safe to use. | No suitable technology yet available to make it economical to use. Limited locations as big tidal range needed. |
| | Wind | Wind is available most of the time, especially in western Europe. Does not pollute environment and is safe. | Winds do not blow all the time or when power is needed. Windmills cause visual pollution and are noisy to people living nearby. Can block local radio/TV reception. |
| | Solar | Sun provides enough energy for everyone on earth. A constant source. Does not pollute environment and is safe. | Ideally needs cloudless conditions. Costly to produce on a big scale. High costs needed to convert energy – insufficient technology. |
| | Waves | Numerous in coastal areas of western Europe. Does not pollute environment. Each wave possesses much energy – even more during storms. | No technology yet available to utilise wave energy. Equipment likely to be damaged in winter storms. Likely to be expensive to produce. |
| | Biomass and biogas | Available from crops such as sugar cane and maize, and other plants, animals wastes and waste tips. Cheap source material. | Expensive to use fermenting equipment. Uses crops originally grown for eating. Can give off methane, a greenhouse gas. |

# Economic gain or environmental loss?

## The Sullom Voe oil terminal

The Shetland Islands were an isolated and sparsely populated area until the discovery of North Sea oil. With the building of an oil terminal, it was hoped that the economic gains would not cause the same environmental losses that the copper and zinc smelting areas of the lower Swansea Valley experienced (page 153).

Sullom Voe (Figure 14.13) was chosen because of its:
- nearness to the North Sea oilfields
- deep inshore waters leading to the even deeper fiord-type Yell Sound
- relative shelter in a gale-prone area
- sparsely populated hinterland
- moraine and peat soils which were easily excavated for the terminal and the associated new power station.

The terminal is a receiving and despatch centre. Oil comes via two pipelines from the Brent and Ninian fields. It is here that the oil is separated from any water and gas before being sent by tanker to refineries on the British mainland. The terminal was designed to take the environment into full consideration (Figure 14.14). Every effort has been made to try to avoid:
- any oil spillage (though should this occur a full containment plan can quickly be introduced)
- ruining the natural scenery and wildlife.

**Economic gain** Jobs have been created at the terminal, at the power station and in support industries. Most of these jobs pay far more and provide greater security than traditional jobs in knitwear (using local Shetland wool), farming (crofting) and fishing. The airport at Sumburgh has been enlarged and modernised.

**Social gain** The extra wealth, and an increase in the Shetland population, have enabled improvements to be made in the service sector, i.e. education, health, retailing and entertainment. With better job prospects, higher salaries and more service provision there is less need for younger people to move to mainland Britain.

**Environmental loss** Despite efforts by the oil companies, the terminal does create some noise and air pollution and is a visual eyesore. But of greater concern are the potential threats of:
- an explosion and subsequent fire like the one on the Piper Alpha oil-rig in the North Sea in 1988
- oil spillage either from a broken pipeline from the North Sea fields or from a fully laden tanker running aground as happened at Milford Haven in 1996.

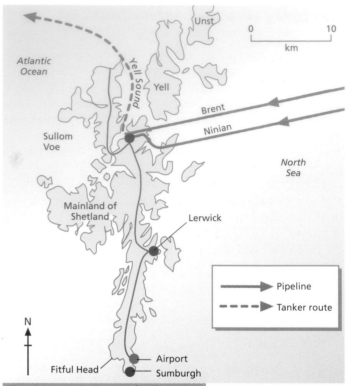

**Figure 14.13** Location of Sullom Voe

Although Sullom Voe is sheltered from the worst of the weather and has the latest radar technology, it is still closed, on average, 50 days a year due to fog and gales.

The Shetland islanders' worst fears were realised on 5 January 1993, although the cause of the disaster had nothing to do with the British oil industry and did not occur at Sullom Voe.

**Figure 14.14** Sullom Voe oil terminal

## The Braer disaster, 1993

'So it's finally happened. No one who lives here is surprised by the disaster. Probably the only surprise is that the tanker was not coming in or out of Sullom Voe, but was a passer-by – one of many – and that the spill happened in the Ness rather than further north.'

*The Shetland Times*, 8 January 1993

The weather conditions and events which caused the *Braer* oiltanker, en route from Norway to Canada, to run aground near Fitful Sound on 5 January (Figure 2.1) and to break up five days later (Figure 2.2) have already been described (pages 18 and 19). Figure 14.15 describes some aspects of the islands' natural environment, and Figure 14.16 some of the effects of the event on the local environment, people and economy.

Fortunately, the storm-force winds and their mountainous waves crashed the sea against rocks and the cliff coastline. The light crude oil was rapidly emulsified and broken down into small droplets which were dispersed naturally. The impact was far less than predicted. Within days most of the coastline was clear of oil and the otters seemed unaffected. By the end of April fresh grass had grown on the sixteen affected farms and scientists believed the sea to be safe enough to continue fishing, except for shellfish. Attempts were later made to ban tankers from taking the short cut to the south of Shetland. What is still unknown, however, are possible unnoticed long-term effects.

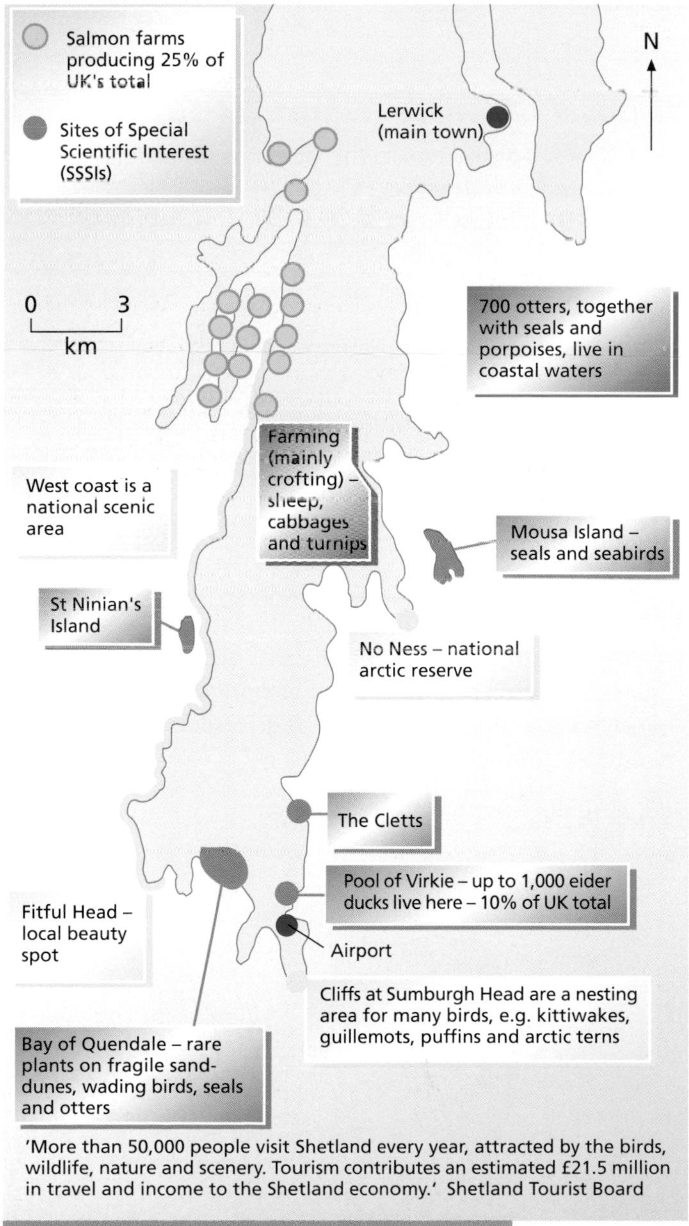

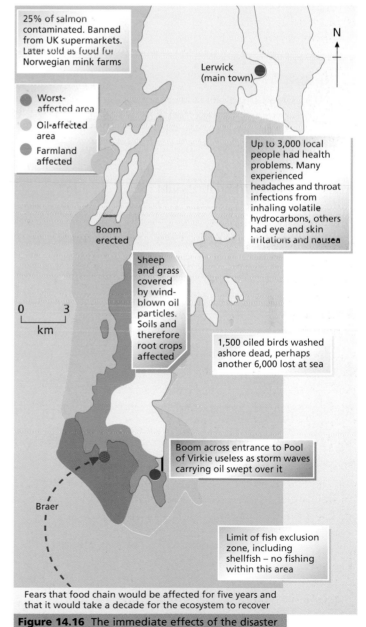

**Figure 14.15** Shetland before the *Braer* disaster

Salmon farms producing 25% of UK's total

Sites of Special Scientific Interest (SSSIs)

Lerwick (main town)

N

0    3 km

700 otters, together with seals and porpoises, live in coastal waters

Farming (mainly crofting) – sheep, cabbages and turnips

Mousa Island – seals and seabirds

West coast is a national scenic area

St Ninian's Island

No Ness – national arctic reserve

The Cletts

Pool of Virkie – up to 1,000 eider ducks live here – 10% of UK total

Fitful Head – local beauty spot

Airport

Cliffs at Sumburgh Head are a nesting area for many birds, e.g. kittiwakes, guillemots, puffins and arctic terns

Bay of Quendale – rare plants on fragile sand-dunes, wading birds, seals and otters

'More than 50,000 people visit Shetland every year, attracted by the birds, wildlife, nature and scenery. Tourism contributes an estimated £21.5 million in travel and income to the Shetland economy.' Shetland Tourist Board

**Figure 14.16** The immediate effects of the disaster

25% of salmon contaminated. Banned from UK supermarkets. Later sold as food for Norwegian mink farms

N

Lerwick (main town)

Worst-affected area

Oil-affected area

Farmland affected

Up to 3,000 local people had health problems. Many experienced headaches and throat infections from inhaling volatile hydrocarbons, others had eye and skin irritations and nausea

Boom erected

Sheep and grass covered by wind-blown oil particles. Soils and therefore root crops affected

0    3 km

1,500 oiled birds washed ashore dead, perhaps another 6,000 lost at sea

Braer

Boom across entrance to Pool of Virkie useless as storm waves carrying oil swept over it

Limit of fish exclusion zone, including shellfish – no fishing within this area

Fears that food chain would be affected for five years and that it would take a decade for the ecosystem to recover

# Waste material

Around 400 million tonnes of waste are produced each year in the UK. Reliable estimates are difficult to obtain as very little waste is actually weighed and data is not updated annually. Bearing this in mind, the latest available information (early 1990s) is given in Figure 14.17. The graph also shows that only about one-third of the total waste is controlled by a Government Act.

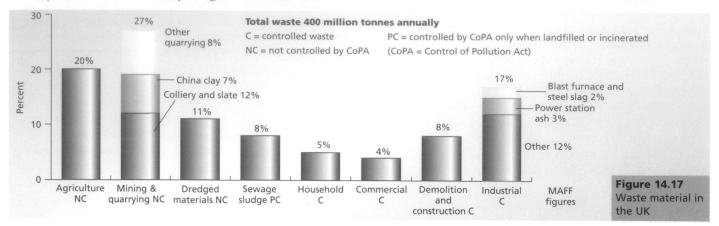

**Figure 14.17** Waste material in the UK

## Types of waste

**Controlled**
- Household and commercial.
- Demolition and construction, e.g. building materials and planed asphalt road surfaces.
- Industrial – mainly from power stations but also slag from steelworks, organic chemicals and heavy metals.
- Special (hazardous) waste – about 0.5 per cent of total waste is defined as 'dangerous to life'.

**Partly controlled**
Sewage sludge (partly treated raw sewage) disposed of in landfill sites or incinerated is controlled, but not when it is disposed of at sea or used in agriculture.

**Uncontrolled**
- Agricultural – mainly excreta from animals.
- Mining and quarrying – e.g. coalmining spoil, china clay and slate waste.
- Dredged materials – mainly dumped at sea (phased out by 1998).

## Disposal of waste (Figure 14.18)

The UK is self-sufficient in the disposal of waste. This is achieved in several ways.

- **Landfill** accounts for the disposal of most of the controlled waste and 70 per cent of special waste. It includes the disposal of most sewage sludge (Figure 14.19). Despite strict controls, there is always the risk of some sludge being leached out of landfill sites and into water supplies, and biodegradable material giving off methane – a greenhouse gas.
- Incineration accounts for a small percentage, mainly from clinical (hospital) sources.
- Sewage sludge, which contains nutrients, is often used to improve soil fertility. The rest is either released into rivers or, until 1998, deposited at sea.
- Recycling could account for half of the UK's domestic waste. At present only 5 per cent, mainly paper and glass, is recovered. Recycling also includes the use of agricultural waste as manure and fertiliser.

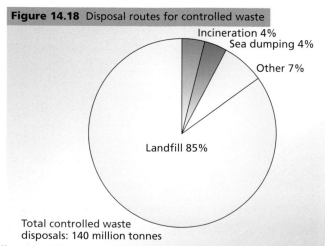

**Figure 14.18** Disposal routes for controlled waste

Total controlled waste disposals: 140 million tonnes

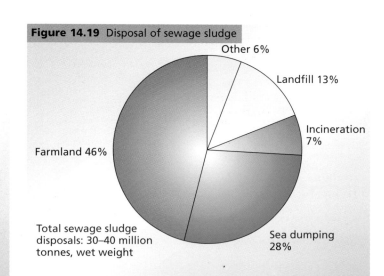

**Figure 14.19** Disposal of sewage sludge

Total sewage sludge disposals: 30–40 million tonnes, wet weight

## Special (hazardous) waste

Special waste includes toxic, ignitable, corrosive, explosive, oily, irritant and other dangerously active materials. A major environmental and health problem is how to store, or safely dispose of, these wastes (Figure 14.20). They include arsenic, mercury, paint sludge, detergents, residues from metal plating industries (Figure 12.15), microchip degreasing agents (from modern high-tech industries) and especially those from the nuclear industry. The leakage of these wastes has been linked with various cancers, birth defects and miscarriages, brain damage, and blood and nervous disorders.

Three current methods of disposing of special waste in the UK are:

1 Sealing waste in drums which can then be stored. However, the drums are not always labelled and may,

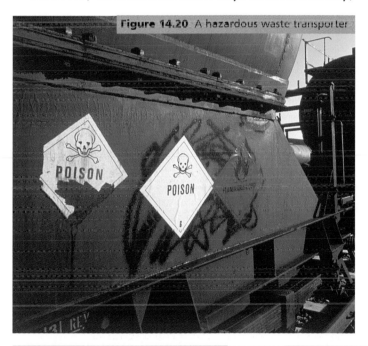

**Figure 14.20** A hazardous waste transporter

at a later date, explode or corrode allowing the contents to spill out. In 1990 unlabelled drums washed ashore at Brighton were found to contain lethal poisons.

2 Using landfill sites: this may prove to be of short-term economic advantage but can create longer-term environmental damage if material is leached out.

3 Incineration: this can, if not supervised, release toxic gases into the air.

## Nuclear waste

Most radioactive waste comes from the production of nuclear energy for electricity. The remainder comes from the production of nuclear weapons, medical use and research, radio-isotopes, and the dismantling of old nuclear power stations and submarines.

Every radioactive substance has a 'half-life'. This is the time needed for half its initial radioactivity to die away. Iodine, with a half-life of eight days, becomes 'safe' relatively quickly. In contrast, plutonium 239, produced by nuclear reactors, has a half-life of 250,000 years (it is still lethal after half a million years), and uranium 238 a half-life of 2.4 million years.

Figure 14.21 shows how radioactive waste can be divided into three types based upon the level of radioactivity and the half-life. The transport of nuclear waste to Sellafield in Cumbria and its subsequent reprocessing is highly controversial. Opponents claim it is dangerous and unsafe, is responsible for high rates of leukaemia among local children, and has polluted the Irish Sea killing marine life and making Cumbrian beaches unsafe. Supporters argue that there is no proven link with leukaemia, that the industry is the major source of employment in an area traditionally known for its high unemployment, brings in wealth for the UK and does not contribute to global warming.

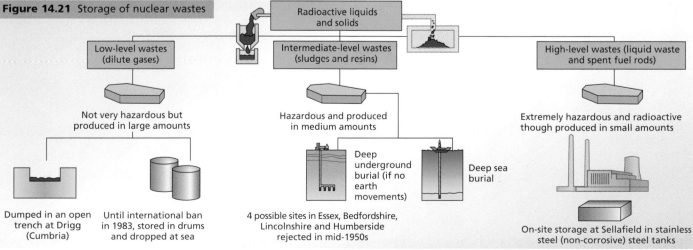

**Figure 14.21** Storage of nuclear wastes

Radioactive liquids and solids

Low-level wastes (dilute gases) — Not very hazardous but produced in large amounts — Dumped in an open trench at Drigg (Cumbria) / Until international ban in 1983, stored in drums and dropped at sea

Intermediate-level wastes (sludges and resins) — Hazardous and produced in medium amounts — Deep underground burial (if no earth movements) / Deep sea burial — 4 possible sites in Essex, Bedfordshire, Lincolnshire and Humberside rejected in mid-1950s

High-level wastes (liquid waste and spent fuel rods) — Extremely hazardous and radioactive though produced in small amounts — On-site storage at Sellafield in stainless steel (non-corrosive) steel tanks

## 1 (Pages 182, 183, 187)

**a** Give the meaning of the following terms.
i) Resources
ii) Natural resources
iii) Human resources
iv) Renewable (sustainable) resources
v) Non-renewable (finite) resources

**b** Look at the drawings below.
i) Name the fuel or energy source in each drawing.
ii) Which of the resources are renewable?
iii) Name one other source of •renewable energy and •non-renewable energy.

**c** The need for resources is growing very rapidly. Suggest two reasons for this.

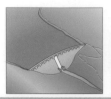     

## 2 (Page 187)

**a** Look at the graph.
i) Which country *produced* most energy?
ii) Which country *used* most energy?
iii) How much energy did the UK use?
iv) Which country or countries have an energy surplus?
v) Which country has the greatest energy deficit?

**b** Explain why economic growth is difficult for countries that produce less energy than they use.

Energy produced and used in some EU countries, 1993

## 3 (Pages 184 and 185)

**a** Lignite mining in northern Greece has brought many benefits but it has also caused problems.
i) List the benefits of mining under the headings:
   * Local      * National.
ii) Describe the problems under the headings:
   * Human   * Environmental.

**b** Look carefully at the drawing below.
i) Briefly describe what needs to be done to restore the land after a mine or quarry has closed.
ii) Suggest two uses for areas that have been restored after mining or quarrying.

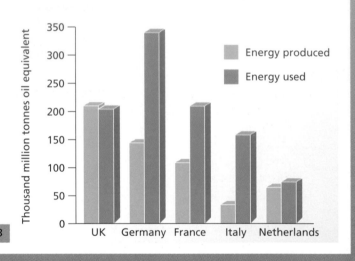

## 4 *(Pages 182, 183, 187)*

**a** Look at the drawings of energy sources in question 1.

   i) Choose any one *non-renewable* resource and give its advantages and disadvantages.

   ii) Choose any one *renewable* resource and give its advantages and disadvantages.

**b** Study the cartoon, which was part of a newspaper advertisement.

   i) Explain why decisions to build nuclear power stations may lead to *protests* from people.

   ii) Make a list of the factors that could be used on an advertisement *supporting* nuclear power.

## 5 *(Pages 182, 183, 187)*

**a** Give two advantages and two disadvantages of using the power of the wind to make electricity.

**b** Study the sketch map, which shows four possible sites for a wind farm in a coastal area of the UK.

   i) Match locations (Z) (X) (Y) and (Z) on the map, with the following advantages.
   (Some sites may be used more than once.)

   ^ Away from main settlements.
   * Near existing industry.
   * In a windy location.
   * Accessible by road.

   ii) Give a disadvantage for each location.

**c** Which of the four sites, (Z) (X) (Y) or (Z) do you think would be the best location for a wind farm? Give reasons for your answer.

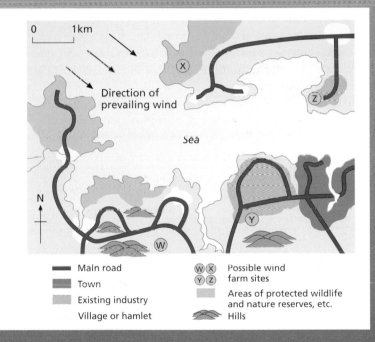

## 6 *(Pages 184, 185, 188, 189)*

Look at the information which shows how economic activities such as the oil industry can bring many benefits but may also cause problems. For the oil industry at Sullom Voe:

**a** describe why Sullom Voe was chosen

**b** explain what benefits it brings

**c** say what problems there might be

   i) for the local community

   ii) for the environment

**d** suggest how these problems might be reduced.

**NIGHTMARE!**
Wildlife faces disaster as 22 million gallons of oil gush into the sea off Shetland

**MASSIVE OIL SLICK THREATENS WILDLIFE**

**Haven for seabirds faces black tide of death**

*Jobs bonanza hits Scotland's far north*

Shetland Oil – Better Jobs, Better Pay, Better Life

Braer disaster – "no longer a problem"

Fishermen in massive compensation claim

**BLACK DEATH IS HERE AGAIN**

# 15 DEVELOPMENT

## Employment structures

### Classification of industries

Traditionally, industry has been broken down into the three groups of *primary*, *secondary* and *tertiary* although, since the 1980s, *quaternary* has been added as a fourth group (Figure 15.1).

- **Primary** industries extract raw materials directly from the earth or sea. Examples are farming, fishing, forestry and mining.
- **Secondary** industries process and manufacture the primary products (e.g. steelmaking, furniture making and shipbuilding). They include the construction industry and the assembly of components made by other secondary industries (e.g. car assembly).
- **Tertiary** industries provide a service. These include health, education, office work, transport, retailing and entertainment.
- **Quaternary** industries provide information and expertise. The new micro-electronics industries fall into this category.

Employment structures can be shown by three different types of graph. In each case the employment figures for the primary, secondary and tertiary sectors have to be converted into percentages.

**Figure 15.1** Classification of industries

### 1 Pie graphs

Figure 15.2 gives the employment structures for the UK and shows how they have changed *over a period of time*. Two hundred years ago, before accurate figures were available, most working people in Britain were engaged in the primary sector. At the beginning of the twentieth century most people found employment in the secondary sector, while today most people work within the tertiary (service) sector.

Employment structures can also be used to show changes *between places*. Figure 15.3 shows regional employment in Italy. Notice how people employed in primary activities increase towards the south of the country, and people employed in secondary industries increase towards the north. The proportion engaged in the tertiary sector is more evenly spread across the country, with a peak in the region that includes the capital city of Rome.

Usually there is a link between employment structures and levels of economic development (page 197). Generally it is places, either regions or countries, with a higher percentage in secondary and tertiary activities that are considered to be the more economically developed, and those with a higher proportion in primary activities that are regarded as economically less developed.

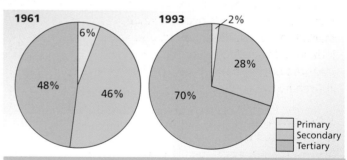

**Figure 15.2** Changing employment structures in the UK

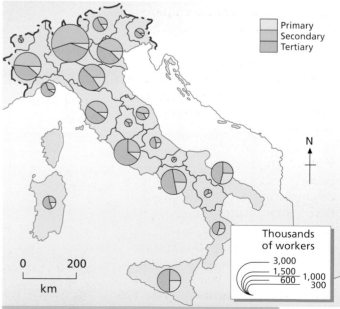

**Figure 15.3** Regional employment structures in Italy

## 2 Triangular graphs

A triangular graph is an equilateral triangle with each of the three 'bases' divided into percentage scales. Each base represents one of the three variables of primary, secondary and tertiary industries. It is convenient, though not essential, to make the sides of the triangle 10 cm long (so that 1 cm = 10%).

Figure 15.4 shows how the three variables are plotted to show the employment structure of Town A. The figure for the primary sector is found by using the left-hand scale (see the green graph), for secondary industries by using the right-hand scale (blue graph) and for tertiary industries the base (orange graph). The answer for Town A is given underneath the graph. Try to complete the table for Towns B and C. These three towns represent, but not necessarily in this order, a small market town, a holiday resort, and an industrial town. Match the figures with the appropriate letter (and be able to justify your answer).

## 3 Percentage bar graphs

A percentage bar graph is a horizontal bar, again ideally drawn 10 cm long. The bar is then divided into three, to show the percentage of the working population employed in each of the primary, secondary and tertiary sectors.

Figure 15.5 shows the employment structures for European countries. The countries have been ranked according to the proportion of people engaged in the primary sector. Remember that countries with a high proportion in the primary sector are more likely to be economically less developed and to have a lower standard of living than those countries with a low proportion in that sector. You will be able to see how accurate this statement is when you look at the GNP of these countries on page 196.

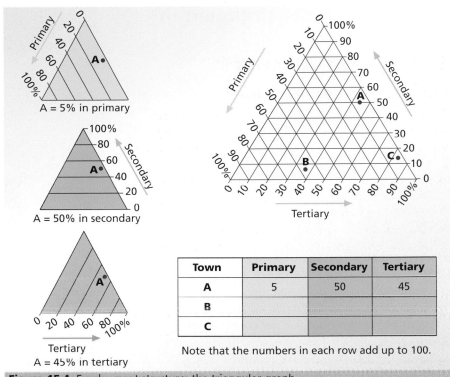

| Town | Primary | Secondary | Tertiary |
|---|---|---|---|
| A | 5 | 50 | 45 |
| B | | | |
| C | | | |

Note that the numbers in each row add up to 100.

**Figure 15.4** Employment structure: the triangular graph

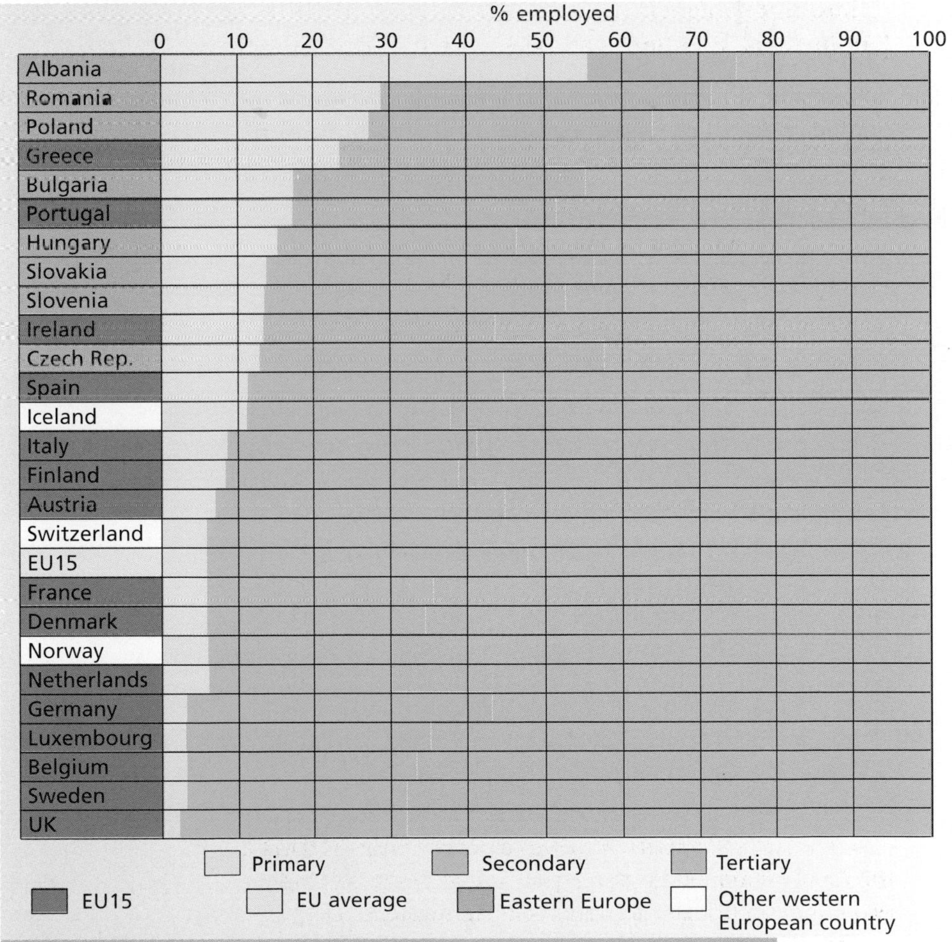

**Figure 15.5** Employment structures in Europe, 1993: percentage bar graph

# Differences in development in Europe

Development means growth. Geographers are interested in differences in levels of development and rates of growth between places across the world and within a continent or a country. However, it is difficult to find an acceptable and accurate method of measuring levels of development. The traditional and easiest method is to compare wealth. The wealth of a country is measured by its *gross national product per capita* – that is, its *GNP per person*. The GNP per capita is the total value of goods produced and services provided by a country in a year, divided by the total number of people living in that country. To make comparisons between countries easier, GNP is given in US dollars (US$). Countries with a high GNP are said to be *economically more developed*, and countries with a low GNP are *economically less developed*.

Figure 15.6 gives the GNP for countries in western Europe. It shows, for example, that in 1993 every person in the UK would have received US$ 17,970 if the wealth had been shared out evenly (the figure for 1990 was US$ 14,570). GNP does not, however, show differences in wealth between people and regions within a country.

Wealth is not the only way to measure development. A range of social measures can be used which measure human welfare, and differences in standards of living and quality of life between people and places. Several of these social measures can be grouped under population (Figure 15.7).

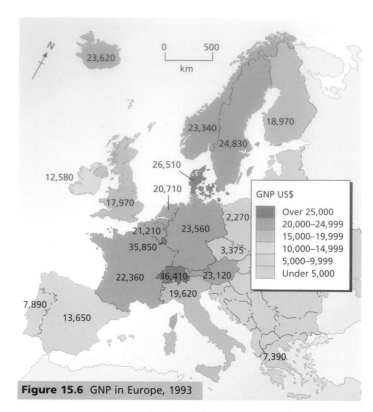

**Figure 15.6** GNP in Europe, 1993

**Figure 15.7** Population indicators in Europe, 1993

| Rank | Birth rate per 1,000 | | Death rate per 1,000 | | Infant mortality per 1,000 | | Life expectancy male/female | | Natural increase % | | % under 15 | | % over 60 | |
|---|---|---|---|---|---|---|---|---|---|---|---|---|---|---|
| 1 | Italy | 9.4 | Iceland | 6.6 | Finland | 4.4 | Iceland | 75/81 | Germany | −1.2 | Switz. | 16 | Sweden | 23 |
| 2 | Spain | 9.7 | Spain | 8.7 | Iceland | 4.8 | Sweden | 75/81 | Italy | −0.1 | Germany | 16 | UK | 21 |
| 3 | Germany | 9.8 | Ireland | 8.9 | Sweden | 4.8 | Switz. | 75/81 | Greece | 0.4 | Austria | 17 | Norway | 21 |
| 4 | Greece | 9.8 | Switz. | 9.0 | Denmark | 5.4 | Norway | 74/81 | Portugal | 0.8 | Denmark | 17 | Belgium | 21 |
| 5 | Portugal | 11.6 | Neth. | 9.0 | Switz. | 5.6 | Neth. | 74/81 | Denmark | 0.9 | Italy | 17 | Austria | 20 |
| 6 | Austria | 11.9 | France | 9.2 | Norway | 5.7 | France | 73/81 | Spain | 1.0 | Lux. | 17 | Denmark | 20 |
| 7 | Belgium | 11.9 | Greece | 9.4 | Germany | 5.8 | Italy | 73/80 | Belgium | 1.3 | Sweden | 17 | Italy | 20 |
| 8 | Switzerland | 12.1 | Italy | 9.5 | Austria | 6.6 | Greece | 74/79 | Austria | 1.6 | Belgium | 18 | Switz. | 20 |
| 9 | France | 12.3 | Lux. | 9.8 | UK | 6.6 | Spain | 73/80 | UK | 1.8 | Neth. | 18 | Greece | 19 |
| 10 | Finland | 12.8 | Finland | 10.2 | Ireland | 6.7 | UK | 73/79 | Sweden | 2.4 | UK | 19 | Lux. | 19 |
| 11 | Neth. | 12.8 | Austria | 10.3 | Neth. | 6.8 | Denmark | 73/79 | France | 2.8 | Norway | 19 | France | 19 |
| 12 | Denmark | 13.0 | Belgium | 10.6 | France | 6.9 | Finland | 72/80 | Finland | 3.1 | Finland | 19 | Finland | 18 |
| 13 | UK | 13.1 | Norway | 10.7 | Spain | 7.6 | Austria | 72/79 | Norway | 3.1 | Greece* | 20 | Portugal | 18 |
| 14 | Sweden | 13.5 | Portugal | 10.8 | Belgium | 8.0 | Belgium | 72/79 | Switz. | 3.2 | Spain | 20 | Spain | 18 |
| 15 | Lux. | 13.6 | Germany | 11.0 | Italy | 8.3 | Ireland | 73/78 | Lux. | 3.8 | France | 20 | Neth. | 17 |
| 16 | Norway | 13.8 | Sweden | 11.1 | Lux. | 8.5 | Lux. | 72/79 | Neth. | 3.8 | Portugal | 21 | Germany | 16 |
| 17 | Ireland | 13.9 | UK | 11.3 | Greece | 8.6 | Germany | 72/78 | Ireland | 4.0 | Iceland | 25 | Iceland | 14 |
| 18 | Iceland | 17.6 | Denmark | 12.1 | Portugal | 8.7 | Portugal | 71/78 | Iceland | 11.0 | Ireland | 28 | Ireland | 14 |

In general, countries that are economically more developed have lower birth, death and infant mortality rates, a longer life expectancy, a lower natural increase, a lower proportion aged under 15 and a higher proportion aged over 65 than countries that are economically less developed (pages 90–95).

Other social measures of development are given in Figure 15.8. Notice, however, that many of these indicators are themselves dependent upon the wealth of a country. For example, the more wealthy, and therefore more economically developed, a country is, the smaller the proportion of its population in agriculture (with more in services), the higher its energy consumption, the higher its level of urbanisation, the greater its car and TV ownership (material goods), the fewer of its population per doctor (better health care), and the higher its adult literacy rate (better education).

In 1990, the United Nations replaced GNP with the *Human Development Index (HDI)*. The HDI is a social welfare index measuring the adult literacy rate (education), life expectancy (health) and real GNP per person – that is, what an income will actually buy in a country (economic). The HDI for European countries (1992) is given in Figure 15.9. The HDI can also be used to show differences in development within a country.

**Figure 15.9** HDI in Europe, 1993

HDI
- Over 0.930
- 0.920–0.929
- 0.910–0.919
- 0.900–0.909
- 0.890–0.899
- Under 0.890

**Figure 15.8** Social indicators in Europe

| Rank | % in agriculture | | Energy consumption* | | % living in urban areas per 1,000 | | Car ownership per 1,000 | | TV ownership per 1,000 | | Population per doctor | | Adult literacy rate % | |
|---|---|---|---|---|---|---|---|---|---|---|---|---|---|---|
| 1 | UK | 2 | Lux. | 14.0 | Belgium | 97 | Germany | 320 | Germany | 558 | Italy | 211 | | |
| 2 | Belgium | 3 | Neth. | 7.1 | Iceland | 91 | Italy | 295 | Denmark | 537 | Austria | 230 | | |
| 3 | Lux. | 3 | Sweden | 6.9 | UK | 89 | France | 240 | Finland | 504 | Denmark | 250 | | |
| 4 | Germany | 4 | Belgium | 6.8 | Neth. | 89 | UK | 219 | Neth. | 489 | Spain | 262 | | |
| 5 | Neth. | 4 | Norway | 6.7 | Lux. | 88 | Spain | 125 | Austria | 476 | Belgium | 298 | | |
| 6 | Sweden | 4 | Finland | 6.6 | Germany | 86 | Neth. | 57 | Sweden | 470 | UK | 300 | | |
| 7 | Denmark | 5 | Iceland | 6.2 | Denmark | 86 | Belgium | 40 | Belgium | 452 | Norway | 309 | | 99 |
| 8 | France | 5 | Germany | 5.9 | Sweden | 83 | Sweden | 36 | UK | 435 | Greece | 313 | | |
| 9 | Norway | 6 | France | 5.4 | Spain | 76 | Austria | 33 | Italy | 429 | France | 333 | | |
| 10 | Switz. | 6 | UK | 5.4 | Norway | 74 | Switz. | 31 | Norway | 426 | Portugal | 352 | | |
| 11 | Austria | 7 | Switz. | 4.9 | France | 73 | Portugal | 30 | France | 408 | Germany | 370 | | |
| 12 | Italy | 7 | Denmark | 4.6 | Italy | 67 | Finland | 19 | Switz. | 405 | Sweden | 395 | | |
| 13 | Finland | 9 | Austria | 4.2 | Greece | 64 | Greece | 18 | Spain | 402 | Neth. | 398 | | |
| 14 | Spain | 10 | Italy | 4.1 | Finland | 62 | Norway | 16 | Iceland | 320 | Finland | 405 | | |
| 15 | Iceland | 11 | Ireland | 4.0 | Switz. | 60 | Denmark | 15 | Ireland | 300 | Iceland | 425 | Spain | 98 |
| 16 | Portugal | 12 | Greece | 3.2 | Ireland | 57 | Ireland | 9 | Lux. | 260 | Lux. | 500 | Italy | 97 |
| 17 | Ireland | 14 | Spain | 3.1 | Austria | 55 | Lux. | 2 | Greece | 200 | Switz. | 585 | Greece | 94 |
| 18 | Greece | 21 | Portugal | 2.1 | Portugal | 34 | Iceland | 1 | Portugal | 189 | Ireland | 633 | Portugal | 86 |

*tonnes oil equivalent per person

## Differences in regional development in Europe

We have already seen that wealth and economic development differ from one country to another (Figure 15.9) and that wealth is not evenly spread across individual countries. Figure 15.10 shows the standard of living within the various European regions. Note especially:

- the differences within such countries as Italy, France, Germany and the UK
- the concentration of most of the more wealthy regions towards the centre
- the isolation of the poorest regions on the edges of the EU.

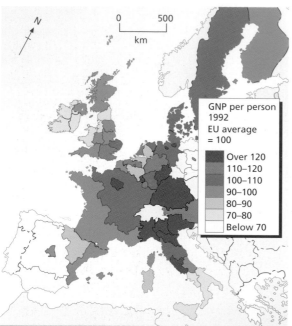

**Figure 15.10** Regional differences in the standard of living in the EU, 1992

### Core–periphery

The most prosperous part of the EU, or an individual country, can be referred to as the *core*. The core usually contains the major cities, industrial areas and ports. As this provides a large local market, it will attract other industries and services such as banking and insurance. As levels of capital, technology and skilled labour increase, the area becomes even more wealthy and so is able to provide better housing, schools, hospitals, shopping centres and transport systems. These 'pull' factors encourage the in-migration of people from surrounding areas.

| | Birth rate per 1,000 (1993) | Migration (% 1993) | Unemployed (% April 1994) | % under 15 (1993) | % over 65 (1993) | GNP per person (ECU 1993) |
|---|---|---|---|---|---|---|
| Italy average | 10.1 | 3.0 | 11.4 | 15.8 | 15.4 | 100 |
| Nord-Ouest (North-West) | 7.6 | 4.4 | 8.9 | 12.1 | 18.6 | 115 |
| Lombardia (Lombardy) | 8.7 | 4.0 | 6.1 | 13.8 | 14.6 | Richest 130 |
| Nord-Est (North-East) | 9.0 | 3.9 | 6.3 | 14.0 | 16.0 | 115 |
| Emilia-Romagna | 7.2 | 7.2 | 6.6 | 11.4 | 19.6 | 124 |
| Centro (Central) | 7.8 | 5.0 | 7.9 | 12.9 | 19.3 | 104 |
| Lazio | 10.0 | 2.9 | 11.0 | 15.3 | 14.2 | 115 |
| Abruzzi-Molise | 10.1 | 4.4 | 11.3 | 16.5 | 17.1 | 87 |
| Campania | 14.6 | 0.4 | 23.1 | 21.5 | 11.2 | 68 |
| Sud (South) | 12.6 | –1.0 | 17.5 | 20.3 | 12.9 | Poorest 67 |
| Sicily | 13.8 | 1.6 | 21.9 | 20.0 | 13.8 | 68 |
| Sardinia | 9.8 | 1.4 | 20.3 | 18.3 | 12.6 | 75 |

Above average development

Average development

Below average development

**Figure 15.11** Development indicators in Italy

In the EU, and in many individual countries, the level of prosperity decreases with distance from the core region. The poorest places are therefore found towards the *periphery*. Here there are fewer jobs, which are less well paid, and more likely to be in the primary sector. There is often a lack of opportunities, poor service provision and insufficient government investment. These 'push' factors force many people to migrate to the core region.

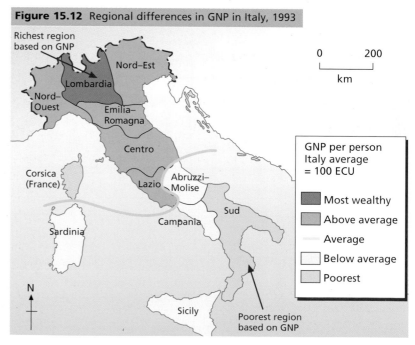

**Figure 15.12** Regional differences in GNP in Italy, 1993

## Italy

Figure 15.11 gives data for several measures of development (pages 196 and 197) for the eleven economic regions of Italy. Figure 15.12 takes one of these measures, that of GNP, to show that there is a distinctive national divide between the 'wealthier, economically more developed north' and the 'poorer, economically less developed south'. Some of the many reasons for the contrast between Lombardy, the wealthiest region, and the South, the poorest region, are given in Figure 15.13.

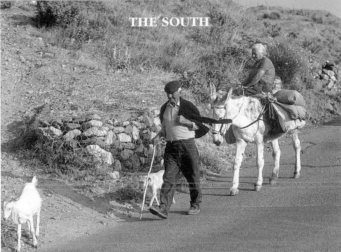

**Figure 15.13** Contrasts between Lombardy and the South of Italy

| LOMBARDY | THE SOUTH |
|---|---|
| Flat land. Fertile soils brought down by the River Po and its tributaries. | Limited flat land. Many steep, high and badly eroded mountains (Apennines). |
| Rain falls throughout the year to give a reliable water supply for agriculture, industry and domestic use. | Summer drought or severe storms. Problem of water supply in summer. Summers are hot – this is the Mezzogiorno ('Land of the midday sun'). |
| Good nearby sources of energy with hydro-electricity, geothermal, gas and some oil. | Limited energy sources other than some unreliable hydro-electricity. |
| Excellent transport system with motorways (autostradas) and railways. Good transport and trade links with rest of the EU. | Poor transport system – few roads (other than the Autostrada del Sole) or railways. Distant from rest of the EU. |
| Intensive, commercial farming. | Extensive, less commercial farming. |
| Only 3% employed in farming. | 21% employed in farming. |
| Low birth rate. Small percentage aged under 15. | High birth rate. High percentage aged under 15. |
| Industrial area, e.g. cars (Alfa Romeo), engineering, fashion (Benetton and Gucci) and chemicals. Much government investment. High level of service provision. | Some new industry (steel, oil-refining and chemicals). Investment by Italian government in 1950s (Cassa per Il Mezzogiorno) and, more recently, from the EU Regional Development Fund. Limited service provision. |
| Low unemployment. In-migration. | High unemployment. Traditionally many people have migrated out of the region (to the North and the USA). Recently many illegal immigrants from Albania and North Africa. |
| A new extreme political party wants the North to separate from the South. It believes too much money is spent and wasted on the South. | People in the South feel they have had far too little financial help from outside. |

## Sustainable development

The term *sustainable development* has been used on several occasions throughout this book (Figure 15.14). But what does it really mean? Ideally, sustainable development should lead to an improvement in people's:

- quality of life – how content they are with their way of life and the environment in which they live
- standard of living – how well off they are economically.

This improvement should be achieved without wasting the earth's resources or destroying the environment. In other words, improvements should not just benefit people living today but should be available for future generations.

Sustainable development needs careful planning and, because it extends across national frontiers and involves a commitment to conservation, the co-operation of different countries. Ideally, sustainable development means the following.

- Using natural resources without spoiling the environment.
- Developing materials that will use fewer resources.
- Using materials that will last for much longer.
- Developing local skills and passing these on to future generations.
- Developing technology that is appropriate to the skills, wealth and needs of local people.
- Encouraging economic development at a pace which a country can afford so as to avoid that country falling into debt.
- Protecting the environment, both its landscape and

| Example | Page number |
|---|---|
| Water management | 21 |
| Coastal management | 74–75 |
| Ecosystems (including wetlands) | 80, 84–85 |
| Farming (organic) | 143 |
| Industry (Consett) | 159 |
| Tourism | 178–179 |
| Resources (including energy) | 182–183, 187 |
| Recycling waste | 190 |

**Figure 15.14** Examples of sustainable development

wildlife, so that it can be enjoyed by later visitors and generations.
- When using resources, to consider the three Rs – *renewable* resources such as solar power and the wind, *recycling* resources such as paper and glass, and *replacing* resources by replanting trees and adding manure to the soil.

## *The Flow Country of Caithness and Sutherland*

This area contains the largest natural blanket peat bog environment in Europe. It consists of vast open expanses of peat and pools (Figure 15.15), moss and rare flowers. It forms a habitat and breeding ground for a wide variety of rare birds. Although it is recognised as one of the world's few remaining natural ecosystems (page 80) and is protected by four international treaties, it is under threat from local people, foresters and gardeners.

Peat is a soil that consists of layer upon layer of partly decayed vegetation. It is found where the climate is too cold and too wet for soil organisms to break down the vegetation. Blanket peat is very acidic, lacks oxygen and nutrients, and formed between 5,000 and 8,000 years ago. Due to the length of time it takes peat to form, scientists consider it to be a finite rather than a renewable resource (page 182).

**Figure 15.15** The Flow Country

(a) Hand cutting peat in South Uist

**Figure 15.16** Peat cutting

(b) Machine-cut peat

Peat has long been cut in parts of Britain for use as a fuel. It was cut in relatively small amounts and by hand (Figure 15.16a). Today's main use of peat is by gardeners, either to improve their soil or to help plant growth. It is now cut in large amounts and by machine (Figure 15.16b). Modern peat extraction involves clearing the vegetation by bulldozer and then draining the land. Fortunately this method, which totally destroys the peat ecosystem, is not yet widespread in the Flow Country . . . but for how long will it remain that way?

A more immediate threat in the Flow Country is from afforestation (Figure 15.17). Conifers have been planted by developers to form several large plantations in areas where, conservationists claim, the land is unsuitable for economic forestry. To local people, forestry means a welcome source of employment and, therefore, an improvement in their standard of living. Referring back to the definition on the previous page, how can development in this area be made sustainable?

To answer this, the Highland Regional Council set up a working party which included representatives from the Countryside Commission for Scotland, the Nature Conservancy, the Forestry Commission and the Highlands and Islands Development Board. Their report stated that it is possible 'to safeguard the integrity of the wetlands (blanket bogs) and allow for development of a sustainable forestry-based industry'. It concluded that:

'a total forest area of 100,000 ha in Caithness and Sutherland is desirable to sustain a viable forest industry, which would mean a land-use change of less than 6% of the total area [Figure 15.18]. A balance can be struck between development with its forestry-related jobs and conservation of an ecosystem of global importance.'

**Figure 15.17** Afforestation in the Flow Country

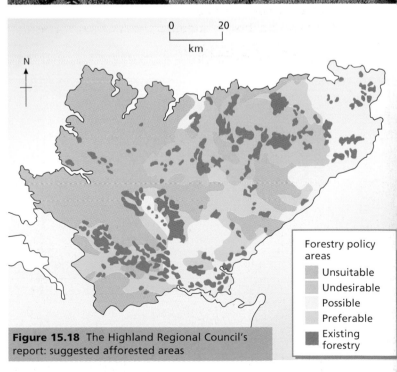

0    20
km

N

Forestry policy areas

Unsuitable
Undesirable
Possible
Preferable
Existing forestry

**Figure 15.18** The Highland Regional Council's report: suggested afforested areas

# The EU and the world – trade and aid

## Trade

Trade is the flow of commodities from producers to consumers. It is achieved through the buying (*importing*) and selling (*exporting*) of goods. Although no country is self-sufficient in all the raw materials (food, minerals and energy resources) and manufactured goods that its inhabitants need, it is likely to have a surplus in some of them. Countries that earn more from their exports than they have to pay for their imports have a *trade surplus* (Figure 15.19a). These countries, and their inhabitants, are likely to become more wealthy. Countries that spend more on imports than they earn from their exports have a *trade deficit*. Usually, though not always, they are likely to become poorer. (At present the USA has a large trade deficit.)

In order to increase their trade, countries may:
- create barriers to restrict the amount and value of goods that can be bought and sold, for example by adding *tariffs* (import duties) to make the imported goods more expensive than locally produced goods, or
- group together to form trading groups such as the EU.

The EU, with 15 member states, is now the world's largest single trading market, with a population of 370,000 million (1996). By removing tariffs between members it has reduced the cost of products and increased the number of potential customers. For most EU countries, over half of both their imports and exports are with other member states (Figure 15.19b). Of the remainder, most are with economically more developed countries such as Japan and the USA, and relatively little with the economically less developed countries in Africa and South America (Figure 15.19c).

**Figure 15.19** Trade in Europe

(a) Balance of trade in the EU15, Iceland, Norway and Switzerland

(b) Proportion of trade between western European countries and the EU

(c) Direction of EU trade

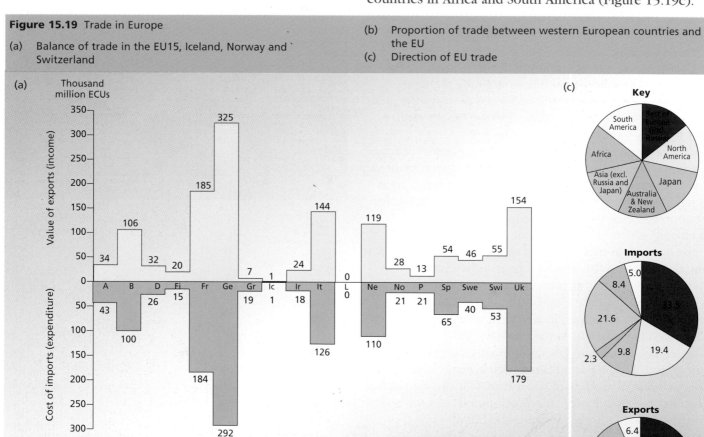

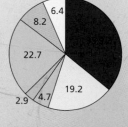

(b)

| Country | Aus. | Bel. | Den. | Fin. | Fra. | Ger. | Gre. | Ice. | Ire. | Ita. | Lux. | Neth. | Nor. | Por. | Spa. | Swe. | Swi. | UK |
|---|---|---|---|---|---|---|---|---|---|---|---|---|---|---|---|---|---|---|
| **Balance** | –9 | +6 | +6 | +5 | +1 | +33 | –12 | 0 | +6 | +18 | 0 | +9 | +7 | –8 | –11 | +6 | +2 | –25 |

Trade with other EU15

| | Aus. | Bel. | Den. | Fin. | Fra. | Ger. | Gre. | Ice. | Ire. | Ita. | Lux. | Neth. | Nor. | Por. | Spa. | Swe. | Swi. | UK |
|---|---|---|---|---|---|---|---|---|---|---|---|---|---|---|---|---|---|---|
| % imports | 67 | 71 | 54 | 46 | 64 | 51 | 60 | 48 | 69 | 55 | – | 66 | 49 | 72 | 61 | 55 | 73 | 49 |
| % exports | 60 | 74 | 54 | 45 | 61 | 50 | 56 | 60 | 69 | 53 | – | 74 | 67 | 75 | 62 | 53 | 57 | 53 |

## Aid

Aid is the transfer of resources from one country (the UK), a group of countries (the EU) or an organisation (Oxfam) to another country (usually one in an economically less developed continent). The resource, given by a *donor* and received by a *recipient*, may be in the form of:

- money, which can be given as a grant or a loan but which has to be repaid together with (usually) a low rate of interest
- goods, food, machinery, technology or people (nurses, teachers).

There are two main types of aid, each of which can be given for a different length of time:

- *official aid*, which is usually political
- *voluntary aid*, which is often charitable (Figure 15.20).

The basic aim of aid is to help poorer countries to develop their economy and to improve their services in order to raise their standard of living and quality of life. It should reduce poverty and promote sustainable development. In reality, the giving of aid is far more complex and controversial as it does not always benefit the country to which it is given (Figure 15.21).

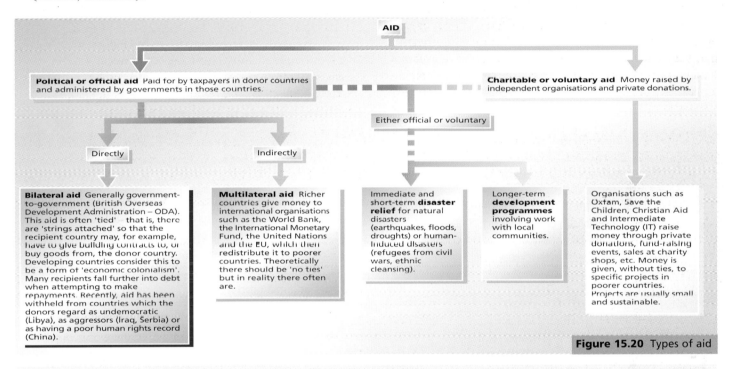

**Figure 15.20** Types of aid

| For | Against |
|---|---|
| • Rapid response to emergencies, both natural and human-induced. | • Aid is a conscience-salver for the rich and former colonial powers, or is in their commercial interest. |
| • Helps in the development of raw materials and energy supplies. | • Better to use money on the poor people living in the donor countries. |
| • Encourages, and helps to implement, appropriate technology schemes. | • An exploitation of physical and human resources. |
| • Provides work in new factories and reduces the need to import certain goods. | • Used to exert political and economic pressure on poorer countries. |
| • Helps to increase yields of local crops to feed rapidly growing local populations. | • Increases the recipient country's external debt. |
| • Provides primary health care, e.g. vaccines, immunisation schemes, nurses. | • Often only goes to the rich and to urban dwellers in recipient countries, rather than to the real poor. |
| • Helps to educate people about, and to implement, family planning schemes. | • Encourages corruption amongst officials in donor and recipient countries. |
| • Grants to students to study in overseas countries. | • Distorts local markets.<br>• Does not encourage self-reliance of recipient countries. |
| • Can improve human rights. | • Often not given appropriate technology and is not sustainable. |

**Figure 15.21** Arguments for and against the giving of aid

**1** *(Page 194)*

**a** Give the meaning of *primary, secondary* and *tertiary activities.*

**b** i) Sort the jobs shown in the drawing under the headings:

   \* Primary    \* Secondary    \* Tertiary

   ii) Give two more jobs of each type.

**c** Study the OS map of Newcastle on page 206. Name the economic activity at each of the following grid references. State whether each one is a *primary, secondary* or *tertiary* activity.

   203714    185640    244714

   221711    176643

JOB CENTRE
\* Teacher  \* Miner  \* Farmer  \* Banker
\* Shop assistant  \* Steel worker
\* Forester  \* Car maker  \* Engineer
\* Fisherman  \* Shipbuilder  \* Pop star
\* Builder  \* Table maker  \* Bus driver

**2** *(Pages 194 and 195)*

**a** i) Look carefully at the triangle graph. Give the percentage of workers in primary, secondary and tertiary activities for each place **A**, **B**, **C** and **D**.

   ii) Match each of the town descriptions below with a letter on the graph. Explain your choices.

**b** Describe the likely employment structure in:

   i) an economically developed country

   ii) an economically developing country.

   Give two examples for each.

% employed in primary activities

% employed in secondary activities

% employed in tertiary activities

**1**
A town famous for its pottery. It developed because of nearby raw materials, which are still mined.

**2**
This is a small countryside area where most jobs are in farming. Some agricultural machinery is made, and tourism is on the increase.

**3**
A large industrial town. Most jobs are related to heavy industries and mill products.

**4**
A typical seaside resort where the leisure industry provides most employment.

**3** *(Pages 196 and 197)*

**a** i) Give the meaning of the term *gross national product (GNP) per capita.*

   ii) Suggest one problem with using GNP per capita to measure wealth.

**b** Look carefully at the graph.

   i) Name the two richest countries by GNP.

   ii) What is the GNP of the UK?

   iii) Which two countries use most energy?

   iv) Describe the relationship between energy consumption and GNP.

**c** Describe two other indicators of development and say how they could be used to compare the level of development in different

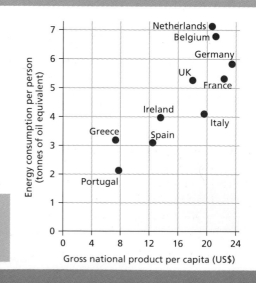

Energy consumption per person (tonnes of oil equivalent)

Gross national product per capita (US$)

Relationship between GNP and energy consumption

countries.

## 4  (Pages 198 and 199)

a  Look at Figures 15.11 and 15.12 on page 198. In which region or regions of Italy are:
  i)   incomes highest
  ii)  the fewest people unemployed
  iii) the highest birth rates
  iv)  people most likely to migrate from?

b  Choose any three of the factors shown below, and use them to explain why the North of Italy is wealthier and more

Physical features

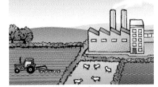
Economic features

Transport and energy

Population factors

## 5  (Page 202)

a  Look at the drawing below and give the meaning of each of the following terms.
  i) Trade   ii) Imports   iii) Exports
  iv) Trade surplus   v) Trade deficit

b  Describe two ways in which countries can increase their trade.

c  How has the EU helped improve trade between member countries?

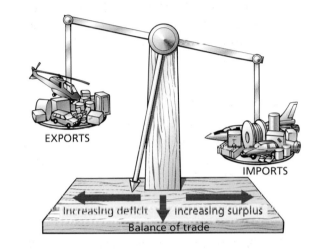

EXPORTS

IMPORTS

Increasing deficit   Increasing surplus

Balance of trade

## 6  (Page 203)

a  Look at the table below which shows some types of aid given by European countries.
  i)   What is the meaning of the term *short-term aid*?
  ii)  Give an example of when short-term aid may be used.
  iii) Explain why long-term aid may be more useful to a poor country than short-term aid.

b  Look at the newspaper extract.
  i)   What name is given to:
     * aid provided by the government
     * aid given by organisations and individuals
     * aid that has conditions linked to it?
  ii)  What are the advantages to Britain of giving aid?

c  Look at the cartoon below. Describe how receiving aid may be a problem for some countries.

| Short-term aid | Long-term aid |
|---|---|
| * Food  * Blankets<br>* Tents  * Lorries<br>* Medicines  * Clothing | * Education  * Training<br>*Financial aid  *Transport |

Aid is given by governments and individual organisations to those in need. Often the aid must be spent on goods and services from the country providing the aid. For example, the British government paid for a road in Kenya but insisted that the road was built by a British company.

AID

INCREASED DEBT RESTRICTS FREEDOM

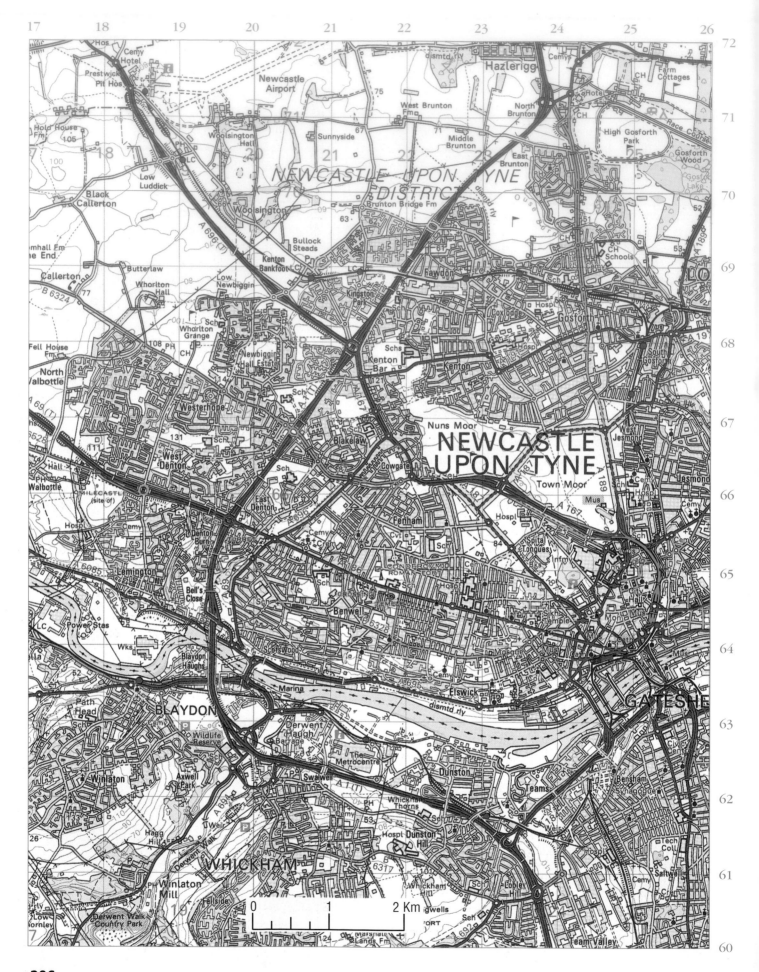

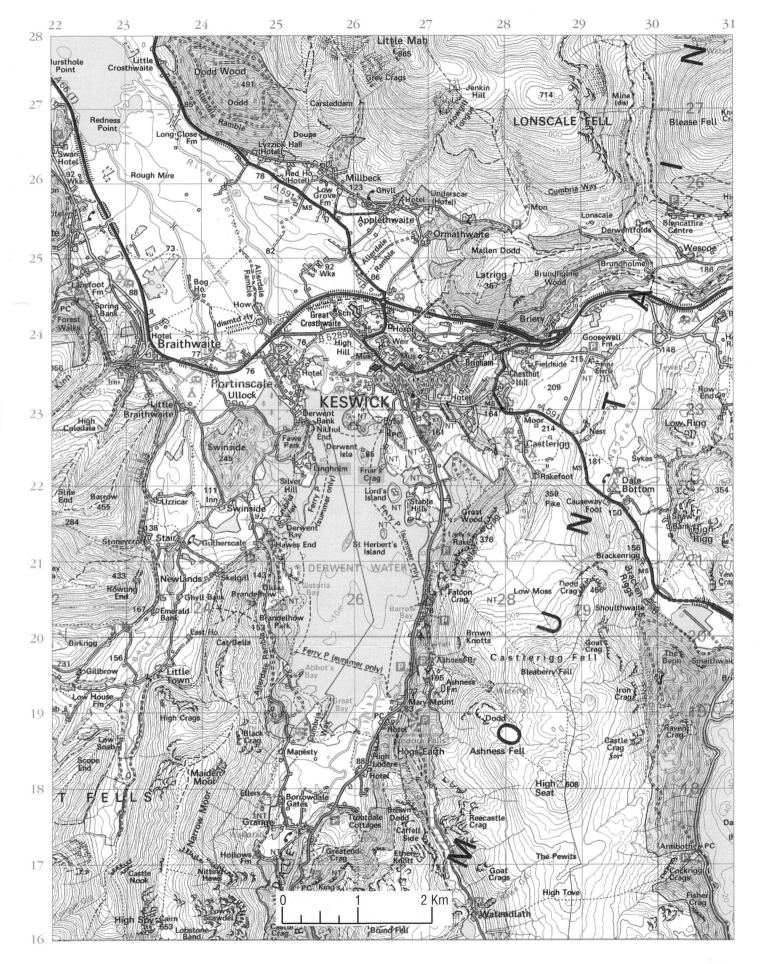

# Index